RACE, SEX, & ENVIRONMENT

J. R. de la H. MARETT

B.Sc., Dipl. with Distn. Anthropology (Oxon)

RACE, SEX, AND ENVIRONMENT

A Study of Mineral Deficiency in Human Evolution

Hutchinson's Scientific and Technical Publications

32–36 Paternoster Row, London, E.C.4

1936

Made and Printed in Great Britain at
The Mayflower Press, Plymouth. William Brendon & Son, Ltd.
1935

TO

MY MOTHER AND FATHER

PREFACE

THIS BOOK IS THE RESULT OF A MODERATELY PROTRACTED period of thinking upon the very large question how mineral deficiencies of the soil and the resulting vegetable food could have influenced animal and human evolution. The problem first presented itself to me in 1929 when I happened to receive a review copy of Sir John Orr's book *Minerals in Pastures.* I was, however, already interested in the theory of animal husbandry, in the origin of domesticated breeds, with special reference to the relationship of form to function, and in the sex-linkage of milk-yield in dairy cows, a matter which Gowen, Buchanan Smith and others had shown to be of such great importance. Not only did Sir John Orr's array of evidence draw attention to the wide-spread and ever-increasing incidence of disease, death, and sterility attributable to various mineral deficiencies, of which pathological effects I already had some practical experience; but, in addition, cases were cited in which the size and the rate of growth in animals appeared to have been altered by shortage of bone-forming material. Accordingly I formulated the theory that a physiological economy of mineral elements, and especially of calcium, was associated with the external display of secondary sex-characters of markedly feminine type. This notion of differences in the degree in which sex-linked characters are developed had in its turn gained currency through the work of Crew and of Goldschmidt; both of whom have done so much to establish a connection between the genetics and the physiology of sex.

It thereupon seemed obvious that research on similar lines might throw light upon some of the more obscure problems of human evolution. For instance, there was reason to suppose that the robust skeletal development of Neanderthal Man and other earlier fossil Hominidæ might have been due to a former abundance of bone-forming material. If so, modern or "Neanthropic" Man might be regarded as a more feminized variant of the type manifested in his few known predecessors. After a preliminary training in general anthropology I was able to proceed to an intensive investigation of this subject. It then became plain to me that climate, which the Russian school of soil-science has found to provide a sound basis for soil-classification, must also determine the mineral content of the vegetation grown on these soils. Aridity could be shown to cause calcium to be accumulated at the soil-surface; whereas pluvial conditions would result in acidity. Moreover, Sir John Orr's writings had made it clear not only that the mineral content of the soil is reflected in the food; but also that soil acidity, such as is produced by heavy rainfall, brings about the accumulation of iodine, which forms the raw material of the thyroid hormone. Such considerations help to define the long-suspected bearing of the endocrines on Evolution—a topic to which Sir Arthur Keith has repeatedly drawn attention.

In exploring these matters I have found it necessary to indulge in a number of remoter but none the less connected speculations concerning the evolution of vertebrates and the mammal. Perhaps the most important of these, and the one least obviously connected with the primary problem, relates to the origin and validity of sexual selection. This had served me as a bridge between the study of ecology, anatomy and physiology on the one hand, and that of behaviour and its psychology on the other. All these general problems, together with my tentative solutions of them, have been outlined in the first chapter and also summarized at its end.

Chapters II to V contain some of the more important ecological and physiological facts that are intended to supply means for the formulating and checking of the theories of physical and social evolution constituting the remainder of the book. This main object is to trace the distribution of the more important minerals together with their effects outside the human body ; and in particular to determine which of them are abundant and which rare as a result either of aridity or of humid conditions. Wherever this can be done an attempt is then made to envisage the kind of physiology best suited to each special environment ; and sometimes characters displayed by particular types of man or animal can be explained as probably adapted to withstand disadvantageous deficiencies or abundances of particular food constituents.

The rest of the book applies the foregoing theories to the problem of human evolution. Mineral deficiency is held to have influenced selection both for bodily and for mental characters, some of which appear to have become linked even before the emergence of the vertebrate on to the land. Three chapters embody a discussion of the origin of Man, and a good deal of space is devoted to a hypothesis whereby mineral deficiency is credited with the power of removing or simplifying characters whose over-specialization might otherwise have prevented further and alternative adaptation. Besides providing this useful means of phylogenetic retreat, mineral deficiency is also held responsible for a series of arrests of bodily growth, during each of which the relative size of the brain to the body has been increased. Two subsequent chapters deal with the probable conditions responsible for the evolution of some of the better-known fossils, and for the more important of the living races of Man.

In both contexts it has been found necessary to lay great stress upon a theory of racial mixture between a quick-developing Southern and Neanthropic strain and another, equally hypothetical, of Palæanthropic affinities. The latter is held to have been more masculine than the former. On the whole, however, the variation in the rate of metabolic and developmental change would appear to constitute the more important aspect of the difference. This theory of racial mixture seems capable not only of explaining certain anomalous associations of bodily characters alike in the living and in the fossil races of man ; but also it offers a chance of understanding the cause of Kretschmer's observed correlations between differences of physique and character. Indeed the mineral hypothesis promises to facilitate greatly the biological approach to psychology. I have attempted to extend the theories of the late Dr. Rivers and to apply them, as he did, to an interpretation of the findings of Freud. Sexual selection seems to have an important bearing upon the nature of the Œdipus complex. The encouragement of an instinctive aggressiveness in the adult male would necessitate its hereditary repression in the adolescent and in the female. Thus the fœtalization of man—due to mineral deficiency—may be held responsible for the inhibition of intra-group pugnacity, as also for the corresponding strength of the hate felt towards the enemy on the rare occasions when these repressed and thus strengthened emotions happen to be released. Indeed, the whole mineral hypothesis has a most important bearing upon many of the causes of war as well as upon some of the primary problems of peace.

So far, however, I must frankly admit, my enquiries have led to the asking of far more questions than have been answered. Important results, theoretical as well as practical, could not fail to follow from organized research on the part of those who specialize in the very various subjects to which the present theory applies. Though the problem as a whole falls within the domain of the anthropologist, nevertheless he will require constant assistance from the geologist, the geographer, the soil chemist, the geneticist, the physiologist and the psychologist ; so true is it that each can enrich his own science by helping that of his neighbour.

J. R. de la H. M.

OXFORD,
NOVEMBER, 1935

CONTENTS

CHAPTER V

MINERAL METABOLISM AND THE ENDOCRINES

CHAPTER VI

THE ORIGIN OF MAN

CHAPTER VII

THE HUMAN BODY

CHAPTER VIII

SEXUAL SELECTION IN HUMAN EVOLUTION

CHAPTER IX

ENVIRONMENT AND MORPHOLOGY

CHAPTER X

THE EXTINCT HOMINIDÆ

CHAPTER XI

THE DIFFERENTIATION OF MODERN MAN

CHAPTER XII

SEX AND SOCIETY

CHAPTER XIII

RACE AND CULTURE

CHAPTER XIV

SKY GOD AND EARTH GODDESS

CHAPTER XV

BODY, MIND, AND CIVILIZATION

CHAPTER XVI

STRUGGLES OF THE ECONOMIC MAN

LIST OF DIAGRAMS

CHAPTER I

PROGRAMME AND BIOLOGICAL BACKGROUND

The Problem in General : Race and Sex : Sex-Determination and Survival Value : Parallel Association of Environmental and Hereditary Factors : Iodine Shortage and Fœtalization : Mineral Deficiency and Growth-Rate : The Evolution of the Mammal : Size-Control and Lactation in the Mammal : Giants and Dwarfs : Translocation and Sex-dimorphism : Environment, Adaptation and Natural Selection : The Environment of the Gene : The Evolution of the Endocrines : A Theory of Somatic Revolutions : The Endocrines and Environmental Change : Population, In-breeding, and Sexual Selection : In-breeding : Sexual Selection : Racial Mixture : Conclusion

It is a commonplace of science that a causal connexion must exist between environment and race. In other words, the theory of evolution implies habitat as being somehow bound to have exerted a formative influence on the heredity of man as on that of any other animal kind. But to say " somehow " is hardly to say " how." An effective explanation would demand the construction of a causal chain connecting environment and race by various intermediate links, some of them of a physical and others of a physiological or even psychological order. Hitherto the anthropogeographer has been obliged to exhibit the two principles more or less in simple juxtaposition. Such purely descriptive material is all to the good ; but the time has come when the necessary bridge-work can and ought to be attempted. The following enquiry has thus resolved itself into a search for causes : that is to say, into an attempt to associate the discordant categories of the organic and the inorganic by as close a nexus as the existing evidence allows.

The general hypothesis running through the book will be that a natural selection for an economy of various food substances has played a very important part in guiding the evolutionary process. This is held largely responsible for the selection and arrangement of the parts of the material inheritance—the genes—whose interaction with the environment will presumably account for most of the recognized vertebrate and human characters. More especially the relation of the particular habitat to the ductless glands would seem to reveal a design corresponding to a constant variation of solar radiation, together with the changes in humidity and all the other complex environmental factors, many of them affecting nutrition, which follow from that single and initial root-cause. The evolution of the land animal can thus be regarded, not as a series of disconnected attempts to fit in with single sets of surroundings, but rather as a continuous search for improvements on a single arrangement which is easily modified and will thus be adaptable to all stages of the many previously experienced oscillations of climate. When attempting to explain a significant evolutionary change, I have started from the postulate that the organism usually receives an initial stimulus from a change in the environment. Nevertheless, it will be pointed out how the essential " aliveness " of the higher species would appear always to react with an energy greater than the mere minimum required to maintain a *status quo*. Both the individual and the race would appear to be elastic rather than merely plastic in a passive way, so that the evolutionary process derives a momentum and rhythm of its own.

The phylogenetic significance of differences in the degree in which sex-linked characters may be expressed is put forward as an important part of the mechanism with which the animal has come to adapt itself to the more frequently experienced changes of its environment. The sex-linked genes are the special protectors of the next generation. Hence their full expression is held to promote physiological efficiency and the storage of nutrients. Thus increased sexuality becomes more necessary to both sexes at times when the reduced quantity or inferior quality of the food is the main difficulty with which members of the species must contend. Conversely, the unfettered expression of the remaining, or autosomal, inheritance will allow a better focussing of energy upon the task of defeating rivals whether of the same or of another species. This will be most necessary when external circumstances, combined with an increasing efficiency of the sex-inheritance, succeed in producing a high pressure of population. Much of the great success of the mammal is attributable to the double set of sex-linked genes possessed by the viviparous homogametic female ; for life on land had suddenly thrust upon her the far heavier portion of the reproductive burden.

As for the means whereby these changes of racial sexuality are brought about, it is argued that there is a natural selection for the correct ratio of reproductive to individual energy-expenditure ; and, further, this first process is held to have given rise to the many elaborate systems of sexual selection. In this way an artificial intensification of the intra-specific struggle is utilized to accelerate changes in whichever direction is desirable. Systems of sexual selection are held to have evolved and to possess survival value on this account. Thus such complex features as the marriage systems of mankind, their forms of social organization, and even their religions, have here been related to the types of sexual selection believed to possess the greatest survival value in each case. This last question is in its turn decided by the ecological factors as a whole, and especially by the relationship of the race to its climate and food supply. In some cases the individual development, dependent upon the autosomes, will be too great, and in such circumstances greater sexuality and fertility will be in demand. Rivalry with other groups, together with the competition between individuals in the same society, will tend to exert a greater selective influence than that imposed by disease. In such cases an increase of masculinity and an improved anatomical development would probably follow.

Though in some respects this professes to be a pioneer study, it has nevertheless been inspired by recent movements of thought, which, starting from one side or another, may be seen to converge upon the same point. It will, at this stage, suffice to call attention to two especially notable collections of evidence which, taken together, seem able to relate the effects of its physical surroundings to the development of the land animal. Firstly, great attention has recently been paid in Russia to soil as conditioned by climate—more especially as it is affected by the degree of humidity, which, by causing certain salts to be either abundant or rare in the upper layers of the ground, modifies the soil type, and through it the nature of the vegetable food supply. Secondly, two important reviews, dealing respectively with Man and with his domesticated livestock, have shown how mineral deficiency, in the shape of a lack in the staple food of iodine, lime, phosphorus, iron, common salt, and so on, is responsible for human suffering and death, and likewise for great economic loss on the part of the breeders of domesticated animals.[1,2] Indeed, among the latter there is a growing tendency to adjust the inorganic constituents of the diet to the requirements of the grazing animal, as also to try to mould the heredity of the animals in directions favourable to an improved ecological adjustment to the physical characters of the country. Thus, mineral deficiency, which is here related to climate and geology, must be believed to play an important, though hitherto often unrecognized, part in directing the course of human and animal evolution by natural selection.

An attempt has been made to correlate various classes of habitat with corresponding types of animal and human physiology. In particular a distinction has been drawn between lime-rich and lime-poor soils, and between the differences of heredity governing endocrine activity, physiology and anatomy in each case. Lime-rich soils may result from climatic aridity or from the nature of the parent rock. In either case a resultant alkalinity of the soil will inhibit the retention and adsorption of iodine. Thus, in these areas every means of economizing iodine, the basis of the thyroid hormone, will be in demand. Correspondingly, animals or men specialized for life in the lime-deficient areas, which are almost always humid, will suffer no lack of water or iodine. The physiological requirement in these areas is an economy of lime, and probably of its usual associate, phosphorus, as well.

[1] Orr, J. B.: "Iodine in Nutrition," Special Report Series. Medical Research Council, London, No. 123 (1929).
[2] Orr, J. B.: *Minerals in Pastures*, London, 1929.

Heavy rainfall will also render these soils deficient in common salt; the sodium being lost, and the chlorine combining with potash. Thus in humid areas we may expect an economy of calcium and phosphorus to be encouraged by a reduction in the mass of the skeleton. The capacity to utilize an abundance of iodine and potash, and to cope with a deficiency of sodium, may accordingly become associated with an inheritance making for small bones.

The main importance of these considerations lies in the fact that they enable us to explain several disadvantageous changes of morphology in terms of correlated physiological advantages. Survival value can be increased through the reduced consumption of a rare structural substance, even when a mechanical disadvantage due to an anatomical defect must thereby be incurred.

RACE AND SEX

It will be noted that in the title "sex" figures by the side of "environment" and "race," so that it might be easily mistaken for a third principle co-ordinate with the other two. Actually it will be treated in its due subordination to race, being in point of fact no more than one race-making factor amongst others. Its importance in this respect, however, has hitherto passed almost unrecognized. Thus, it seems worth while at the outset to call special attention to what almost amounts to the middle term of the subsequent argument. Briefly, the theory is that mineral economy has been secured through an increase of sexuality, and that mechanical efficiency has sometimes been sacrificed to meet this requirement.

These ideas have been largely inspired by the work of Crew on sex-determination in birds and mammals, and by that of Goldschmidt on inherited experimental intersexuality in the Gypsy moth (*Lymantria*).[1] The sex-linked genes are held to have been selected for the purpose of improving the chances of survival for the offspring, even when this endangered the continued existence of the parent. Such a distinction seems broadly the same as that already drawn between anatomical and physiological requirements. Thus, after sex-dimorphism is evolved, we may expect the sex having most need of reproductive efficiency to be homogametic; that is, to carry a full allowance of genes for physiological efficiency. As a result the heterogametic sex, being less hampered by a need to retain structural material in a form readily available for the production and nutrition of offspring, is better able to develop specialized limbs and organs for the purpose of modifying and controlling its environment for the benefit of itself, its mate, and its species.

[1] Crew, F. A. E.: "Studies in Intersexuality," *Proc. roy. Soc.*, Lond. B. XCV, 1923-24. Crew, F. A. E.: "Animal Genetics," London, 1925. Goldschmidt, R.: "Experimental Intersexuality and the Sex Problem," etc., *Amer. Nat.*, 50, 705-718 (1916). Goldschmidt, R.: *The Mechanism and Physiology of Sex Determination*, London, 1923.

This division of function between the sexes is believed subsequently to have played an important part in the adaptation of the species to changes of its environment. Thus, when food was scarce or ill-balanced, a full outward or somatic expression of the sex-linked genes for food economy would confer survival upon all individuals of either sex in whom such a state happened to exist. Correspondingly, an abundance of well-balanced food is suspected of leading to a natural selection for greater anatomical perfection ; that is, to the full outward expression of the autosomal parts of the germinal inheritance hampered by only a minimal degree of sex-linked repression.

These changes in the extent of the somatic, or outward, expression of whole groups of characters, such as are exemplified in *Lymantria* by the alterable interaction between the sex-linked genes and the remainder, are themselves assumed to be the work of genes. Fisher, in his theory of the evolution of genetic dominance by an initially recessive primary mutation, suggests a natural selection of secondary modifying mutations which eventually enable the mutant to achieve a cumulatively large effect even when inherited in the simplex condition.[1] In speaking of the evolution of a similar reinforcement of somatic effect, when applied to a whole chromosome or set of chromosomes, it has been thought better to introduce the word "predominance," reserving "dominance" for the relationship between a gene and its immediate allelomorph or partner.[2] The mechanism, however, is assumed to be the same. Some space will be devoted to a detailed hypothesis in regard to this point.

SEX-DETERMINATION AND SURVIVAL VALUE

Most of this book is directly concerned with the problem how changes of environment affecting the mineral supply of the soil and food have influenced the evolution of Man. It is thus legitimately concerned with the way in which mineral deficiencies affect the selection for relative degrees of sex-linked predominance in the mammal. An interesting side-light, however, is thrown upon the survival value of the mammalian sex-determining mechanism by considering the case of birds and reptiles, in which the male, rather than the female, may be homogametic for the two sex-chromosomes. Under the still earlier aquatic conditions this arrangement seems to conform to the theory that physiological and reproductive efficiency is most needed by the homogametic sex. A great production of sperms would be of more use than a corresponding extra expenditure on the larger and so more vulnerable eggs. Autosomal characters would thus be allowed to inhibit a sex-linked catabolic gametogenesis and lead to the production of a few large ova by the heterogametic female.

[1] Fisher, R. A. : *The Genetical Theory of Natural Selection*, Oxford, 1930.

[2] The technical expression "epistatic" has been used to express a dominant relationship between genes situated in different loci of the homologous chromosomes obtained from either parent.

Now on land sperms may be economized, if conception is to take place within the body of the female. Thus the need for a physiological superiority of the male will vanish ; more especially as land life imposes a new need to be met by the female physiology, namely, liquid economy. If, then, we imagine an aquatic form newly adapted to land life, there appears a danger of unstable equilibrium as between the previously balanced needs of anatomy and physiology. The now less important males, if still homogametic, will be adapted faster to any change in their environment than the females, to whom such modifications are actually more necessary. This will result in a great surplus of males, followed by fierce selection for still greater degrees of efficiency as measured by purely masculine standards. Thus the needs of the male may oppose and overthrow many of the opposite and more important needs of the female. In this way it may be possible to explain such run-away processes as those responsible for the extinction of the dinosaurs and of many giant birds. The persistence of the homogametic male among birds, despite the inherent danger of a run-away to large size, is here attributed to the balancing factor introduced by the need of small size necessary to maintain survival value through flight. Similarly, the power of flight is deemed to inhibit in-breeding, which might otherwise still further accelerate this dangerous type of phylogenetic change.

PARALLEL ASSOCIATION OF ENVIRONMENTAL AND HEREDITARY FACTORS

The selection for ever-increasing size both in the dinosaurs and in the new homogametic vertebrate female, ancestral to the mammal, is held to have been directed by a demand for adaptation to progressive degrees of aridity or to other conditions usually associated, now as formerly, with a need to economize liquid. Of these last iodine shortage is considered the most important. Fresh-water plants contain less iodine than sea plants, and land plants least of all. In addition to this, as already mentioned, aridity results in a basic soil-condition which inhibits both the adsorption of iodine from the primary rock and hinders its subsequent retention by the humus. Thus we may expect most of such mutations as can assist a defiance of drought to have been selected under conditions of greater iodine deficiency than those predecessors that will subsequently become their allelomorphs or partners. In consequence, a full expression or predominance of such genes could serve to improve the chances of survival under conditions either of increasing drought or of increasing iodine shortage, even if these happened to be experienced separately. These genes for liquid and iodine economy are believed to have become sex-linked owing to their paramount importance in reproduction. They could have secured their results through size and tissue-hydration, probably by encouraging an activity of the anterior-pituitary, seeing that the latter mobilizes vitamin E, the fruit of the sex-genes of the vegetable kingdom. This suggests a synergism between vitamin E and iodine far earlier than the appearance of the vertebrate. The former is probably abundant in arid habitats, and may be deficient in rain forests where vegetative, as opposed to sexual, reproduction is common, and soils abound in iodine.

IODINE-SHORTAGE AND FŒTALIZATION

There is a further factor which, besides humidity, may be considered to govern the iodine-contents of a soil. This is the passage of time. The liberation of iodine from the primary rock is a slow process. Hence, it seems fair to assume that, other things equal, later epochs will tend to provide a greater abundance of iodine than would be available at earlier periods. Thus, just as mutations for the overcoming of aridity will have been selected so as to operate in an internal environment providing a low iodine concentration, so will later mutants tend to have been selected in a higher iodine concentration than their predecessors. As a result, selection for iodine economy may be expected not only to favour the predominance of genes selected in periods of aridity, but also to encourage a predominance of old as against later mutants. Selection for increased iodine-economy, whenever such be needed, may thus be expected to select modifying mutations or, by other means, result in the phenotypic expression of atavistic characters. These last, on a theory of recapitulations, must at the same time be infantile or fœtal characters. Despite an advance in genetic complexity the somatic development may be checked and so simplified. This hypothesis is adopted to explain several of the salient characters of Man such as his hairless skin and the unspecialized form of the human hand.

MINERAL-DEFICIENCY AND GROWTH-RATE

Lime-deficiency is thus thought to encourage femininity, and iodine shortage to favour fœtalization. Yet, since many of the aspects of youth and femininity are similar, it will not be easy to distinguish between the two possible causes of a similar state. It may be easier to distinguish types evolved for a mineral abundance, as contrasted with those resulting from single or multiple deficiency.

Lack of any structural material would seem in the long run likely also to result in a slow rate of growth. This tendency has been partly verified by observation. When fast-growing English breeds of cattle are moved to pastures on which slow-maturing native Indian breeds do well, the former are found to die out. Even when crossed with the native stock the cross-bred offspring still grow faster, and, as a result, display many bone-defects, unless fed with additional calcium phosphate. In these cases phosphorus rather than calcium seems to be the main deficiency concerned.[1]

Phosphorus-shortage can thus be responsible for slow growth, and we may reflect that it is required for the building of the soft tissues no less than for the bones. Lime, on the other hand, is needed mainly

[1] Orr : *Minerals in Pastures.*

for the latter. Hence it can be better economized by a limitation of the eventual size than by a slow growth-rate and a consequent delay of sexual maturity.

It seems probable, though there is no direct proof, that iodine shortage, like phosphorus-deficiency, would favour a delay of sexual maturity and consequently a slow rate of growth. Iodine-deficiency, as manifested by goitre, is most common in adolescents. Thus, the longer the period of childhood, the greater the chances of storing a reserve necessary to bring about the difficult and long delayed change to full reproductive capacity.

Now it will be argued later that iodine-economy is encouraged by great size and a consequent economy of heat. The mechanism whereby this size-increase may be brought about could, however, depend upon the previously mentioned need to delay the onset of sexual maturity. Even if the final stages of adult development are postponed for a year or more, a slow but continuous growth could be expected during this extra period of immaturity.

It is proposed, then, to erect the superstructure of this hypothesis upon the basic theory that most mineral deficiencies, certainly a shortage of phosphorus, and probably one of iodine, encourage a slow rate of growth. A further point to be noted, however, is that an economy of any one structural substance secured in this manner must, almost automatically, confer the advantage of a similar economy in the use of all others. Thus phosphorus-shortage might result in a pre-adaptation to withstand iodine-deficiency or *vice versa*. The ratio of the total ash-content of milk to its calorific value is a good guide to the mineral requirements of the adult animal. It is worth noting that in the case of man, and of that other slow-growing and intelligent animal, the elephant, this ratio is wider—indicating a greater degree of mineral economy—than in any other species of land mammal.

THE EVOLUTION OF THE MAMMAL

It was argued that, when the male was both homogametic and of less physiological importance than the female, male competition would overthrow any limiting capacity inherent in the greater need of the heterogametic, and therefore less physiologically efficient, female.[1] It is assumed that this process might proceed until female fertility was greatly reduced. If the environment was still arid—as it would appear to have been in the Triassic—large size would be favoured and the runaway process would be in this direction. Now what was required, if only it could evolve, was a species in which the females were larger, and therefore of greater physiological efficiency, than the males. I suggest, therefore, that a change occurred whereby some of the homogametic, and therefore more efficient, males were enabled to have issue as phenotypic females. The occasional failure to develop complete masculinity might be assisted by iodine-shortage. Granting

[1] See previous section : "Sex Determination and Survival Value," p. 21.

this, all the offspring would be homogametic. In other words, the sex-chromosomes, with their genes for water- and iodine-economy, would have become autosomes. Somewhere else in the chromosomes, however, would be the gene responsible for the occasional failure to develop full masculinity. When it occurred in the duplex condition this would be even more likely to happen. Mutations of special value to the female would then be encouraged to collect in its neighbourhood. Thus could evolve a new sex-chromosome, this time homogametic in the female.

SIZE-CONTROL AND LACTATION IN THE MAMMAL

It will be assumed, then, that following upon the evolution of the homogametic female it became more possible to strike an accurate balance between the conflicting needs of the parent and of the offspring. Necessary as this may have been under conditions of increasing aridity, it would become still more so if there were to occur a sudden environmental change requiring a new kind of physiological efficiency. This last I believe to have been lime-economy.

The ancestral aquatic vertebrate was probably a carnivore, and it may be assumed that the first land-forms retained this means of obtaining food. The change to plant-eating on land would probably supply a welcome addition to the supply of calcium. This would be needed, since on land gravity must be resisted by the growth of bone. Thus, only later, when the hitherto arid land became partially depleted of its calcium, would there arise a sudden need for the economy of this once plentiful substance. I suggest, then, that the mammal evolved sex-linked genes for lime-economy at a time of increasing rainfall subsequent to the development of the homogametic female. The latter would have been larger than the male owing to her greater need to economize fluid.

Now lime-economy is assisted by small size. Not only are the areas of the gut and the skin enlarged relatively to the bulk of the body—thereby encouraging the intake of lime and the autosynthesis of vitamin D—but also the ratio of skeletal to body weight can be reduced.[1] Moreover, the relative increase in the bone surfaces probably favours an increased reserve of calcium, which is specially useful to the lactating female.[2] Lactation can, without doubt, throw a considerable strain upon the lime reserves of the female, and would cause death and sterility in areas where lime was deficient. The mechanism of lactation is, in consequence, believed to have been first evolved under arid conditions when lime was plentiful. Under such circumstances the rapid ossification of the hitherto plastic fœtal bones immediately after delivery would offer a clear case of survival-value by benefiting the offspring at no cost or risk to the mother. If so, lactation was

[1] Cf. Haldane, J. B. S. : Essay " On being the Right Size." Possible Worlds.

[2] Cf. Chapter IX.

evolved primarily as a means of transferring fluid, and was at first only of secondary use in supplying lime. Later it became a tax upon the calcium reserves, and so led to the perfection of a physiological economy through reduction of the bodily size. This happened as soon as the vertebrate was required to adapt itself to humid conditions, probably in the Cretaceous. These originally sex-linked genes for lime-economy are considered of great importance as a means of explaining the fine bone of so-called "Modern Man" when compared with the coarse-boned Hominidæ.

GIANTS AND DWARFS

I was led to this theory of the essential importance of the sex-linked characters as determinants of racial as well as of individual size by noticing that, in general, isolation in islands seems to reduce the size of mammals, whereas birds and reptiles tend to grow bigger. The observation would require further confirmation by a competent zoologist. My theory is that mammals are in a state of greatest physiological efficiency when a predominance of the sex-inheritance has reduced size and resulted in an economy of calcium; and that in-breeding hastens a move in this direction. Incidentally the smaller numbers reduce the intensity of a male rivalry otherwise liable to annul the former influence. In the case of birds and reptiles, on the other hand, where the male is generally both larger and genetically more complex (since homogametic) than the female, he is also deemed to be physiologically the more efficient. Thus, even after a removal of male rivalry, a corresponding acceleration of phylogenetic change, due to in-breeding, would seem bound to favour large size as a correlate of reproductive superiority. This may explain why birds have adopted æsthetic or "aeronautical" forms of masculine display. Sexual selection for masculine size, strength or weight must at all costs be avoided.

This theory is not, of course, without its difficulties. The fact that in islands large size seems correlated with reptilian and avian survival, and small size with mammalian success, could be attributed to the fact that mammals have already displaced reptiles in most situations where lime-economy is an advantage, and that the sex-linkage of large size in the reptile and bird serves to economize heat, or some heat-releasing material, such as iodine. When mammals are isolated in cold or iodine-deficient regions they might be expected to grow bigger. Thus the large bears of Kodiack Island, and possibly the extinct giant dormouse of Malta, might serve as the exceptions proving the rule.

TRANSLOCATION AND SEX-DIMORPHISM

The theory that the whole, or a major part, of the primitive sex-chromosome may have become an autosome has already been mentioned. Later, however, in dealing with the probable evolution of human races, the possibility has been recognized that genes once evolved on the sex-chromosomes might become translocated to the autosomes. Observations bearing out this possibility have already been obtained from a comparison of the genetical analyses of two sub-species of the fruit fly (*Drosophila*).[1]

Since the female mammal is smaller than the male an augmented predominance of the sex-linked inheritance might increase sex-dimorphism to a disadvantageous extent. At the same time the males might still continue to suffer from a relative lack of physiological efficiency (e.g., lime-economy) even after the homogametic, and so smaller, females had achieved a proper adaptational adjustment. Under these circumstances the translocation of a few hitherto sex-linked size-reducers would benefit the males at no cost to the females, and so advance the interests of the species as a whole.

Similar translocations from the autosomes to the sex-chromosomes might also be of value. Supposing the mechanical efficiency of the female to be hindered by a sex-linked repression of some single character, we may assume that genes favouring its full expression must exist upon the autosomes. Thus, if the latter became translocated, and so sex-linked, the females would gain at the expense of the males. A better arrangement still would be for the duplicate genes to arise in the sex-chromosomes, while their originals retained their positions in the autosomes.

ENVIRONMENT, ADAPTATION AND NATURAL SELECTION

Now, in attempting to explain a complex adaptational escape from an otherwise impending calamity, lip-service is often paid to a theory of random mutation and selection. It might rightly be objected, however, that a mutation can hardly be regarded as random if it be deemed to have stepped in only at the eleventh hour and at a time when a decrease in female fertility has probably reduced numbers. Small numbers may intensify in-breeding, and so hasten the doubling up and full somatic expression of recessive mutants.[2] It can do nothing, however, to speed up the mutation rate.

More space will hereafter be claimed for this fundamental problem. Here it must suffice to point out that the influence of use and disuse upon the development of the individual, and also the arrests of development due to adverse environmental changes, are regarded as a means whereby the individual can experiment, and so contrive a safe path for the later adaptational progress of the race. When a given form of individual reaction confers survival-value, we may expect it to be perfected by a subsequent selection of modifying factors ; and in-breeding could accelerate the latter process. As an incidental result

[1] Koller, P. C. : " Pointed, and the constitution of the X Chromosome in Drosophila Obscura," *Journal of Genetics*, Cambridge, 1932, Vol. 26, No. 2.

[2] See page 37.

of these secondary mutations, a return to the original non-adapted condition would, to a large extent, be cut off; and this accidental and partial irreversibility insures that the initial adaptive stimulus will be persistently applied.[1]

This subsequent perfecting and inheritance of an initially acquired or ontogenetic character seems of assistance in explaining the last-mentioned case of the inheritance of an accidental sex-reversal, no less than those of many other fundamental happenings, such as the probable hypotrophy of the anthropoid arm, and the consequent adoption of the erect stance at the dawn of Hominid evolution. Supposing small numbers of a badly adapted species to be struggling against an adverse environmental influence, say iodine deficiency, the chances of large and frequent developmental arrests and distortions will greatly increase. In the earlier example this might conceivably lead to the failure of full masculine development, and to that alternative production of the female sex-organs postulated to explain the emergence of the homogametic mammalian female. In the other, the specialized anthropoid hand, with its long fingers and shortened thumb, could cast off these later-developed characters and so offer better opportunities for acquiring manipulative skill.

THE ENVIRONMENT OF THE GENE

The nature and evolutionary significance of the individual's reaction to changes of the external environment, especially alterations of growth in response to variations in the quantity and nature of the food supply, are fundamental to this whole enquiry. If such reactions are at random it would be difficult, though perhaps not impossible, to place much faith in the previous theory according to which the ontogenetic reaction proceeds in advance of the phylogenetic adaptation. A process, to be termed "selective predominance," is therefore postulated which would appear capable of experimental verification. In the meantime, it promises to explain certain puzzling alterations of size which occur when pedigree livestock are exported overseas. For it is unsatisfactory to attribute these either to mutation and selection, since the process seems to occur within as few as three generations; or again to mere ontogenetic reactions affecting each generation afresh, since the degeneration of exported breeds is not immediate. Moreover, the same theory of selective predominance provides an explanation for the recapitulation of racial history by the individual, as also for the survival of polyploid races of plants and animals; and it has been used here as the groundwork of a theory of endocrine evolution and action in plants and animals. It could also account for the mobilization of genes into linkage groups.

[1] Cf. Thomson, J. A., and Geddes, P.: *Evolution*, pp. 108 and 200, Home University, 1912; also Baldwin, J. Mark: *Development and Evolution*, 1902. The latter stresses the influence of behaviour as a form of plasticity paving the way for the selection of germinal variations.

The basis of the theory is as follows : *A gene is deemed only to exert its full somatic, or outward, effect upon the body if and when its own intra-nuclear environment is similar to that prevailing at the time of its selection as a new mutant.* Also, the intra-nuclear environment of the gene is held to be controlled by other genes as well as by the nature of the external environment with which they must interact. Thus, Fisher's theory of the evolution of genetic dominance through modifying factors is regarded as implying a secondary selection of such modifying factors, each of which helps to adjust and maintain the environment of the primary mutant in a manner consistent with a full somatic expression of the latter.

On this theory the development of the growing individual may be conceived as beginning with an interaction between the forces of the external environment and some very primitive genes. The resulting modification of the physico-chemical state within the dividing cells will then allow later selected genes to exert their influence upon their still later selected neighbours and so upon the organism. Thus there will occur an ontogenetic unfolding that runs parallel with a serial transference of the environmental stimulation passed on by the primitive to the more recently evolved hereditary factors. Hence, the theory—which is now almost a verified fact—that ontogeny recapitulates phylogeny supports the hypothesis of selective predominance.

Perhaps the main importance of this theory, as applied to the question of the animal and human reactions to recurrent variations in the nature of the climate, soil, and food, lies in its power of helping us to understand the nature of the evolved reactions to food deficiencies. It seems possible, for instance, that arid conditions will have tended to build up a system of reinforcing genes all dependent for their somatic expression upon a few primitive factors selected to perform their duty under the associated conditions of calcium abundance, and water and iodine shortage. Similarly, one might suppose that another and alternative organization would be perfected for the purpose of maintaining life, and its own somatic expression, under conditions of lime deficiency and iodine abundance.

Only when characters achieve outward expression can they be improved by further mutation and selection—a fact which Fisher points out. Thus, supposing one set of characters to express itself only under arid conditions, it would become further perfected for these conditions alone ; the same holding good for the gene-train evolved in response to humidity. The critical period would be the time when the more primitive genes were struggling for predominance. This would be shortly after conception. Thus the nutritional state of the mother might be expected to pre-condition the phenotypic expression of her offspring's heredity. Moreover, the direction of this influence, being presumably a faint reflection of the external environment through the internal environment of the mother, would be in a direction calculated to improve the survival chances of the offspring as compared with those of its dam.

On this theory we must expect a given hereditary outfit to display the possibility of a limited and evolved phenotypic plasticity. Anthropometrical facts, as marshalled by Boas and his school, and also the common experience of pedigree livestock breeders, suggest that in Man and his large domesticated animals, if not in small fast-developing laboratory mammals (about which more is known), some such process must take place.[1] In the case of smaller and more specialized animals it seems possible that a change in the size of the population, rather than in the form of the individual, serves as the sole method of ecological adjustment.

As for the origin, as opposed to the final perfecting, of this or any other alternative set of environmental reactions, it is useful to look to the possible survival-value of polyploidy. Suppose two sub-species to undergo secondary adaptation in opposite types of environment, their subsequent re-combination might result in a new polyploid species, having the inherent capacity to evolve in either of the two opposite directions. Similarly, any doubling of a chromosome, due to a failure of normal disjunction, would offer a chance of alternative somatic reactions developing between its own genes and those once homologous with them. Thus, if two such chromosomes differed in the matter of a few heterozygous genes, the former allelomorphs would be encouraged to collect secondary supporters ; each side tending to select modifiers whose action, besides assisting their own somatic expression, also inhibited that of their opponents.

This theory of an inherent hostility between linkage groups is deduced from the idea that modifying factors will generally be valueless unless inherited in conjunction with the primary mutation that they were selected to serve. Consequently points at which disjunctions occur might represent conflicts in the possible evironmental demand. Indeed, supposing the physiological behaviour of the gene to depend upon a reaction to a previously evolved environment in immediate contact with itself, it seems possible that disjunction would be encouraged by any circumstance able to destroy an essential factor of this physico-chemical state. Thus a nutritional deficiency might be felt at a certain stage of ontogenetic development, and the gene responsible for this next step would thus not only fail to affect the soma, as a result of its lost activity, but might also be more inclined to break away from its immediate neighbour. This, of course, is pure speculation. It is tempting, however, to imagine waves of gene-stimulation proceeding along the lengths of each chromosome ; the crests, or points of high potential, corresponding to the various evolved, but conflicting, tendencies severally striving for somatic expression at any given moment of ontogenetic development.

[1] Boas, F. : *Changes in Bodily Form of Descendants of Immigrants.* New York, 1912.

Obviously the foregoing is too conjectural a construction to furnish a ground for further hypothesis. It is necessary, however, to apply the general theory of selective predominance in an attempt to understand the evolution, and so the action, of the endocrines. The latter control the blood concentrations of at least three of the more important minerals, namely, iodine, lime and sodium. Moreover, on quite other grounds they have for some time been regarded as the points at which differences of heredity responsible for racial characteristics may be supposed to act. The "hormone theory" is thus reinforced by, and itself supports, the "mineral hypothesis," here in the course of formulation.

I suggest, then, that an endocrine is essentially an organ evolved for the purpose of maintaining the uniformity of the body's internal environment; and in particular for controlling the concentrations of the electrolytes, of which the mineral elements form an important class. As regards the need for this environmental uniformity, I suggest that it allows a continuous predominance, or expression, of the later evolved genes, which are in this way subjected to continuous selection, improvement, and specialization.

On this theory the endocrines must be thought of as controlled by the agency of the more primitive genes that react with the variable and relatively uncontrollable factors of the external environment. For example, the inorganic iodine-content of the food, which may vary from place to place and from day to day, is mobilized into the colloidal thyroxin which can be stored and issued in more regular amounts. Thus all tissues, except the thyroid itself (and, possibly, the pituitary controlling it), may be thought of as governed by genes that have been selected to react with thyroxin, but not with inorganic iodine. Presumably the cells of these tissues also contain the genes identical with those responsible for the behaviour and growth of the thyroid. In their case, however, the reaction to thyroxin must be held to have overthrown the influence of the more primitive genes; for the latter have shot their bolt.

The thyroid might thus be considered as part of a first line of defence useful in safeguarding the predominance and somatic expression of a large number of more recently evolved characters. We know, however, that the endocrines play a further part in altering the state and behaviour of the organism in response to various stimuli. This is explicable if the alternative reactions of a tissue to variations in the strength of a hormone are put down to alterations in the predominance of linkage groups within the cells of the tissue in question. The hormonic fluctuations may then, in their turn, be attributed to similar alterations in the somatic expression of the rival genes struggling for the government of the endocrine itself.

These genes controlling the endocrine must sometimes be subject to deficiencies of special raw materials—such as iodine—whose absence could prevent the full somatic expression of some, while favouring that of others. Indeed, in the case of the genes sensitive to iodine, this capacity for altering the degree of somatic expression may be believed to be very great, and to persist until a considerable age, perhaps, until the full somatic expression of all other genes has been achieved. Thus the growth of thyroid tissue, in response to low nutritional levels of inorganic iodine, known as simple goitre, may be regarded as an assumption of predominance on the part of genes evolved for this very state of affairs. By increasing the size and efficiency of the thyroid gland they will to a large extent, though not completely, succeed in shielding the remainder of the cells. In the latter the genes corresponding to the iodine-sensitive factors of the thyroid must be held to become immobilized after the stimulation of those requiring the more complex thyroxin.

A THEORY OF SOMATIC REVOLUTIONS

Reference has already been made to the possibility of environment effecting a striking change in the phenotypic expression of the inherited genes. These postulated changes have been called somatic revolutions. Their importance would appear to lie in the fact that they can explain an ontogenetic change as an attempt, by the organism, to develop in a manner best suited to the needs of its immediate environment, provided that its more disadvantageous factors have already been encountered during the previous history of the race. This theory reinforces the view that ontogeny may prospect ahead of phylogeny. Alterations of development, due to changes of nutrition, or to the use and disuse of organs, may be regarded as initial steps in a direction which, if continued, might very probably lead to success. They are not mere accidents of which only a very few could ever be of value. The theory of somatic revolutions thus follows from the hypothesis of selective predominance. Its results, if indeed they occur, might easily be mistaken for single gene mutations. Indeed the latter, by altering the intra-nuclear environment, might give rise to the former. Little space has been devoted to the question how often, if ever, a somatic revolution is transmitted from parent to offspring; since at the present stage of the argument the point is not fundamental. The view that, so-called developmental arrests and distortions are due to somatic revolutions within the individual is, however, adopted. Moreover, it has sometimes been assumed that the returned predominance of genes now resulting in an anatomical defect are of value to the individual, and of potential value to the race, on account of correlated physiological advantages, for which, indeed, they were likewise selected.

THE ENDOCRINES AND ENVIRONMENTAL CHANGE

The endocrines, when judged by their ascertained functions and mutual interactions, display a wonderful capacity for modification in response to changes of climate, and so of soil-type and mineral and vitamin supply. Several physiological facts seem explicable on the assumption either that the Sun is a variable star, or that heat of radio-active origin is released spasmodically to the Earth's crust. It will be assumed, then, that high temperature has been associated with an increase of atmospheric circulation and rainfall, and that the cold has been associated with aridity. This, incidentally, is the theory adopted by Simpson, to help explain the glacial advances and pluvial periods of the Pleistocene.[1] I have found it more satisfactory than any attempt to explain endocrine interactions in terms of all the present climatic belts, on the assumption that the animal is designed to move from one to another, and is possessed of an inherent capacity to adapt itself to any of them. The hot dry habitats and the cold wet places seem thus to provide conditions which will demand entirely new adaptations, differing from those imposed on the ancestral land vertebrate by the *force majeure* of climatic changes affecting the world as a whole.

To substantiate this theory let it be pointed out how both cold and aridity may be countered by the large size, and metabolic activity, produced by a hypersecretion of the anterior-lobe. Not only will an evaporation of moisture from the relatively reduced skin-surface be inhibited, but heat produced as a by-product of the physiological processes will likewise be saved. The dry soil will provide an abundance of lime, and probably of phosphorus and fluorine as well, for the building-up of a large and strong skeleton and teeth. As for the absorption of this excess of calcium, the intensity of the ultra-violet radiation responsible for the auto-synthesis of vitamin D (the lime vitamin) would likewise be increased, even if the total result, allowing for reduced surface area, were much the same. Of course, the gut surface, too, would undergo relative reduction. This consideration may be serious, implying a limitation to development in certain directions owing to the difficulty of obtaining various substances, such as iodine and iron, that will be rare in the arid kinds of habitat. The main structural substances, however, seem all to be plentiful. Lime and phosphorus having been mentioned, it is significant that the protein or nitrogen content of vegetation is correlated with its phosphorus and lime ingredients. Thus the arid habitat provides an abundance of material not only for the skeleton, but for the soft tissues as well. Further, the excess of nitrogen in the food can be eliminated with a useful release of heat.

Now mention has already been made of the theory that vitamin E, considered as the raw material of the anterior-lobe hormone, is probably more plentiful in arid habitats. It is derived from the pollen of plants, and these, we may reflect, are almost bound to re-fertilize in situations where drought may kill off the mature diploid individual. In rain-forests, however, vegetative reproduction is possible,

[1] Simpson, C. G.: "The Climate during the Pleistocene Period," *Proc. roy. Soc.*, Edinb., 1929-30, Vol. V., Part III, No. 21, p. 261.

C

and the weakness of the seedling places it at a disadvantage with more mature rivals. Assuming, then, that vitamin E is most abundant in cold climates, one can understand its suitability as used by the pituitary to encourage the heat-production and large bodily size necessary in such situations.

The requirements of the arid habitat in the matter of the water-economy of the animal body seem also fairly consistent with the assumption that anterior-lobe activity has been used to assist survival under these circumstances. Anterior-lobe extracts favour the intake—though also the diuresis—of water. Meanwhile, the abundance of sodium in the arid regions probably serves to assist water retention, and might thus otherwise have inhibited diuresis. Sodium retention is encouraged by the adrenal-cortex, and is most necessary in the hot, humid habitats.

The question of the evolutionary significance of the posterior-lobe is more difficult. It is worth remembering, however, firstly, that the posterior-lobe appears to inhibit the anterior-lobe, in so far as the latter influences amphibian metamorphosis ; and, secondly, that the posterior-lobe affects diuresis and constricts the bore of the capillaries, so tending to reduce the volume available for maintaining the liquid reserve. It is thus credible that the anterior-lobe promotes water storage as well as intake, and that the posterior-lobe has been evolved to maintain an adjustment of surface tension and fluid pressure in response to the progressive loss of liquid liable to occur in a primitive amphibian. In an animal species or in a human race that has become adapted to life in a desert we might thus expect either an activity of the anterior-lobe or an inhibition of the posterior-lobe. The long-legged camel would appear to have adopted the former method, and the dwarfish Bushman the latter. This would allow of a capillary dilation, and consequently of a large reserve of liquid. At the same time any mechanism able to reduce the evaporation of moisture from the skin —as by inhibiting the development of sweat glands—would be of value. It is of interest, therefore, to note that in myxœdema, due to iodine deficiency, this dry form of skin—analogous to that of the Mongoloid peoples and the Bushman—is often apt to develop. I suggest that its cause should be regarded as due less to the direct influence of the deficiency, than as arising through a compensating hypersecretion of some other hormone, probably one derived from the anterior-pituitary.[1] Not only iodine deficiency, but also fluorine abundance (an equally adverse condition, since fluorine is a poison), would seem able to produce similar cachexias. In each case I suggest that genes evolved for survival under conditions of extreme aridity gain a selective predominance by somatic revolutions. One case of probable fluorine-cachexia in a rat appears to have been inherited. In man and large animals the condition occurs regularly in certain localities ; as often where phosphates are abundant.[2]

[1] Cf. Chapter IV. [2] Cf. Chapter V.

The idea that vitamin E is most abundant, and anterior-lobe activity greatest, in arid and iodine-deficient situations, whereas rainfall reduces this need by providing more iodine, is supported by the observation that the thyroid and anterior-lobe hormones both promote basal-metabolism and encourage amphibian metamorphosis. A difficulty, however, arises from the fact that, although a pathological anterior-lobe activity (acromegaly) seems sometimes to encourage an increase in stature, the races of man evolved in the iodine-deficient areas of Central Asia are not noticeably large, but rather the reverse. Moreover, iodine, which might be expected to occur in humid areas where small size is an advantage, may sometimes increase stature, as was found in the case of recruits for the Swiss army. A similar difficulty arises in connexion with the Bushman, whose steatopygia, even if produced through sexual selection, suggests a valuable adaptation for liquid economy. Nevertheless, the Bushman, instead of being a giant and so saving water by a relative reduction of surface-area, is actually a dwarf.

These difficulties may be overcome by considering the possible phylogenetic influence of sex in mammalian and human evolution. The demands of lactation require a greater reserve of liquid than is wanted by the more primitive vertebrate. At the same time, the need to economize lime and retain an available reserve upon the bone-surfaces will have tended to inhibit skeletal development and gross size. I suggest, therefore, that the original functions of the anterior-lobe have become divisible ; and that the female sex-inheritance, probably acting through the gonad and the follicular or female sex-hormone, can inhibit the action of the anterior-lobe in so far as it encourages growth in size. At the same time, it seems possible that the same sex-influence preserves, or even positively promotes, the original tendency towards tissue hydration, and does nothing to hinder the efficient utilization of iodine and thyroxin.

This encouragement of tissue hydration in the female could possibly have come about at the time of the evolution of the homogametic female. For it was suggested that the new sex-chromosome was developed at a time of aridity, and in response to a previous inefficiency on the part of the original heterogametic mothers. Thus the new sex-chromosome is likely to have collected genes for liquid economy at a time prior to the selection of the sex-linked mutants for small size and calcium economy. On this theory, sex-linked as well as autosomal characters for iodine and liquid economy should be in existence ; the former linked with genes for small size, and the latter with factors making for an increase of body bulk. If so, it would appear to be largely a matter of chance whether an environmental deficiency of liquid or iodine would result in an increase or in a reduction of size. All one could expect would be that an impaired nutrition of the endocrines would result in a two-fold, but in each case beneficial, deviation from the previous racial average. Acromegaly and giantism, no less than cretinism and dwarfing, might thus possibly be due to iodine shortage. Small races, among which the sex-chromosome was already predominant owing to a selection for calcium-economy in the tropics, might be expected to adapt themselves to drought or iodine shortage by becoming still smaller. Moreover, if the aridity was associated with heat, the small size would bestow an advantage of its own. Larger races that were already principally specialized for these conditions, and in which the autosomal inheritance was already predominant over the female sex-characters, might be expected to react by becoming still larger. Thus the influence of iodine deficiency upon a mixed modern population might be to augment the standard deviation by producing an increase in the numbers of abnormally tall and short people at the expense of those approximating closely to the previous average.

POPULATION, IN-BREEDING, AND SEXUAL SELECTION

A theory of the mechanism of animal and human adaptation having now been outlined, it may be well to say something of the means by which the speed of the process is believed to be governed. Actually there can be no advantage in slow adaptation, provided that an avenue of retreat is left open. This, in the case of the mammal, would appear to have been arranged. Size can be varied in either direction by allowing a greater or less expression of the size-repressing sex-linked genes of the homogametic female. Similarly, when the specialization of an organ precludes its immediate use for a new purpose, iodine-deficiency, or even drought, would appear capable of encouraging the predominance of more primitive genes whose full expression will achieve a beneficial arrest of anatomical development. Thus, organic adaptation, unlike the genetical evolution in which it arises, has become partly reversible.

It would thus appear as though every device able to accelerate the evolutionary process will itself possess survival-value. Consequently it may be useful to consider, first of all, the conditions operating in a small population, already reduced by an adverse environmental change ; and, afterwards, the reverse process, when numbers increase as the result of an abundance of well-balanced food. In the first case, I suggest that in-breeding is bound to occur, and will result in a specific change ; and usually in such a direction as to increase physiological efficiency at the expense of previous anatomical specialization. In the opposite case of large numbers of well-fed individuals, sexual selection will replace in-breeding as the spur to adaptational progress. It will result also in physiological improvement through the alteration of racial sexuality and sex-dimorphism. In addition, however, it will tend to divert the direction of anatomical development through the agency of specialized and more arbitrary forms of competition. Fisher points out that all changes of environment are in some sense disadvantageous. This may be true for the average individual, even when the change increases the population. The conditions of competition are thereby altered, so that adaptability becomes of greater value.

IN-BREEDING

In-breeding, when combined with fierce selection, has been responsible for the fashioning of most of the sub-species or "breeds" of domesticated livestock. It serves to increase phenotypic or bodily variations by providing the increased chance of recessive genes meeting, in the same individual, with allelomorphs, or partners, derived from the same initial mutant as themselves. Thus an increase of somatic variation can be used to hasten the adaptational process in any given direction. All offspring, except some extreme type of variant, can be killed or otherwise removed from the in-breeding group. I suggest, therefore, that the mammal has derived a certain benefit from the very reliance it has placed upon the extremely alterable supplies of soil-salts present in the vegetable food, and used by the reproductive organs. The sterility of parents or the premature death of offspring, either of which seems liable to occur as a result of lime or iodine deficiency, would be of value in reducing the size of the population and in causing in-breeding. Supposing the original population to have been large, we may expect a big crop of recessive, and therefore untested, mutations to arise. Among them might be many which, when doubled by in-breeding, would become capable of acting as modifying factors, and so of assisting the full expression of primary and advantageous mutants—if such occur—and in any case of promoting the full re-expression of primitive or atavistic, though once more valuable, characters.

Haldane draws attention to the absence of typological series illustrating the evolution of the majority of land animals;[1] whereas in the sea the process would appear to have been more gradual. This significant fact I would attribute to the greater environmental instability of the land, and particularly to the influence of climate upon the inorganic constituents of the food. I believe it to have encouraged both in-breeding and sexual selection in alternating periods. Arid conditions, being probably less lethal, and being also liable to assist the preservation of bone, have probably been responsible for the adaptation of most of the known types of fossilized land animals. If, therefore, as I suspect, modern man arose in response to in-breeding under humid conditions, the chance of finding even one missing link is correspondingly remote.

SEXUAL SELECTION

Reason has already been given to suppose that a natural selection for a certain degree of sex-linked predominance, or racial sexuality, could confer survival-value. It would thence follow that any means of

[1] Haldane, J. B. S.: *The Causes of Evolution.*

accelerating a necessary change of this racial sexuality would also receive its reward. Thus any means whereby males could compete so as to excel in some masculine character would sway the development of the race towards masculinity, and vice versa. Moreover, if, and when, correlated instincts were developed, the strength of the instinct would need to be linked with the genes for the anatomical character which the instinct was designed either to direct or to appreciate. That is to say, if the genes for tall stature are autosomal, any genes leading to a feminine appreciation of this character could have no phylogenetic influence unless they also were autosomal. Otherwise the taller and more masculine men would be most admired by the shorter and more feminine women. The result would be offspring of an average sexuality and stature.

Now actually, of course, the question how far feminine appreciation plays a part in sexual selection is most obscure. I would suggest, however, a manner in which it could slowly evolve. As an example, take the development of antlers. These do not appear until puberty, and in the females horns of any sort either fail to materialize or remain very small. It is reasonable to attribute to horns a value for the purposes of offence and defence. Males use them to fight each other for the possession of the females. It is thus legitimate to assume a linkage between the genes making for the growth of horns and those which encourage a combative attitude to other males. Now the immature males do not fight with the adults, and there is no reason to believe that most of them even attempt to do so. I conclude, therefore, that the inhibition of horn-growth and the inhibition of the combative instinct are likewise linked ; and, seeing that the growth of horn in the female is repressed, and that she does not fight the male, it seems probable that they are both sex-linked.

In all mammals many of the features of youth and of femininity are similar. In the developing male these feminine characters are apt to be retained until puberty, and are then suddenly cast off ; being presumably overthrown by an activity of some autosomal parts of the inheritance. This retention of a feminine form could have been encouraged in two ways. Firstly, while growth was proceeding the more efficient female economy of nutrients and structural substances would be of value. Secondly, the jealousy of the mature males would need to be held in check until such time as growth was finished, and the new individual was ready to fight for the survival of such genes as he might have inherited. Thus sexual selection for an autosomal character in the mammal can first of all encourage a full phenotypic expression of autosomal characters in the mature male ; secondly, it will favour a delayed maturity transferable to the females also ; and, thirdly, it will demand a rapid metamorphosis from a sex-linked repression to a full development of all organs and instincts of offence. The psychological implications of this are most important, and will be dealt with apart. This theory of a sex-linked repression of combativeness helps to explain the evolution of Freud's "Œdipus complex," and so relates the pathological to the normal.

Only brief mention will here be made of the theory that in Man a sexual selection for ultra-femininity also exists, and tends to balance the influence of sexual selection for male, or autosomal, characters. The development of the organs used for sex-display in the female are deemed to owe their initial over-development to an accident. The young male would require to arrange for a store of nutrients sufficient to accelerate his anatomical development past the danger point of puberty. He would thus require a special degree of female, or sex-linked, anabolic efficiency during the period just prior to this. Thus a selection for a sex-linked character required simplex by the young male would display itself more powerfully, though at first without reason, when inherited duplex by the female. At a later stage an appreciation of water and fat stored upon the buttocks or breasts could be made use of to reverse part of the results of sexual selection for masculinity. When nutrients were scarce, sexual selection for ultra-femininity, as measured by a capacity to lay on fat, would be of considerable survival value. Sexual selection for ultra-femininity implies an inhibition of male aggression and the exercise of female choice. Infra-masculine men must be free to mate with ultra-feminine women.

RACIAL MIXTURE

A good deal of reliance has been placed upon theories of racial mixture. In particular, the initial change from anthropoid to man is believed to have been followed by a separation into a Northern, or Palæanthropic, type adapted to arid country, and a Southern, or Neanthropic, sub-species adapted to the decalcified soils of the tropical rain-belt. All the more widely dispersed and successful races of humanity are considered to represent various blends produced by a series of racial mixtures separated by periods of specialization within single adverse and selective environments.

Not only in-breeding, as resulting from a contraction of population, but also racial mixture, due to expansions leading to contact between two or more endogamous groups, will produce an increase of outward or phenotypic variation. Thus, a change either from good to bad or from bad to good conditions of life may alike have been utilized to hasten the evolutionary process. Just as in-breeding results in the doubling of recessive genes within the single individual, so may racial mixture bring about the combination of hitherto unassociated dominants. For the previous phase of in-breeding may be expected to have eliminated old dominants and to have promoted recessives into their places; and the latter will in time collect modifying supporters capable of conferring a new, if relative, dominance, even when faced by the return of strange allelomorphs, similarly modified in the evolution of the other sub-species.

It does not seem necessary to suppose that this combination of hitherto unassociated hereditary characters need necessarily produce a mere blending of the outward forms previously recognizable in the parental strains. Indeed, one might expect striking departures from either ancestral form to be at least occasional. Modifiers, evolved to maintain the dominance of a new and hitherto weak recessive, might find themselves equally well adapted to support the original dominant allelomorph, whose mutational crippling had previously called them into being. Thus, if the old dominant was inherited from one side of the cross, and if supporting factors appropriate to its full expression could be obtained from the other, it does not seem impossible for the old character to display a greater phenotypic gain than ever before. Moreover, supposing the dominant to have survival-value, since it is carried by one strain at a time of racial expansion, the over-development might conceivably, and even probably, prove of use.

Much the same conclusion is reached if we think physiologically, and consider the probable effects of racial mixture between sub-species whose main difference lies in the activity of the endocrine system as a whole. It seems fair to assume that, whereas some genes tend to control the concentrations of the internal secretions, others are mainly concerned with governing the reactive thresholds of the tissues. Moreover, there is evidence to show that, when the activity of an endocrine is sub-normal, a standard increase produces a more than usual degree of reaction. This is true of thyroxin, insulin and parathormone. Such an arrangement may be claimed as an adaptation valuable in economizing any rare substance used as a hormone. When a substance is scarce, a small quantity is enabled to produce an enhanced effect.

Now, supposing a racial mixture to occur between endocrine types that are of high and low activity respectively, it is not impossible that the genes for an active secretion might not be inherited in company with others making for a high degree of reaction to a unit rise of concentration. If this can occur, there will result a type in which the endocrine characters in question will be developed in a degree never previously selected by any natural process. The result will be a purely experimental type—one in which the degree of some adaptational development is sure to be extreme. If this adaptation were a response to climate, the new type might thus be enabled to penetrate further into a disadvantageous area than had ever been possible before.

It is not inconceivable that the production of pygmies and giants might thus follow from the racial fusion of two less different types. In the dwarf there would be the low endocrine activity of the small race linked with the high reactive threshold evolved for the tissues of the larger one. The case for the giant has already been outlined. Could the Nilote and the Pygmy be the result of the same Negro and Bushman intermixture? Could an identical process have produced the Lapp and the Nordic? I suggest, then, that racial mixture, besides producing a blend, may also result in a rebound to even greater extremes than those separating the original constituents. If racial mixture occurs at a time of expanding population, the production of those extreme types will serve still further to extend the limits of the habitat occupied by the species in question.

In later chapters dealing with the living and extinct races of man I have been driven to the expedient of explaining several anomalous combinations of characters in terms of racial mixture. Taken by themselves such features seemed only explicable as the products of selective processes occurring in opposite types of habitat ; yet they have somehow managed to combine in the same individuals. In order to escape from this difficulty, the analogy of Goldschmidt's *Lymantria* intersexes can again be used. The intersexuality itself has, of course, already been brought under the main theory of phylogenetic change through sex-dimorphism. It remains to use it to cover the notion of a high-speed Southern heredity slowly overtaking and masking the influence of a slower-developing set of Northern characters. It might also be claimed that the mineral hypothesis helps to explain the initial facts. Iodine abundance should encourage a high metabolic rate. The early-evolved, and ontogenetically developed, characters might well display a true blend between those of either parental sub-species. The later-evolved and developing vertebrate characters, however, such as the limbs and mandible, when compared with the neurocranium, may be expected to reflect mainly the features derived from the Southern ancestor. Thus may be explained some otherwise puzzling combinations, such as the association of Neanderthaloid skulls with modern limb bones, or that of an ape-like jaw with a human cranium.[1] Thus, too, we may attempt to account for the extreme variations of physique and character found in modern civilized communities.[2] In such a way the synchronization of the evolved checks to growth, and also the development of certain " strata of dissociation " in the mind, are deemed to have been upset. All modern races, and all the known fossils, are regarded as probable results of racial mixture between less plastic and previously inbred sub-species.

CONCLUSION

In this first chapter, the attitude of the writer to the whole complex problem of human and animal evolution has been outlined in order to explain the unusual stress that will be laid upon several hitherto neglected groups of facts here assumed to be of ecological and so of genetical importance. Present heredity has been moulded by past habitats ; and a combined study of soil-science and mineral-deficiency affords a new method of proving geographical and geological conditions to be a main agency in regulating the incidence of natural selection upon animal and human evolution.

The phylogenetic significance of inherited variations in the degree in which secondary sexual characters are expressed is shown to be of primary importance as a means of adapting the species to abundance

[1] Cf. Chapter X. [2] Cf. Chapter XV.

or deficiency of mineral supply, and to the requirements of arid and humid habitats. This harnessing of the mechanism of sex-dimorphism for the sake of adaptation to the environment is believed to have reached its highest development in the mammal; for in this case an ability to regulate body-size in two directions has been evolved. Humidity and lime-shortage are assumed to favour small size, whereas lack of iodine and cold may encourage large size. Iodine-shortage might also be expected to encourage slow-growth and fœtalization, both of them characters that are fully developed in Man. Since iodine supplies are deemed to have slowly accumulated during the course of animal history, the means of accommodation to renewed deficiencies may have been secured by the reappearance of atavistic characters.

The more specific cases of organic adaptation are explained by an extension of Fisher's theory of the evolution of genetic dominance by modifying mutations. Similar secondary mutations are held to perfect the ontogenetic reactions in any series of related individuals subject to the same recurring stimuli.

The ontogenetic reaction itself is regarded as an evolved character; and hence as more likely to start the adaptational process in a favourable direction than if it were merely at random. Ontogenetic reactions, indeed, are explained as the returned "predominance" (allied to Mendelian "dominance") of subsequently modified or repressed primitive characters; the changes in the outward expression of a gene being attributed to an alteration of its intra-nuclear environment, brought about by the agency of mutations, or possibly by the direct agency of nutritional changes. The endocrines are explained as devices whereby the more important aspects of the immediate environments of the genes responsible for the later-evolved, and ontogenetically differentiated, tissues are prevented from losing their somatic expression and thus falling outside the influence of natural selection. Environmental change, however, is thought able to affect the activity of the endocrines; and so, by altering the genetic "predominance" between the genes of the subservient tissues, to bring out old, but previously evolved, characters of a sort more likely to be of value under the new conditions.

The evolutionary influence of alterations in the size of the population is touched upon. When numbers are reduced, owing to a disadvantageous change of climate and food-supply, in-breeding is held responsible for subsequent adaptations, which, in the case of the larger mammals, will probably result in a reduction in the size of the individual. When numbers increase, however, owing to an improvement in ecological adjustment, a sexual selection operating between the males will tend to reverse this process, and to favour strength at the expense of physiological efficiency. In Man, too, a second form of sexual selection resulting in reduced size and racial femininity seems to have become highly developed, as an alternative to the reduction of numbers and the in-breeding otherwise inevitable. This last process would be hardly compatible with the successful transmission of a social inheritance. Thus the human race has avoided frequent in-breeding and the concomitant danger of extreme specialization.

Increase in the size of population is liable to result in racial mixtures, which not only combine and blend characters previously specialized apart, but may also result in the production of a few extreme types. The latter may be enabled to invade habitats previously impossible to the less extreme parental forms. Thus conditions which are favourable to the numerical expansion at the centre will furnish specialized pioneers capable of extending the range of the whole inter-breeding group. If the analogy of Goldschmidt's moths be extended further, it may be expected that in such crosses the predominance of the Southern inheritance will be greatest in respect of the later evolved and developed vertebrate characters.

CHAPTER II

A STUDY OF ENVIRONMENT

Function and Distribution of Minerals: Classification and Calcium-Content of Soils: The Distribution of Iodine.

IT IS PROPOSED HERE TO DISCUSS MAINLY THE DISTRIBUTION OF minerals in the soil, and the relation of soil types to climatic and geological areas. In addition, however, the opportunity will be taken to review some fundamental physiological principles without which the importance of mineral distribution cannot be appreciated. Since the distribution of minerals is controlled either by purely physical forces, or by the related activity of low, and probably primitive, soil organisms, it seems sound method to place these data in the forefront of the argument. Subsequently, the evolutionary significance of the more complex biological facts may thereby be elucidated. After an examination of the principles on which the distribution of phosphorus, calcium, and iodine depend, an attempt will be made in the next chapter to account for certain observed deficiencies in the different continents, using the theories that emerge in combination with a hypothesis of Quaternary climate as influenced by Polar Shift. Thus, to some extent, each theory can serve to check the other. Incidentally, the probability that past climate is responsible for present mineral deficiencies, and will consequently influence the heredity of future animals and men, draws attention to the fallacy of expecting to derive the laws connecting heredity and environment solely from an examination of the present distributions of various hereditary types.

FUNCTION AND DISTRIBUTION OF MINERALS

The food of all animals must be derived from the soil, but plants alone can synthesize the organic substances. Thus plants, regarded as animal food, may be considered, in the first instance, as stores of solar energy. They combine the carbon dioxide of the atmosphere with water, using the radiant energy to force out free oxygen in the formation of hydrocarbon. The hydrocarbons are then available as a source of animal energy; but they will require a catalytic mechanism to assist in the more rapid regaining of the lost oxygen, and a return to the state CO_2+H_2O, accompanied by a reconversion of the energy wherewith the original synthesis was first accomplished. It is in this matter of providing material for the catalytic enzymes that the presence of specific mineral elements becomes important to animals and plants alike. Salts of iron, manganese or copper act on peroxides in the same way as the enzyme peroxidase. Indeed, all the metals found to be active as " peroxidases " are those capable of existing in two states of different valency. Salts of all these metals, especially in the dilute solutions in question, are hydrolyzed in water. In other words, the solutions used consist of hydroxides of the metals in the colloidal state. This fact is taken to indicate that their activity is in direct relationship to the extent of the surface.[1] Chlorophyl itself is the ester of a complex acid, linked to magnesium, while iron probably plays some part in the functioning of the chloroplast.[2]

Substances which provide structure in all living cells are phosphorus, sulphur and nitrogen. The latter, for all practical purposes, is available to animals only in the form of certain of the proteins, which must be reduced to their parent amino-acids and then re-synthesized. Proteins can also be used for the production of heat. Plants obtain their nitrogen from the air, or from the breakdown of organic structures. In either case, however, soil bacteria—living sometimes in symbiosis with the plant from the hydro-carbon of which they obtain energy must act as a go-between to supply them with the necessary nitrates of sodium, potassium, magnesium or calcium. The latter element may be held to play a considerable portion of its biological rôle while still in the soil. For, besides providing a plant-food, and a constituent of the animal body, it exists as the base, calcium carbonate, which is chiefly responsible for maintaining the soil, no less than the plant and the animal, in a neutral or faintly alkaline condition—a state necessary in the soil to allow the fullest activity of the nitrifying bacteria.

The natural soil-water is constantly dissolving small quantities of phosphoric acid, potash, and other minerals, in which task it is assisted by the carbonic acid that it also contains. As this water passes by osmosis into the root hairs, it will carry with it all the dissolved material, with the exception of any particular ion or radicle which has already attained a higher concentration in the sap than it possesses in the external soil-solution. Moreover, it has been observed that the particular ions concerned in nutrition enter the root faster than does the water. This diffusion through the cell-walls occurs because the fluid within is maintained in a less concentrated state than the soil-water ; the low concentration being due to a withdrawal of the necessary elements by the living protoplasm of the cells.[3]

The same kind of plant, then, is by no means constant in regard to the relative quantity of each substance absorbed. The ash of swedes, for instance, may contain anything between 9 and 16 per cent of phosphoric acid ; a matter of far more importance to the animal kingdom

[1] Bayliss, W. M. : *Principles of General Physiology*, London, 1924, p. 586.
[2] Ibid., pp. 577-578.
[3] Hall, A. D. : *The Soil*, London, 1920, p. 178.

than to the plant itself.[1] Again, certain clovers may substitute potash for calcium, or vice versa ; though the former seems to be seldom required by the animal in amounts falling short of the supply. In other cases, sodium may replace the almost valueless potash.[2] Orr shows that there is a definite correlation between the protein and mineral contents of pastures. Pastures which are low in minerals tend to be low also in protein. There is no evidence, however, of any correlation between the mineral contents of pastures and their calorific values, though it is possible that a lack of minerals may lower the digestibility.[3] To generalize, then, we may conclude that, to the plant, minerals are mainly necessary for the metabolism of nitrogen.

Regarding the ratios of the separate minerals to each other, there would seem to exist a minimum percentage of each capable of establishing a limiting factor for vegetative growth. Thus Thompson

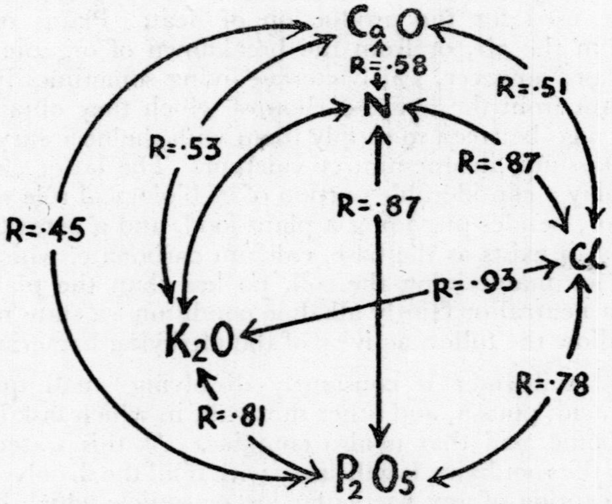

Correlations of Mineral-Contents of Pastures.
(Falkland Islands, Forty Samples.)

shows that in forty samples of the mineral-poor pasture of the Falkland Islands, where lack of calcium would appear to be the limiting factor, the correlations between the percentages of the various minerals are closer than in other comparable groups of samples obtained from richer cultivated and hill pastures in England. All the closest correlations exist between potash, nitrogen, chlorine, and phosphoric acid. The lowest are between calcium and the other four. The lowest of all is that between calcium and phosphoric acid.

Calcium, then, in comparison with the other four key-substances of

[1] Hall, A. D. : *The Soil*, London, 1920, p. 177.
[2] Orr : *Minerals in Pastures*, pp. 20 and 22.
[3] Ibid., p. 16.

vegetable growth, may be regarded as the mineral least necessary to the plant. Indeed, the fact that we find it more highly correlated with the nitrogen-content of pastures than with the other minerals that they contain may be explained best perhaps upon the theory, already put forward, that this affords direct evidence of its function in stimulating the nitrifying bacteria. Moreover, since we have here been considering pastures of mixed flora, it is probable that this nitrifying ability of the more calcareous soils is responsible for the plant-forms normally demanding a high nitrate-concentration before achieving success in " the battle of the meadow." Calcium, however, can help little towards the initial fixation of nitrogen from the air. In this matter the key-substance is undoubtedly phosphoric acid, though deficiencies of the remaining salts may at any time inhibit its action.

The ability of phosphorus to pass simultaneously into a higher and a lower oxide would seem largely to account for its importance as a constituent of living things. Meanwhile, as against the other substances capable of this autoxidation, it may well owe its " selection " as a cell-constituent to its relative immobility in the soil. For, as our consideration of calcium and its functions likewise made clear, we may regard soil-phenomena as constituting a relatively simple outer network of causality distinguishable from the complex organization of life itself rather in respect to degree than kind. The environment, no less than the organism, may be said to have evolved.

Whatever may be the origin of phosphoric acid—and possibly it is apatite, $Ca_5(PO_4)_3F$, which is present in many of the fundamental rocks—it is readily absorbed by the soil.[1] Chalky soils, as also those of fine texture, possess this power to an even greater degree than sands. Soils containing sufficient calcium can absorb phosphoric acid with the precipitation of di-calcium phosphate, wherever the acid meets with a particle of calcium carbonate. The di-calcium phosphate will then remain *in situ* until dissolved either by water containing carbonic acid, or by the organic acid of the root-hairs. In the absence of calcium carbonate the precipitation will be effected by the hydrated iron and aluminium compounds ; and the resulting phosphates are then practically insoluble in the water containing carbonic acid, and to a lesser degree even in the presence of the weak organic acids. At Rothamstead only 17 per cent of phosphoric acid was found to have been lost from a total comprising all applications over a period of fifty years.[2] In nature, too, one would expect an even smaller loss. The phosphorus balance between soil-content and plant-demand is doubly upset under artificial conditions. Trees, not corn crops, are the natural covering of the English plough-lands ; and artificial applications of manure must have increased the total phosphorus content of farm-land far beyond the original amount.

[1] Hall, p. 24. See also Blackwelder, E. : " The Geological Rôle of Phosphorus," *Proc. nat. Acad. Sci. Wash.*, Vol. II, p. 490 (1916).
[2] Ibid., p. 256.

Within the plant, the importance of phosphorus appears to depend upon its usefulness in the forming of special protein compounds, especially those found in the nucleus of the plant cell. It is also present as an element in inorganic compounds.[1] Where phosphorus is lacking, vegetation may utilize large quantities of any existing nitrogen and potash to expand the leaves, stems and vegetative organs. The development of reproductive organs and seeds will, however, be inhibited. Moreover, since the nitrates and potash are both highly soluble, they will often tend to be lost by leaching ; or, in localities where the rainfall is seasonal, they may sink in the rainy season, to creep upward again during the dry remainder of the year. It is clear that a vegetation whose seed-bearing capacity is impaired by lack of phosphorus will seldom thrive in situations subject to climatic variation. Indeed, only in the climatic uniformity of the tropical rain-forest need we expect a lack of phosphorus to pass without being clearly reflected in the sparsity of plant growth.

To return, then, to its nitrogen-fixing properties, these are best displayed, perhaps, in the case of natural or cultivated grass-land, though the principle would seem to hold of most other localities as well. Somerville showed that by the application of a phosphatic fertilizer—basic slag—to English pasture, the growth of the nitrogen-fixing leguminosæ was at once stimulated. As a secondary effect it was found that all the herbage, including even the grasses normally depending for their nitrogen upon the nitrate derived from the decomposition of organic matter by the soil bacteria, was eventually stimulated. This second result might, of course, be expected to be aided by the redistribution of nitrogen effected through the agency of grazing animals. Even without this assistance, however, it has long been known that crops of the leguminosæ, although harvested and removed from the land, can nevertheless encourage the subsequent fertility of other plants grown in the same soil. Indeed, the importance of Somerville's experiments would seem to have rested more upon this primary demonstration than upon the quite remarkable effects observed in the growth-rates and lactation of the animals through which the economic values of phosphatic fertilizers were being estimated. Great as was the quantitative improvement in the pasture, the qualitative change was even more striking.[2] This system of estimating the value of a manure in terms of meat and milk may be said, indeed, for a time to have somewhat obscured the question how minerals react upon the development of plants and of animals respectively. It is now recognized, however, that in certain circumstances it is financially more

[1] Percival, J. : *Agricultural Botany*, London, 1921.

[2] Somerville, W. : " Poverty Bottom," *Journal of Board of Agriculture*, Vol. XXIV., No. 11, Feb., 1918, Reprint No. 20 ; also " Manuring of Pastures for Meat and Milk," Min. Agric. and Fish. Miscl. Pubn., No. 30, 1921.

profitable to supply mineral, especially phosphates in the form of bone flour, by feeding it direct to the animal.[1]

Nature, too, would long seem to have established this same emergency-method of balancing the often mineral-deficient rations of wild animals. Names such as "Big Bone Lick," the fossil bed of Kentucky, serve to point out how, in a period of desiccation, animals will congregate and die in the regions where water last remains unevaporated.[2] Moreover, it is in these same drainage areas that sodium chloride and other salts will tend to accumulate. The result must often be a salt-lick containing all the calcium phosphate once constituting the bones of the early fauna, together with an admixture of such more soluble minerals as are less permanently retained either in the soil or in the animal body. During succeeding epochs these accumulations will again tend to be consumed and redistributed. We may consider, then, that in Nature phosphorus owes to the animals most of such slight mobility as it may be considered to possess.

From the foregoing brief discussion of phosphorus and its properties it will be realized that it occurs both in the soil and in the animal ; being in each case usually combined with calcium. In the plant, however, as we already observed, the ratio of phosphorus to calcium may be variable. Only when a surplus of calcium-salts exists in the soil are we likely to find a high concentration of this latter element in the vegetation.

It will be seen, then, that the phosphorus content of a soil can control not only the volume of vegetation, but the numbers and bulk, of the animals as well. Calcium, on the other hand, is far more variable in its distribution ; and even its absence will imply no reduction in the quantity of vegetation, though it may be expected to bear directly upon that of the animals. Thus, on the assumption that some animals are more economical than others in their utilization of calcium, it follows that calcium may control selection. If, then, the supply of phosphorus, often determines the quantity of life within an area, the amount of available calcium may well decide its quality.

It is at this point that the influence of climate and geology upon the distribution of minerals must be examined. For it is the soluble salts, and especially calcium, that are controlled by the action of water. Now calcium, unlike phosphorus, exists in relatively vast quantities. It constitutes as much as 20 per cent of such primary rocks as the felspar anorthite, while in combination with magnesium it is contained in hornblende and augite in amounts varying from 10 to 15 per cent. In addition, D'Orbigny, quoted by Hall, estimates the carbonate of lime and magnesia as constituting one per cent of the total crust of the earth.[3]

[1] Orr : *Minerals in Pastures*, pp. 130-131.
[2] Osborne, H. F. : *The Age of Mammals*, New York, 1921, p. 480.
[3] Hall : *The Soil*, p. 17.

Now, according to Wegener's theory of continental drift, of which much must be said presently, the calcium and magnesium contents of the oceans may have been increased in relatively late geological times. The rocks forming the ocean beds are, on this hypothesis, deemed to consist of a larger proportion of magnesia, iron oxide, and lime combined with water ; and it is held that a drift of the lighter and more acid land-masses has been accompanied by a series of submarine eruptions whereby additional quantities of this " sima " (silica and magnesium) have been exposed.[1] This theory is at least consistent with a belief that life, which requires a neutral or slightly alkaline environment, was started in the sea. Moreover, it would seem to adduce further testimony in support of the theories of Bunge and Macallum, who each suggested that the salt-content of the blood of land-vertebrates is an inheritance from marine ancestors. Close as are the proportions of sodium to calcium in the two cases, namely, 100 to 2.58 for blood serum, and 100 to 3.84 for sea-water, it will be noticed that the latter is richer in calcium, and thus, in accordance with this theory, may be deemed to have increased its concentration since Cambrian times. Moreover, the difficulty already pointed out by Macallum, namely, that magnesium is now in a far higher ratio to sodium in sea-water than in blood plasma, is explained.[2]

It even seems possible that an initial rise in the calcium and magnesium concentration of the sea may have applied an external stimulus encouraging the original, presumably soft-bodied, cell-aggregate forms of marine life not only to enclose themselves from the outer sea, but also to secrete hard ectodermal parts, the precursors of shell, bone, teeth, tusk, and antler. By so doing they could afterwards maintain their now internalized fluids, or plasma, at a salt concentration such as that to which the individual cells had become long accustomed. Moreover, as already suggested, the extrusions of excess mineral, if even temporarily retained, could not only be utilized for purposes of structure, defence and even attack, but could form a portable reserve of calcium salts such as would render the organism independent of environmental variations of supply. In support of some such theory we may perhaps draw attention to the observations of Robison, who has pointed out that pathological calcifications in the mammal are most liable to occur in those of the soft tissues which happen normally to contain the greatest amount of magnesium.[3] The fact that bone, unlike shell, is comparatively poor in this element may be attributed, perhaps, to some inherent defect of magnesium, in its relation to phosphorus, as a substance wherewith rigid structures may be com-

[1] Wegener, A. : *The Origin of Continents and Oceans*, trans. by J. G. A. Skerl.

[2] Bayliss, pp. 209-210. The theory of an estuarine origin of life, mentioned in Chapter VI, also bears upon this problem.

[3] Robison, R. : Lecture, unpublished ; read before Junior Sci., Oxon., 1932.

posed. The 30-40 per cent of magnesium in marls and limestones does not seem to owe its position to animals. If so, the exclusion of magnesium must be regarded as a character evolved at the same time as bone.

Some large portion of the free calcium, then, may be believed to have had its origin in the sea ; though undoubtedly the sub-aerial weathering of primary rock has likewise contributed. The sea, too, must in any case provide the main deposit of the world's calcium ; for, with the exception of the small fraction immobilized through its association with phosphorus, the remainder, when once rendered soluble, will sooner or later percolate thither, so as finally to be fixed as calcium carbonate through the agency of marine organisms. Geologically, then, it is from deposits of marine origin that the calcium available in the soil will have been obtained.

Now the movement of calcium may be effected through the agency either of wind or of water. The former process is of interest mainly in reference to the wind-formed loëss soils of the Pleistocene. It is, however, to the action of water containing carbon-dioxide in solution that a far more important influence may be attributed. Water, then, may wash calcium from one formation and transfer it horizontally so as to deposit it in another. To do so, however, the water will normally have to evaporate. It is in this way that the lime salts frequently present in drainage areas have been transported. Normally, however, the most common and also, from the point of view of this enquiry, the most important movement of water-borne calcium proceeds vertically either upwards or downwards in the soil. Thus, it is through tracing the movements of calcium that the relations of climate to soil type, originally worked out in detail by the Russian school of Glinka, can be made to throw so much light upon the whole theory now under discussion.

CLASSIFICATION AND CALCIUM-CONTENT OF SOILS

According to the Russian system, soils may be classified largely in terms of evaporation and rainfall. The point is, whether the soil-moisture may be considered to rise and evaporate, thus drawing to some extent upon a subterranean water supply ; or whether the current tends on the whole to flow downward. In the former case salts will accumulate on, or close to, the surface. In the latter case the same salts, and often the colloidal portions of the soil itself—the clay fraction—may be washed out, whereupon the salts find their way into the rivers and the sea, while the clay forms a substratum beneath. Robinson, in a recent discussion of this rather intricate subject, points out how well the climatic classification answers for an interpretation of continental effects.[1] Applied to a country such as England, on the

[1] Robinson, G. W. : *Soils, their Origin, Constitution and Classification.*

other hand, which is subject to no great extremes of climate, and where narrow strips of different geological formation may be observed to determine the farm practice, the climatic criterion in its simpler forms proves utterly inadequate. According to Glinka's soil map of the world, for instance, it will be seen that, for the British Isles, only three classes of soil can be distinguished.[1]

Glinka himself, however, would appear to have propounded a nomenclature, if not a solution, capable of dealing with this difficulty. He has distinguished between "Ektodynamorphic" soils, that is soils in which the external factors predominantly affect the soil-chemistry; and "Endodynamorphic" soils, where the parent material determines the main character. Ramann,[2] discussing this same problem, points out that extreme conditions of heat and cold, such as characterize a continental climate, make for a uniformity of soil-type irrespective of geological conditions. During the heat of the summer the surface particles may become stripped of their last vestige of moisture, this baking effect preventing them ever afterwards from resuming their colloidal properties. Similarly, freezing may arrest bacterial action during a large portion of the year, when the moisture might otherwise be expected to favour the decay of organic matter. These facts seem highly relevant to the present study. We seem to be entitled when dealing with the continental climate of the Pleistocene, and even perhaps with that of the Bronze Age, thus to some extent to neglect geology and to classify the probable calcium-content of the soils almost entirely in terms of climatic theory and observation. During temperate periods, however, the nutritional values of lands situated close to the sea must be judged according to their parent material also. With regard to the Endodynamorphic soils, then, it is obvious that for the purposes of animal nutrition deficiencies are unlikely to occur on formations where the parent deposit contains some quota of the mineral in question. Moreover, when dealing with primitive man and with the wild animals, both of them free to roam over wide tracts of country, it seems unlikely that the specific nature of small areas due to boundaries imposed by geological exposure can seriously affect selection. Let us concentrate, therefore, upon a study of the climatic zones, and of their reactions upon the mineral content of the soil.

In order, then, to facilitate nomenclature and to offer some account of the interactions of temperature and humidity—the mathematical relationships of which, in their bearing on soil type, seem to have defied exact analysis—we may reproduce the provisional scheme suggested by Vilensky. Even if it be descriptive rather than ætiological, the scheme possesses at all events the cardinal virtue of simplicity.

[1] Glinka: Soil Map of the World attached.
[2] Ramann, E.: *The Evolution and Classification of Soils*, trans. Whittles, Cambridge, 1928.

SOIL CLASSIFICATION
(after Vilensky.)[1]

	ARID.	SEMI-ARID.	MEDIUM.	SEMI-HUMID.	HUMID.
POLAR	Tundra	Semi-peat soils	Peat and meadow soils	Podsol	Peat and meadow
Cold	Dry peat	—	Black meadow	Degraded meadow	Podsol
TEMPERATE	Grey earth	Chestnut	Tchernozem black earth	Degraded forest	Podsol
SUB-TROPICAL	—	Yellow of dry steppe	Yellow earth	Degraded yellow	Podsolized yellow
TROPICAL	Red soil of desert	Red earth	Laterite	Degraded red	Podsolized red

N.B. For a comprehensive review, with literature, covering the whole question of soil classification see Encyclopædia Brit., 14th Ed., Russia.

It will be seen that the nomenclature depends largely on colour; which, in its turn, is often dependent on pigments excreted by bacteria.[2] Each type, however, has peculiarities of its own when considered in profile, that is, in vertical section.

Turning now to Glinka's map, and comparing its data with the distribution of rainfall, it will be seen that the bands of the different soil-types run roughly along the parallels of latitude, and correspond generally with the areas of heavy, medium, and low precipitation. In areas of heavy rainfall, even in the tropics, and elsewhere wherever the rainfall may be described even as medium, it will be found that the soils tend to be described as podsolized. A typical podsol is a soil in which the soluble portions are apt to be washed out from the upper layer. From the point of view of this work, then, all podsols may be suspected of being deficient of calcium.

[1] Vilensky, D. G.: "Concerning the principles of a genetic soil classification." Contributions to the study of the soils of Okrainia, 1927, 6, pp. 129–151.
[2] Hall: *The Soil*, p. 216.

Perhaps the next most important class consists of the Tchernozems or black earths of the wheat belts. These mostly occur on the loëss or glacial deposits, and it is arguable, perhaps, that their striking uniformity may in part be attributable to that of their parent materials. Their most remarkable feature, however, is undoubtedly an effect of climate, which would seem to have adjusted evaporation and precipitation so as neither to allow of podsolization on the one hand, nor of the surface precipitation of dry salts on the other.

The result has been the growth of grass under natural conditions. These soils would be unsuitable to the growth of trees, which, as already indicated, seem to flourish best where salts are tending to sink, and may thereupon be intercepted and returned to circulation only through the agency of deep rooting vegetation.

The Tchernozems, then, which owe their black colour to the chalk-loving nitrogen-fixer Azotobacter, tend to accumulate vast stores of organic matter, or humus, while at the same time remaining alkaline or at least neutral in their reaction.[1] Calcium may exist as carbonate or oxide. Most of the chalk will be found deposited in lumps at a horizon below the surface, while the soil water above this contains sufficient CO_2 to retain its lime in solution. In these soils, the bacterial decomposition, probably inhibited by winter frosts and summer drought, would seem to lag behind vegetative production. The outcome has been an accumulation of humus, more important, perhaps, to the new tillers of these soils than to the original grazing animals, together with their hunters and their herdsmen. Phosphorus will tend to have been distributed uniformly throughout the humus content, and will be more available, therefore, to the cultivated crops than to the numberless generations of surface-rooting grasses that have preceded them.

Hence the Tchernozems may be placed within the class of arid, and on the whole lime-rich, soils ; or, alternatively, it may be preferred to regard them as forming an intermediate class by themselves. The arid soils proper will be found in Europe to occur mostly to the south of the Tchernozems so far as they are not in the same latitude.

It is worthy of note, too, that on the calcareous formations the arid soil-types extend further towards the poles—a phenomenon connected with the flocculating effect of lime upon the clay fractions.[2] A second class of arid soil does, however, exist in the Arctic, and, although the literature dealing with this type is extremely sparse, its great interest in connection with the question of Pleistocene conditions must not be forgotten. Towards the Equator, then, moisture, rather than mineral concentration, tends to replace even phosphorus distribution as the supreme factor regulating the bulk of vegetable and animal life. It will be, therefore, in the areas of high barometric pressure and low rainfall bordering the Equatorial belt that the saline

[1] Hall: *The Soil*, p. 216.

[2] Hall: loc. cit., pp. 45, 305.

soil-deposits occur ; and we find there, moreover, a class of vegetation, no less than an animal life, remarkably adjusted to an environment in which this salt-abundance and water-shortage would seem each to have been utilized as a means of overcoming the drawbacks of the other. Halophytic forms such as the Australian salt-bushes, *Atriplex semibaccatum*, etc., are eaten readily by stock ; and in the tropics, when such types are not available, it becomes necessary to feed large amounts of salt to all live stock as a means of balancing the sodium chloride lost through perspiration.[1]

A further characteristic of the arid soils is their tendency to form alkaline carbonates of sodium, which, by their action on the clay fraction and humus, give rise to the so-called " black alkali " soils. Alternatively, sulphates of sodium and calcium may be deposited as " white alkali." In either case the result would seem to have more influence in the way of producing vegetable sterility than it has upon fauna.[2]

Turning, then, to the arid soils of the polar regions, we find saline soil reported from an area of low rainfall in Norway.[3] Ramann, writing on this subject, states : " Arid soils may be met with in a cold climate. Such soils occur typically in the interior of Spitzbergen and Greenland. It can be assumed that the soils of the table-lands of Central Asia belong here."[4] He quotes Weigner on this subject.[5] A single example from the Antarctic would seem likewise to confirm the essential fact of a prevailing alkalinity. In this case a rock flour was found to contain an abundance of calcium phosphate and little organic matter. The phosphate was almost certainly derived from the sea, through the agency of fish, birds, and their guano.[6]

This question how far phosphorus derived from the sea may, under natural conditions, find its way to the soil has not hitherto been discussed. Nor can it be considered important when we are considering any except the Arctic types of soil. In these regions, however, it seems probable that radiation rather than mineral deficiency limits the growth of vegetation. Thus, even a small, if regular, addition to the mineral of the soil would seem likely in the long run to affect the composition of such vegetation as did grow, and not merely to increase its volume. It is along coasts washed by cold currents, moreover, that marine and consequently avian life will flourish ; for it is normally in the cold waters of the ocean depths that the denser salts will tend to accumulate.

[1] Orr : *Min. in Past.*, p. 126.
[2] Hall, A. D. : *The Soil*, p. 284.
[3] Robinson, loc. cit.
[4] Ramann, loc. cit., p. 50.
[5] Weigner, G. : *Boden und Bodenbildung*, 1921, p. 24.
[6] Jensen, H. I. : " Report on Antarctic Soils." Publ. of Brit. Antarctic Expedn., 1907–1909. *Geology*, Vol. 2, p. 89, 1911.
See also Jochelson, W. : " The Yakut," Anthropological papers of the American Museum of Natural History, Vol. XXXIII, Part II, p. 67, who confirms the arid nature of much of the existing Tundra.

When these denser and therefore colder waters are brought to the surface, as in the case of the Humboldt or Peru current, large amounts of sea phosphorus are converted into food for sea birds, and are then distributed on islands and along the coast.

A further phenomenon connected with the neutral reaction so characteristic of the polar soils is the low CO_2 content of the air, to which Jensen, in his study of the Antarctic soils, draws attention.[1] Under these conditions carbonate of lime will remain undissolved except when in actual contact with organic acids. Ramann refers to the neutral reaction of the " mountain peat " class of soils in which, as in the Tchernozems, an abundance of black humus occurs. Indeed, most of the Tundra would seem to consist of peat soils formed from such plants as the moss *Betulana* and *Empetrum*, which can shatter the mat that the latter creates.[2]

The fact that the sub-soil remains permanently frozen is also, probably, of importance as a factor helping to prevent complete podsolization and a total loss of mineral. The existence of a frozen " pan " or stratum below the surface may to some extent check rapid movements of moisture either upward or downward ; and it will, in any case, prevent a total loss of the soluble portions. It has been conjectured that the frozen layer is a survival from the glacial period, and it actually would seem to extend to the south of the Tundra region and to underlie the more northern podsols.[3]

In short, then, there is strong indirect evidence for a belief that polar soils tend not only to be of the arid type, but to be rich in mineral. The recorded observation that they often consist of peat, which in temperate climates is associated with sour soil, and the further fact that they are useless for agriculture, may often have led to their true character having been overlooked. They would seem sometimes to have been confused with what are really the more extreme podsols, though the process whereby localities that were formerly dry become converted into bogs and marshes (Hockmoor) is not fully understood. This process occurs in Sweden, Finland, and N. Russia, though in a region agreeing with the distribution of the typical podsols. It seems probable that this effect may be due to progressive loss of soluble plant-food, formerly kept in circulation by the trees. It is of interest as indicating that dry soils may formerly have extended much further to the South.[4]

THE DISTRIBUTION OF IODINE

It has been necessary to deal with the distribution of calcium and the more common soluble salts before going into the question of the iodine

[1] Loc. cit.
[2] Ramann, loc. cit.
[3] Nikiforov, C. F. C. : " The perpetually frozen subsoil of Siberia," *Soil Science*, 1928, 26, pp. 66–77.
[4] Ramann, loc. cit.

supply ; for there is evidence to show that in a general way the presence of an excess of calcium is associated with a lack of this rarer element. Orr,[1] in his critical discussion of the whole literature concerning iodine, quotes largely from the work of V. Fellenberg and his co-worker Lunde, who have investigated the amounts present in both primary and secondary rocks, in soils, in air, and in waters. Of course, as also in the case of the other important minerals, the best evidence for their present distribution has been derived directly from observation of the various food deficiencies affecting the domesticated animals and man. For the time being, however, we shall only mention briefly the occurrence of so-called goitre areas as evidence of a local deficiency of iodine ; for in this enquiry, dealing as it does with the distribution of mineral in time as well as in space, it becomes essential to try and establish the principles on which the relative abundance or deficiency in various epochs, as well as areas, would seem to depend.

Iodine, although very widely distributed in nature, is present in such minute quantities that chemical methods capable of affording trustworthy quantitative estimates have yet to be perfected. The unit used is a millionth of a gram or microgram, usually written γ. It has been ascertained that the amounts contained in igneous rock and crystalline schists is fairly uniform, namely, between 200γ and 450γ per kgm., with the exception of gneiss-granite where the amount per kgm. was 810γ.

Among the sedimentary rocks, the quartzites yielded from 1100 to 8850γ as an upper figure, while in gypsum, limestones and dolomites the amounts varied from 250 to 400γ per kgm.

This comparative deficiency in the calcareous deposits is further borne out by V. Fellenberg and Lunde in their investigations of some typical geological horizons in Switzerland and Norway, reproduced below :[2]

	Iodine γ per kgm.		
Formation.	HCl Soluble.	HCl Insoluble.	Total.
Post-Tertiary	310– 650	440– 780	970–1380
Tertiary	60– 350	150–2070	200–2300
Cretaceous	50– 380	120– 400	170– 780
Jurassic	500–5800	100–3400	320–9200
Triassic	320– 940	40– 858	250–1000

It will be seen that, while the Cretaceous is lowest, the next older, the Jurassic, is phenomenally rich, and may be suspected of having somehow obtained the share originally present in the strata which, formerly at any rate, overlaid it.

The Triassic desert-deposits are also deficient in iodine. Hercus,

[1] Orr, J. B. : "Iodine in Nutrition," *Spec. Rep. med. Res. Coun.* Lond., No. 123, 1929.

[2] V. Fellenberg and Lunde (1926) : *Biochem. Z.*, 175, 162 ; quoted by Orr : *Iod. in Nut.*, p. 11.

Benson, and Carter, found a low iodine-content associated with river-beds and alluvial flats in New Zealand ; and Orr suggests that iodine is leached out of calcareous soils in company with the humus, which the calcium tends to break down.

It is fairly certain, in any case, that acid humus tends to accumulate iodine. V. Fellenberg has shown that the iodine-content of soils is much higher than that of the rocks from which they have been derived. This he attributes (*a*) to the accumulation of iodine in the living plant, and (*b*) to the adsorption of iodine from the parent material and from the air ; and he confirms this by showing that adsorption by weathered rocks and soils is stronger when the reaction is acid rather than basic. This work has been confirmed by Tezler, using charcoal and buffered solutions ; and it is again borne out by the findings of a high iodine-content in acid moor-soils by Bleyer and also by Stoklasa. In view of the importance to this examination of the arid and probably basic tundra soils, where, however, peat also is formed, it would be interesting to know whether the iodine originally present in the constituent mosses can be retained. The theory that iodine is absorbed by acid material and not by basic substances is further borne out by observations of processes that occur within the animal body. Iodine, as shown by Keeser, tends to concentrate in any pathological tissues where inflammation may have brought about a local acidosis.

Experiments carried out at the Rowett Institute have demonstrated the plants' ability to concentrate iodine four hundred times in fifty days ; while Heymann has shown a difference of 340γ to 1065γ between the iodine-contents of similar soils, the first kept bare of vegetation for several years and the second growing grass. Fresh-water plants contain even more iodine than land plants, and salt-water plants contain most of all.[1] Despite the well-known iodine-abundance in the brown and red seaweeds ($2,640,000\gamma$ per kgm. of dry matter) and in plankton (2400γ per litre of surface water), Orr points out that the iodine-content of the sea-water itself is very low (17-18γ per litre). The green seaweeds contain less iodine. It seems, therefore, as if this high iodine-concentration in the dark pigmented algæ may, like the pigmentation, be associated somehow with the utilization of the short green-blue, and perhaps ultra-violet, radiation ; of which the former, as suggested by Englemann, is the only fraction of the sun's visible rays that can penetrate to them.[2] The point is noted since the question of pigmentation in Man and in the animals seems to turn, not only on the reception of short-wave radiation by the skin, but also on the iodine and other salts available in the food.

The iodine-content of inland seas does not seem to have been ascertained, except in the case of the Great Salt Lake, for which McClendon gives it as 70γ per litre. According to Osborn this same area in the

[1] *N.B.* This suggests a motive for the return to an aquatic life on the part of certain mammals and reptiles.

[2] Bayliss, p. 568.

Pleistocene carried a sheet of water (Lake Bonneville) with an area of 19,000 square miles and 1000 feet deep, whereas its present representative is only 50 feet deep.[1] From this it would seem as though the original iodine-concentration of the water may well have been lower than that of sea-water, approximating more closely to the very low iodine-contents of river waters, which yield figures of the order of 1 γ per litre.

In the drying of inland seas, or in the case of lands that have recently emerged from the sea, there is good reason to believe that the iodine of the water will be lost to the new soil. The amount of iodine found in evaporated sea-salt, according to McClendon, is only from 1 to 10 γ per kgm., though obtained from a mass of water holding originally about 1500 γ. He considers that in the evaporation of sea-water magnesium chloride is hydrolyzed with the formation of hydrochloric acid, which liberates iodine. To retain the iodine it would be necessary for an alkali, e.g., sodium carbonate, to be present. According to this theory, then, some alkali-soils might be rich in iodine, but, since they support little or no life, the fact seems biologically unimportant. It appears to be otherwise, however, with deposits such as the Chile nitrate fields, which are probably deposits of plant- or bacteria-fixed material washed from the mountain sides and crystallized on the flat lands of the coastal fringe. Crude sodium nitrate contains as much as 0.2 per cent of iodine, i.e., 2,000,000 per kgm. Actually it is these deposits that now supply all the commercial iodine, the process being cheaper than the extraction from seaweed—an alternative process formerly developed in the Channel Islands and elsewhere. This fact is important, since there are many soils of transport, situated at the base of hills, table lands and mountains, into which the rain falling upon the higher arid rocks must eventually drain. The sparse seasonal vegetation will be killed and its salts crystallized by summer drought, and the few constituent salts, derived often from the direct weathering of the rock, will thus tend to be removed each year, and will concentrate in the beds below. Soils of very high fertility are known to exist in these lower situations (e.g., Sundays River, South Africa), and it seems probable that in these localities a very high nitrate calcium- and iodine-content might be encountered. The point is mentioned, as it is suspected that a similar state of affairs may exist at the sources of the Nile.

Before concluding this account of the possible ways in which iodine may be mobilized in nature, we must mention its occurence in the air in the form of spores, algæ, dust and coal-smoke. Hercus, Benson, and Carter calculated the amounts that would be transferred from the sea to the land by winds, but arrived at the conclusion that an addition of not more than 0.08 γ per kgm. of soil per annum was of little significance. Goitre-areas, however, have been known to migrate, and in this connection the high iodine-content of soot, 38,900 γ per kgm.,

[1] Osborn, H. F.: *The Age of Mammals*, New York, 1921, p. 448.

may possibly be relevant. Moreover, it may well play a part in mitigating the goitre incidence in coal-fields, all of which must be situated on carboniferous, and hence probably calcareous, formations. In the next chapter it is proposed to generalize upon the probable distribution of calcium, phosphorus, and iodine typical of various types of environment. In doing so, I shall attempt to imagine the effects of past climatic change ; for it seems unlikely that a change in the flora could of itself cause rapid alterations in the phosphorus or iodine distributions. Calcium, on the other hand, may, as we have seen, be expected to rise at the direct dictate of drought, though its subsequent loss may then be prevented by trees even after a long period of pluvial conditions. I have purposely delayed a discussion of the present-day mineral-deficiencies actually observed in live stock and Man, but it is felt that they can at this point be usefully employed as a means of checking the more general theories. There has been no systematic world-survey of mineral-deficiencies ; so that a mere mapping of those actually reported, on the assumption that where there had been no report of trouble none might therefore be taken to exist, would be dangerous. Moreover, unarmed with any theory, we are powerless to reconstruct conditions in past ages. Again, too, in the present distribution of deficiency-disease, especially the kind due to lack of phosphorus, there is plenty of evidence to show how modern commerce with its export of animal products has most seriously upset the distribution of the otherwise static element. India, for instance, although much if not most of the soil is already short of phosphorus, and deficiency-disease in both man and beast is common, exported more than 100,000 tons of bone a year, with a return in the form of patent fertilizers of only one per cent of this huge weight.[1] Similar depletion must have been going on in all grazing and dairying countries. Indeed, in Scotland, the case which Orr cites merely as an example, it can be shown that for Sutherland, which is mostly grazing land, the yearly exports of cattle and sheep have decreased 38 and 32 per cent in fifty years despite an increase of 40 per cent in the grazing area.[2]

Another consideration, for which allowance must be made when reviewing present deficiencies, is the increase of population of all areas where even the more static and traditional forms of agriculture and civilization are, or have been, practised. Grain and rice are both apt to be deficient in mineral, as well as in vitamin, when contrasted with their carbohydrate values. Thus, their cultivation may be expected to have increased population at a cost of a diminished mineral and vitamin allowance per individual. An area altogether suitable for graziers or hunters might thus seem deficient when brought mainly under the hoe or plough.

[1] Orr : *Minerals in Pasture*, p. 113.
[2] Ibid., p. 142.

CHAPTER III

PAST CLIMATE AND PRESENT DEFICIENCY

Deficiency and Disease: Exophthalmic Goitre and Rainfall: Eurasia: North America: Central America: South America: Australia and Iron Deficiency: New Zealand and Volcanic Soils: Africa and Polar Shift: Other Areas of Deficiency: Conclusion (Chapters II and III).

WHEN WE CONSIDER THE EVIDENCE OF MINERAL DEFICIENCIES as affecting human beings, or more frequently grazing animals, the exact connection between the disease and its cause is often far from clear. Moreover, similar pathological symptoms may be reported under widely differing names. It is often difficult to distinguish between calcium and phosphorus shortages, since the symptoms are usually reported to be allayed by feeding or manuring with calcium phosphate. On the whole, however, calcium- and phosphorus-deficiencies, which cause malformations of bone, hoofs, and horn, besides low milk yield, sterility, depraved appetite, liability to infection, and a reduction of size, may be distinguished from iodine-deficiency, which causes goitre—or swelling of the thyroid gland. The proportion of deaf-mutes in a population has likewise been proved to show such a close correlation with goitre as to be useful as an alternative means of estimating iodine-deficiency. Hairlessness among domesticated animals would also appear to mark goitre areas.

DEFICIENCY AND DISEASE

The proof that the diseases in question are, in truth, caused by the several types of deficiency has been established, firstly, by observing cures to follow from the administration of the various inorganic substances—mainly calcium, phosphorus, iron, and iodine; while, secondly, analysis of food grown in the areas liable to disease has usually revealed abnormally low values of the element in question.[1] In regard to iodine-deficiency, the extreme difficulty of making quantitative estimates of the minute amounts necessary to the animal organism leaves the biological method of estimating a shortage still superior to the purely chemical procedure. Indeed, satisfactory methods of iodine extraction are still in need of further development. Nevertheless, it is far from certain that iodine-deficiency is the sole cause of goitre, though it would now be idle to deny that it does

[1] Orr: *Min. in Past.*

play an important if not, indeed, a major part therein. The theory that it may be communicated by infection is not dealt with in these pages; it being assumed that where, and if, this occurs the host must be weakened by iodine-deficiency before goitrogenic organisms or toxins can achieve their effects.[1] The old idea that goitre was caused by an excess of lime might, even now, be defended. Besides the fact that the presence of lime in the soil prevents the accumulation (and may encourage the dissipation) of iodine, there are experimental data which show that this is true physiologically as well as ecologically. It has been found that an excess of calcium, when fed to animals on a "borderline" diet previously adjusted so as not to produce goitre, would reproduce the original type of thyroid swelling.[2] Substances have also been extracted from plants which produce goitres; though whether their presence in a food is beneficial or a hindrance to prolonged life and fertility does not seem to have been ascertained.

EXOPHTHALMIC GOITRE AND RAINFALL

The full causes of goitre and their evolutionary significance must await fuller discussion. Let it here be mentioned, however, that two kinds of goitre are recognized: "simple" and "exophthalmic." In the former cases the patient is lethargic, and in the latter nervous and highly strung. In simple goitre the blood contains an excess of calcium, whereas with exophthalmic symptoms there is a deficiency. These facts, when viewed in conjunction with the soil and climate theory, led me to correlate rainfall with the incidences of simple and exophthalmic goitre found among recruits from the various States enrolled in the American Army. I found that, whereas simple goitre was correlated with climatic aridity ($R = -\cdot43 \pm \cdot08$), a fact bearing out the theory that lime-rich soils supply less iodine, the ratio of exophthalmic to simple goitre was correlated with high rainfall figures ($R = +\cdot40 \pm \cdot07$). Similarly, the death rates from exophthalmic goitre for the English counties showed a positive correlation with rainfall ($R = +\cdot52 \pm \cdot02$). Nevertheless, the assumption that both simple and exophthalmic goitre are each mainly the result of the same agency, almost certainly iodine shortage, is borne out by the even larger positive correlation between the incidences of these two phases of thyroid trouble. For America this worked out as $R = 0.61 \pm .06$.[3]

It is not claimed that the entire responsibility of rainfall in producing exophthalmic goitre in limestone, or other iodine-deficient, regions is due to its capacity for removing soluble calcium from within reach of the plant roots and thereby affecting human nutrition. This, however, is suggested as an important contributory factor and one easily coun-

[1] McCarrison, R.: *The Etiology of Endemic Goitre,* London, 1913.

[2] McCarrison, R.: "The Effects of the Excessive Ingestion of Lime on the Thyroid Gland and the Influence of Iodine in Counteracting Them." *Indian J. med. Res.*, 13, 817, 1925–26.

[3] Author's unpublished material.

tered by preventive measures. On the other hand, the direct influence of a humid atmosphere upon the body—though not understood—might possibly be important as well. So, too, the influence of a humid atmosphere upon the total and fractional incidences of various radiations could play a part both in affecting the synthesis of vitamin D and in influencing ionization within the body. Provided that these influences all work together, they must be assumed to have likewise been encountered during the evolutionary history of the mammal and Man. It is interesting, therefore, to reflect that, whereas lime-abundance and iodine-deficiency cause simple goitre and a lethargic reaction, a deficiency of the two minerals associated with aridity (lime and phosphorus), when combined with a shortage of the element usually associated with humidity (iodine), causes nervousness. The lethargic reaction would lead to a stay-at-home behaviour followed by selection and specialization ; the exophthalmic reaction, being more dangerous, would both require and encourage migration as an alternative to death and racial extinction.

It is time, however, to review the mineral-deficiencies occurring in the various parts of the world. Goitre will be encountered mainly in mountains, or, again, in flood or drainage areas where evaporation is, or has been, intense. Lime- and phosphorus-deficiency may be expected, firstly, in areas of heavy rainfall ; secondly, in areas subject to heavy rainfall in the past ; and, thirdly, in very dry areas where the plant is unable to assimilate the mineral which—so far as the calcium is concerned—must nevertheless be assumed as present in the surface soil.

EURASIA

Goitre is reported from the Alps, Tyrol, Pyrenees, and Himalayas. In addition to these existing mountain-systems, Carboniferous and Cretaceous deposits occur over very wide areas. Moreover, limestones of most other remote ages are also to be found.

With regard to the British Isles, the Carboniferous deposits are confined to Ireland, where they constitute the centre and major portion of that island, together with the moors of Northumberland, Yorkshire, the Pennine Chain, and Dartmoor. The Cretaceous deposits are confined mainly to the North and South Downs. It would seem, however, as though the Oolite must also be included among the calcareous and therefore iodine-deficient soils, as goitre areas are reported from the Cotswolds and Mendips ; while the goitre map shows another area on Oolite in Yorkshire. Indeed, a comparative study of the goitre map of England seems, on the whole, capable of endorsing the thesis that goitre and iodine-deficiency are associated with the presence of lime ; though, since the map is of death-rates from the dangerous exophthalmic goitre, this correlation does not become clear unless due allowance is made for the contributory influence of the heavy rainfall on the West Coasts.[1]

[1] Stocks, P. : *Goitre Map of England*, Biometrika.

To resume, however, what must be but a summary account of the principal Continental areas of calcareous rocks, we find in France a continuation of the same chalk that forms the English Downs. This lies in an area extending from the Eastern Channel and encircles Paris. The mountains to the East of the Rhone, together with the river-valley itself, are Cretaceous ; indeed, these same deposits go to form the Alps, spreading in an arc North-East from Lyons until they pass to the South-East of Berne. Parts of the Carpathians are Cretaceous, as is also the region South of the Danube between the Black Sea and the Iron Gates.

Most of the coastal region of the Black Sea is likewise Cretaceous. The deposits begin at the Asiatic shore of the Bosphorus and extend almost to Trebizond. After this, a further line runs along the Caucasus to the Southern Crimea. There is a vast area threaded by the head waters of the Don and extending from the Volga to the Dneiper ; and there is a further area bordering the North-East Caspian, between that sea and the Southern Urals. After this—with the exception, of course, of the Himalayas to the South and some rocks in the Tarim Basin—most of the remainder of North-East Asia may be regarded as a Continental shield, which, however, is now covered with a loëss much of which may have been derived from lime-rich formations.[1]

The goitre-incidence covering this vast area has not been systematically surveyed. Janney (1924), however, who is quoted by Orr, regards the Himalayas, including Northern India, parts of the South and West of China, and Eastern Mongolia, as forming one big area subject to iodine-deficiencies. I have been unable to obtain his original paper. The rocks of Mongolia are described as granites, gneisses, and crystalline schists of Archean and probably Primary Age. Coal, however, usually associated with limestones and iodine shortage, exists in the basin of the Yenisei and South-East of Kobdo.[2] We may expect the low precipitation to encourage a basic soil-condition likely to inhibit the absorption of iodine from the primary rocks.

These findings seem, on the whole, to accord with the theory ; since, even where the formations of goitre-areas are not calcareous, the soils are of the arid type. In the river valleys of China, however, floods are in all probability the main cause of iodine loss, just as occurs also in New Zealand. It would be interesting to know the goitre-incidence among the northern hunters of Siberia. Czaplicka reports a case where a man, his father, and grandfather had died of " sick throat," which might indicate goitre. She also points out that further to the South, near the Altai, the maral, a large antelope, is trapped by a bait of rock-salt. The reindeer, too, exhibit salt-hunger.[3] The question of Sodium and Chlorine, however, must wait. Dr. L. H. Dudley Buxton informs me that during his travels in Central Asia he did not observe any goitre.

[1] Beyschlag, F. : *Geological Map of the Earth*, Berlin, 1932.
[2] *Encyclopædia Britannica*, " Mongolia."
[3] Czaplicka, M. A. : *My Siberian Year*, London, 1916.

Regarding the distribution of other kinds of mineral-deficiency in Europe and Asia, it seems probable that modern agriculture, and not climate, or geology, is responsible for many of the troubles in Europe. For Orr reports deficiencies of one sort or another from Germany, Hungary, Belgium, Bohemia, France, and Norway. The symptoms are usually the same—emaciation, brittle bone and depraved appetite, sterility and low milk yield. It seems impossible by inference from the symptoms to distinguish phosphorus- from calcium-deficiency. Both may be counteracted by the administration of bone flour to the stock, and usually by the application of the basic phosphates to the land. Salt-starvation also occurs, and in all cases bacterial infection may complicate the symptoms.

The draining of land has been found sometimes to improve nutrition, e.g., in Württemberg, as reported by Neyen. Correspondingly, in Scotland it has been observed that prolonged depletion of minerals by overstocking, unbalanced by manure, is wont to encourage acidity and the formation of a water-logged peat. In Europe goitre seems on the whole more common in Man than in animals ; and the same is reported to be the case in India. With regard to North America, however, the very reverse is found. We may, perhaps, attribute this to the higher standard of living, and to the greater consumption of animal products in the United States and Canada. Domestic animals, and game too, have certainly played an important part in shielding human beings from the full influence of soil-deficiency.

Looking last of all to the thickly populated areas of India and China, we are offered a very small body of evidence, all of it, however, pointing to the existence of a widespread phosphorus-deficiency in India, and none of it running counter to such a view. Even less seems to be known about the state of affairs in China.

Davis showed that a low phosphorus-content of rice was correlated with a deficiency of the same element in the soil. More interesting still, perhaps, Lt.-Col. Matson, quoted by Orr, points out that, when European and Indian breeds of cattle are crossed, the second cross display a number of defects of health, which can, however, be assuaged by the addition of mixed minerals to their diet. Not only does this indicate the existence of mineral-deficiency, but it goes far to prove the thesis of the animals' adaptation to withstand it.[1] Clearly, without the intervention of the artificial mineral addition, natural selection would soon operate so as to weed out many, if not all, of the hereditary characters introduced by the European animals. This consideration must point to the strong probability that in the case of Man, too, the same rules would be likely to apply. Adaptation to withstand phosphorus-deficiency seems to have been forced upon the more recent, at least, of the human migrants into India. The original Aryan-speaking invaders were probably more robust of build than even the most pure-blooded of their descendants, the Brahmans of the Punjab and

[1] Orr : *Min. in Past.*, p. 114.

Rajputana. But it must be pointed out, that it is hard to reconstruct human evolution in terms of adaptation to withstand phosphorus-deficiency, since no clear and satisfactory connection between climate and phosphorus-distribution has yet been traced. In old centres of agricultural civilization, however, it seems safe to postulate that some progressive impoverishment of phosphorus is always likely to have occurred ; though, doubtless, it has been to some extent checked by the invention of manuring, even if modern transport has now practically annulled this influence owing to the consumption of food and subsequent wastage of phosphorus in the modern city.

On the whole, then, Man, rather than climate, seems responsible for the fact that a majority of the European and Asiatic areas lack bone-forming material. A great deal more research is required, however, before the two sets of influences can be distinguished.

NORTH AMERICA

Turning to North America we find, as in Europe, a considerable number of reports from which it is hard to gather whether calcium- or phosphorus-deficiency is the pathogenic factor. In Texas the cattle may suffer from "loin disease," the chief symptoms of which would appear to be pica or depraved appetite, stiffness of gait, and incoordination of movement. Schmidt, who reports it, recommends the feeding of bone-meal to overcome this trouble. A similar result is reported from the wire-grass region of Southern Alabama, where the land is stated to be sandy and poor in lime. Hart and his co-workers have done valuable research work upon the calcium-deficiency of the Wisconsin soils, and its adverse effect upon the health of grazing animals. This region, it is interesting to note, forms part of the great goitre-area surrounding the present reduced limits of the Great Lakes. The soils in this region can scarcely be classed as arid, since they occur in the belt of 25 inches to 50 inches rainfall, the limits of which include most of Western Europe. We here have proof, then, that the drying out of a flood-area is likely to remove iodine ; and this whether the new land is calcareous or not, and irrespective of the subsequent climate and its resultant effect upon the salt concentration and soil type. Within this same goitre-area of the Great Lake basin we find deficiencies, probably of phosphorus, reported from Wisconsin, Northern Michigan, and Minnesota. We can only speculate as to how much of this phosphorus-deficiency may be due to the advance of the Great Ice Sheet. By dictating a southern migration of animals some such movement of phosphorus may perhaps have been initiated. Again, the subsequent melting might be expected to carry much hitherto frozen organic matter, and its contained phosphorus, straight to the rivers and sea.

Turning now to the iodine-deficient areas of the Western States, we see that they are no longer, as in the East, confined to within the limits of the terminal moraine. We seem here to have encountered a complex interaction of effects, of which I would postulate, firstly, drought conducing to an arid soil type ; secondly, in the case of Utah, the drying of Lake Bonneville, already referred to ; lastly, too, the export of stock, and consequently of phosphorus, with a reduction of the vegetative growth and a consequent increase of aridity and alkalinity. Welch reports a deficiency of lime and phosphorus from Montana, which, owing to its position just south of the terminal moraine, may possibly be due, as in the case of the Great Lake Basin, to the thaw and pluvial conditions probably accompanying the glacial retreat. In

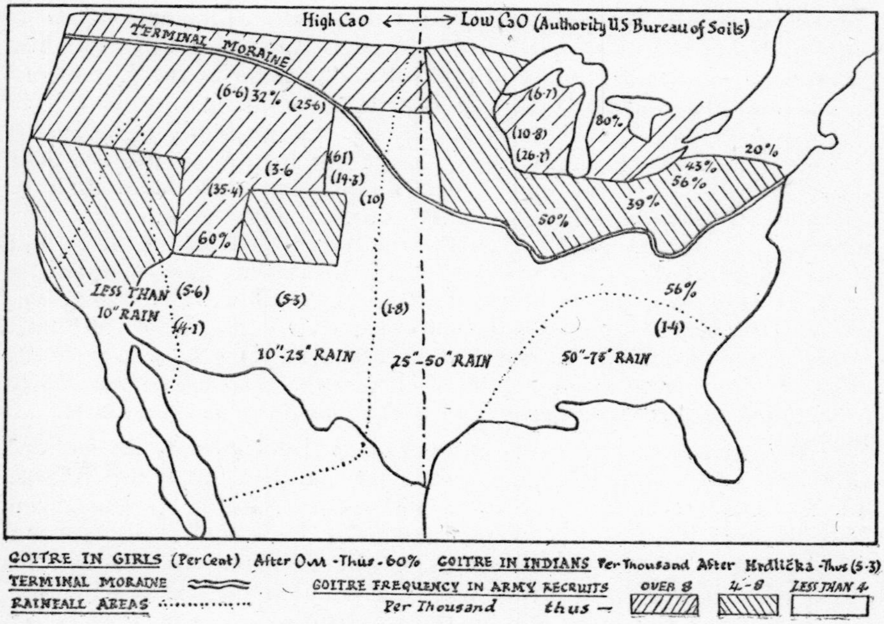

Goitre Map of North America.

Canada phosphorus-deficiency does not seem serious, though goitre in man and beast is common on the calcareous formations. Calcium-deficiencies also occur, particularly in the Maritime Provinces. Here, though the precipitation is still within the limits 25 inches to 50 inches, the colder climate would inhibit evaporation and so encourage the formation of true podsols. It is unfortunate for the purposes of this enquiry that no soil map of North America is available. A map ready prepared by the U.S. Bureau of Soils has not been published owing to expense.

CENTRAL AMERICA

Information with regard to mineral-deficiency in Central America seems scanty. In British Honduras (as also in British Guiana), as the result perhaps of heavy rainfall, sterility of cattle is high, malformation of bone occurs, and milk yield is low.[1] From Trinidad and Jamaica Hammond reports a degeneration in size and type, though in discussing the causes he regards lack of protein in food rather than of mineral in the soil as being the deficiency responsible.[2] This whole question of size-alteration must be dealt with under a separate head. In general, then, we may say that such scanty information as exists confirms the theory that deficiencies of phosphorus and calcium are bound to characterize the tropical rain belt.

SOUTH AMERICA

There seems to be practically no trustworthy information about mineral-deficiency of stock in South America. One would expect a low phosphorus and lime content of the soil to characterize the Equatorial forests and the northern parts of Brazil. The cattle country of the Argentine, however, with its low rainfall, was probably rich, and is still at least sufficiently supplied ; while yet further to the South it seems possible that cold and low precipitation may have directly inhibited vegetation, with the result that soil mineral is high. The arid soils of Patagonia are still rich in the bones of extinct animals, and it was when writing of these that Darwin was led to remark upon the fallacy of supposing that large quadrupeds require a luxuriant vegetation. In confirmation he compares the almost deserted rain-forests of South America with the veldt of South Africa and its (then) teeming herds of game.[3] We would suspect iodine-deficiency to accompany the aridity of Patagonia, and its occurrence in the Andes must be mentioned.

Deniker draws attention to the eating of a kind of kaolin by the Indians of Bolivia, and states that the habit is also indulged in by the Whites. In the latter case the tradition would seem probably to have been brought over from Spain, where "geophagy" is stated also to occur.[4] The question of mineral-deficiency in the Falkland Islands will be dealt with later in connection with the reactions of animals to their environment. Let it be said in the meantime, however, that heavy rainfall, combined with the export of animal products, has resulted in severe phosphorus- and lime-deficiency.

AUSTRALIA AND IRON DEFICIENCY

The usual train of symptoms due to calcium- and phosphorus-deficiencies occurs in Australia under a number of names such as "cripples," "stiffs," "wobbles," "rickets" and "coast disease;" "dry Bible," or impaction of the omasum, is a form in which deficiency may affect the digestive system. In Australia, however, we come

[1] Orr : *Min. in Past.*, p. 109.
[2] Hammond, J. : "Report on Cattle Breeding in Jamaica and Trinidad." Publns. Empire Marketing Board, Vol. 2, No. 8, 1932.
[3] Darwin, C. : *Journal of Voyage of H.M.S. "Beagle,"* London, 1842, and 91.
[4] Deniker, J. : *The Races of Man*, 2nd ed., p. 146.

across the first suggestion of iron-deficiency, which occurs also in New Zealand, but seems otherwise not sufficiently important to be regarded as an influence likely to have directed selection. It seems faintly possible that the nitrifying soil-organism Nitrococcus (Winogradsky), which is peculiar to Australasia and the New World, might in some way fail to render iron assimilable by the animal. In any case, the difference is of interest, suggesting that bacterial evolution and distribution, and therefore soil evolution, may be measured on a time scale comparable with that of the higher animals. Finally, before dismissing the subject of iron-deficiency, it is perhaps worth mentioning another possibility that is also perhaps rather faint. The Australian natives, in common with most, if not all, of the hunters of the Holarctic region, have always displayed a love of red ochre for purposes of ritual and personal adornment. So important is this substance that the Dieri, as described by Howitt, send bands of picked men a distance of three hundred miles to obtain it. This instance is well known to anthropologists, representing as it does what would appear to be an early stage leading up to the development of both war and commerce. Similarly, Orr and Gilks report the even more remarkable fact that the agricultural Kikuyu were formerly in the habit of making raids into the territory of their far more warlike neighbours, the Masai, for the purpose of obtaining a calcium- and salt-rich earth.[1]

Can it be that the application of red ochre to the skin will of itself help physiologically as well as psychologically to impart that feeling of well-being necessary to any full participation in a ceremony? Writing on this subject of personal adornment Sollas cites the use of red and yellow ochre, pipe clay and burnt gypsum, micaceous iron ore, manganese oxides and charcoal as being all used in Australia.[2] The Arunta each carry a stock of these pigments in a "ditty bag."[3] The Tasmanians, too, are reported to have rubbed grease and red ochre on their bodies and into their scalps.[4] In Africa a similar utilization of lime and chalk is common. The question how far, if at all, the skin is enabled to absorb substances applied to it, seems uncertain. Alternatively, it may be pointed out that paint is often made by grinding such substances as kaolin (china clay) in the mouth.[5] It is arguable, then, that man's early search for pure inorganic substances may owe part of its "survival value" to its quite unrecognized function in nutrition. Alternatively, the widespread phenomenon of earth-eating must not be forgotten.[6] Of course, in so far as this has been possible, the selective influence of mineral-deficiency may be believed to have been inhibited. It seems improbable, however, that the instinct of earth-eating would

[1] Orr, J. B., and Gilks, J. L.: "The Physique and Health of Two African Tribes," *Spec. Rep. Ser. med. Res. Coun.* Lond., No. 155.
[2] Spencer and Gillen: *Across Australia*, Vol. II, p. 269.
[3] Sollas, W. J.: *Ancient Hunters*, London, 1915, pp. 223–224.
[4] Roth, H. Ling: *The Aborigines of Tasmania*, Halifax, England, 1899.
[5] Spencer and Gillen: *Across Australia*, Vol. II, p. 407.
[6] Deniker: ibid., p. 145.

come into play until malnutrition had occurred in some considerable degree.

As regards the iodine-content of the Australian soils, there would appear to be a sufficiency, at all events in the sheep-grazing regions. Orr[1] reports no iodine-deficiencies ; and subsequent work by Dawbarn and Farr, who examined the iodine-contents of large numbers of sheep's thyroids derived from most of the pastoral areas, confirms this.[2] These findings, however, are unexpected. Goitre in Man is common in the more or less equally arid parts of Western North America ; and, moreover, much of Australia is calcareous. It may possibly be that the sheep is not subject to goitre except where extreme soil deficiencies are found ; though goitre in lambs is reported by Helmer from British Columbia.[3] Even in the face of this evidence, I would still expect iodine-deficiencies to occur in the more arid central portions of Australia, such as the Arunta country. If, however, this is wrong, and iodine does exist in sufficient quantity, despite the present aridity, it could then be argued alternatively that Australia has become progressively arid owing upon some cause such as a shift of the poles ; and that in a previous phase of luxuriant tropical vegetation sufficient iodine was concentrated to supply all present needs. This latter hypothesis, incidentally, would seem also capable of accounting for the present phosphorus-deficiencies. Indeed, on the whole this explanation seems of the two the more likely to be correct.

NEW ZEALAND AND VOLCANIC SOILS

The study of deficiency-disease in New Zealand has revealed the fact that iron, if present in the soil as a silicate, is unavailable to live stock. It has also been suggested that an excess of manganese may limit the assimilation of iron ; owing presumably to an ability of manganese to replace iron in the plant, but not in the animal. In addition to being deficient in iron the pastures also lack a sufficiency of phosphorus, which when applied artificially mitigates, but does not remove, the effect of iron-starvation. The symptom is anæmia. Iron-starvation occurs also in King Island, Tasmania ; in Australia, as already mentioned ; and in Kenya, where it bears the name "Nakuruitis."[4]

In a more recent investigation of iron-deficiency in New Zealand, Askew, Rigg, Grange, Taylor and Hodgson (1932)[5] have shown that the worst soils are tuffs situated close to the old volcanic cone, and thus

[1] Orr : *Minerals in Pastures*, p. 86–95.

[2] Dawbarn, M. C., and Farr, F. C. L. : "Variations in dry weight and Iodine content of sheep's thyroids under uniform and varying conditions." *Aust. J. exp. Biol. med. Sci.*, Vol. X, III, 1932.

[3] Helmer : Expt. Sta., Summerland, B.C. Report. C. F. Orr : *Minerals in Pastures*, p. 108.

[4] Orr : *Minerals in Pastures*, p. 95–100.

[5] N. Z. Dept. of Sci. and Indust. Res. Bull., No. 32.

composed of large particles. Further away the iron-content of the soil is raised, and that of other minerals also. In particular, calcium tends to be retained in the land of finer texture. The second point of prime importance which they discover is that much of the iron is normally ingested, not through the plant, but inorganically, as dirt adhering to the grass and its roots. Pastures showing a close mat of uneaten grass were more " Bush sick " than those that could be more closely cropped. It will be obvious from this that primitive man, if living on roots, may be expected to have eaten more than his full " peck of dirt," thereby obtaining more iron at least, and perhaps other substances also, than when feeding, say, on fruit, or even for that matter on the flesh of animals.

Regarding iodine-deficiency in New Zealand, Hercus, Benson, and Carter found that a low iodine-content of the soil was associated with river-beds and alluvial flats. Reference to this has already been made.[1] New Zealand, then, affords a valuable lesson in the deficiencies likely to be met with in a recently volcanic region ; the parallel with Kenya in the matter of volcanoes and flood-areas being, from the anthropological point of view, of some interest.

After thus briefly dealing with Australia and New Zealand, those two furthest-detached portions of the " Australasian peninsula," there remains little authoritative information upon the mineral-deficiencies characterizing the islands nearer to the central Eurasiastic mass, though vitamin-deficiency following a rice diet is common.

Deficiencies of iodine might also be expected as a result of the limestone formations which are not uncommon in Indonesia. Hose mentions that the Kayans and Kenyahs of Sarawak were sufferers from goitre, and that they traded a salt—found to be rich in iodine and lithium—with their neighbours, the Kalabits. The latter, presumably as a result of a more regular use of this substance, did not suffer from goitre. The salt was obtained by boiling water from springs.[2] Incidentally, the same author describes how wild pigs seemed to have eaten stibnite or sulphate of antimony crystals.[3] In the Shan States Milne and Cochrane report goitre as common among the Palaungs and Kachins of the hills, but as less in evidence among the Shans of the lower lands.[4] The latter, however, frequently use iron and sulphur as medicines, and, in common with the inhabitants of the whole region, use lime as an adjunct to the chewing of betel-nut.

From the general volcanic nature of much of this neighbourhood, and of Java—a point on which our interest naturally focusses—we might also expect, at the present time at all events, to encounter iron-deficiencies similar to those met with further South. There appears to

[1] Hercus, C. E., Benson, W. N., and Carter, C. L. (1925) : *J. Hyg.*, Camb., 24, 321.
[2] Hose, C. : *The Field-Book of a Jungle-Wallah*, London, 1929, p. 192.
[3] Loc. cit., p. 198.
[4] Milne and Cochrane : *Shans at Home*, London, 1910, p. 180.

be no information relative to our very provisional hypothesis concerning a connection between this trouble and the difference in type of the soil-bacteria ; that is to say, whether the change is clear cut along Wallace's line. It does seem very faintly possible, however, that the iron transference between mother and offspring, which takes place mainly through the placenta and not through the milk, may have been evolved as an improvement upon some alternative device in the marsupials. This minor difficulty of the placental mammals when transported to this more primitive environment is at least significant. In this connection it may be found important that the iron bacteria (also investigated by Winogradsky), and which, according to Molisch, are responsible for the secretion of soluble ferric hydrate, do not seem to thrive in soils containing calcium carbonate.[1] With heavy dressings of limestone the iron-content of the herbage would seem sometimes to decrease.[2]

AFRICA AND POLAR SHIFT

In attempting to attribute the mineral-deficiencies of Africa to past changes as well as to present conditions we seem to be treading on rather more stable ground than before. The whole question of palæoclimatology has been so stimulated by the Continental Drift Theory of Wegener that in attempting to establish the relative chronology between the past climatic changes of countries now situated in opposite hemispheres the whole focus of interest, at the moment, must centre less on the biological effects, than on the further confirmation or disproof of the various contentions comprised in his bold hypothesis.[3] For the purposes of this work, however, any critical discussion of the latter pros and cons must be avoided ; though it may be stated at the outset that, wherever necessary, Wegener's findings have been called in to explain what would otherwise appear to be problems of even greater difficulty.

With regard to Africa, however, we seem safe in assuming no great difference in distance from Europe, whatever movements the Antipodes and the Americas may have made during Man's history. In discussing Africa and its past climates, then, we shall play for safety, taking up the same position with regard to the theory of Continental Drift as that already assumed by Simpson in his very able discussion of the climates of Pleistocene Europe.[4] With Simpson, then, we shall assume a shift of the Poles in regard to Africa, resulting in a corresponding migration of the Equator and its rain-forest such as would at some period of the Pleistocene furnish the Zambesi and its region with the same, or perhaps a much greater, rainfall, than now prevails in the

[1] Hall : *The Soil*, p. 239.
[2] Orr : *Min. in Past.*, p. 21.
[3] Wegener, A. : *The Origin of Continents and Oceans*, trans. by J. G. A. Skerl.
[4] Simpson, C. G. : "The Climate during the Pleistocene Period," *Proc. roy. Soc. Edinb.*, Vol. L, Part III, No. 21, 1930.

region of the Congo. This theory, incidentally, might help to explain the position of the Acheulean implements imbedded in the gravels of the high ledges of the Zambesi, dating as they do to all appearance from a time prior to the cutting-back of the river bed through many feet of solid basalt. The present volume of water, large as it is, would seem, nevertheless, quite inadequate to perform any such stupendous feat even with the longest possible time-allowance.

Wegener suggests the following positions of the North Pole with reference to the present system of co-ordinates, with Africa supposed to be stationary :

Epoch.	Posn. N. Pole.		Posn. Germany.
Recent	90° N.		50° N.
Quaternary	70° N.	10° W.	69° N.
Pliocene	90° N.		54° N.
Miocene	67° N.	172° W.	37° N.
Oligocene	58° N.	180° W.	29° N.
Eocene	45° N.	180° W.	15° N.
Palæocene	50° N.	180° W.	20° N.
Cretaceous	48° N.	140° W.	19° N.
Jurassic	69° N.	170° W.	36° N.
Triassic } Permian }	50° N.	130° W.	26° N.
Carboniferous	25° N.	155° W.	3° S.
Devonian	30° N.	140° W.	15° N.

Just as the figures for Germany show a steady approach of the Pole until the Quaternary, followed by a return to its Pliocene position, so for Africa we may imagine the Equator sweeping down so as to arrive on the North Coast in the Oligocene, passing the Sahara during the Miocene, reaching its present position in the Congo in the Pliocene, and continuing to its furthest towards the Cape—almost touching the Zambesi—before moving back in the Late Quaternary.

Thus, a map of the Quaternary, drawn upon an ordinary Mercator projection, must show the Equator running in an arc ENE. through Africa, cutting the Northern half of Lake Nyassa, and also passing through the present positions of Ceylon, Bangkok, Formosa Strait, and Japan. This, then, may be taken to represent a theory of world-climate during the maximum Southern migration of the Pole in regard to Africa. To simplify matters, I have at the same time depicted a state of maximum glaciation, though it is perhaps doubtful whether this condition would necessarily have been achieved at the precise culmination of polar approach.

Indeed, according to the map of Koppen and Wegener, followed by Simpson, the position of the Pole during the maximum of the Mindel advance was such, in regard to Europe, that the 50th and not the 60th parallel must be made to cut the South Russian boundary of the moraine. Perhaps, then, we may imagine an ice-sheet whose edge in regard to Europe remained relatively stationary, while its centre, the Pole, migrated " northward " or at right angles to its European edge. An increase in precipitation, following upon a widening of the Atlantic, and a simultaneous increase in the sun's radiation—already assumed by Simpson for this exact period—would serve thus to " nourish " the ice cap. Finally, a sudden snapping or foundering of the Wyville-Thompson land-bridge joining Scotland to Greenland by way of Orkney, Shetland, the Faroes and Iceland, occurring subsequently to

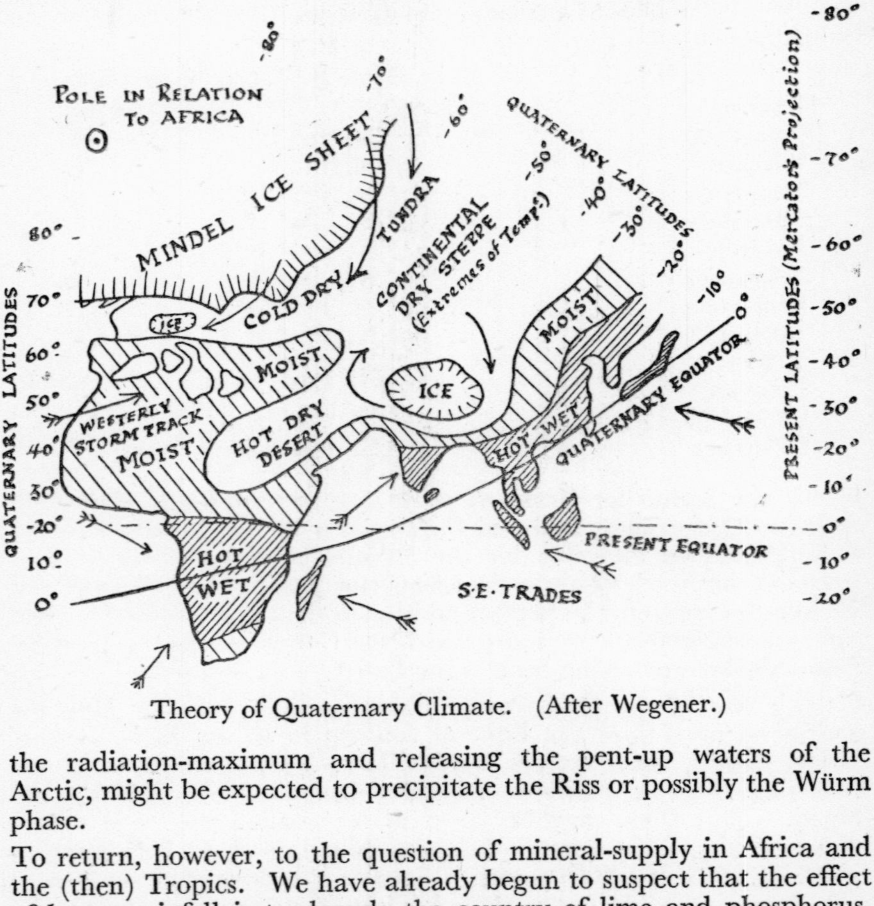

Theory of Quaternary Climate. (After Wegener.)

the radiation-maximum and releasing the pent-up waters of the Arctic, might be expected to precipitate the Riss or possibly the Würm phase.

To return, however, to the question of mineral-supply in Africa and the (then) Tropics. We have already begun to suspect that the effect of heavy rainfall is to denude the country of lime and phosphorus, even if afterwards iodine is to some extent concentrated and conserved. Suppose, then, that, following upon a pluvial period in Kenya and the Congo—the Kamasian pluvial of Leakey and Brooks, perhaps[1]—the same rain-belt may temporarily have moved south to envelop all South Africa except possibly the Cape itself; and later could have

[1] Leakey, L. S. B. : *The Stone Age Culture of Kenya Colony*, Appendix B, by C. E. P. Brooks, pp. 267–270, Cambridge, 1931.

returned. If so, we may expect South Africa and the other countries on the Quaternary Equator to suffer even now from phosphorus-deficiency. Lime, being soluble and able to rise, is likely to reflect present rather than past conditions.

This, almost exactly, is the position we seem to find. Orr states that "in the Union of South Africa there are large tracts of grazing land where deficiency of phosphorus in the pasture is the direct or indirect cause of disease."[1] It was in South Africa that Theiler did much of the pioneer work on mineral-deficiency, and showed how pica, or depraved appetite, due to this cause, was responsible in its turn for the eating of rotten bones; and how, as a secondary trouble following upon the satisfaction of this sometimes useful instinct, "lamsickte" was caused by the ingestion of *parabotulinus bovis*.[2] In another section certain peculiarities of the Cape working-oxen will be attributed to an accommodation to this phosphorus-deficiency. In the meantime we continue to find a poor nutritive power of the land extending over practically the whole African continent. Northern and Southern Rhodesia are mentioned; and in Kenya, besides the iron-deficiency already mentioned, which can be cured by moving the stock a few miles, presumably on to land of finer texture, there is also evidence of phosphorus-deficiency. Common salt would likewise seem to be lacking in the area of iron-deficiency, but it is surprising to find no other mention of it in the reports from the other areas. Africa, like Siberia and Canada, has been a shield formation over which seas have seldom stood. Moreover, Lapicque has found ample evidence of acute salt-hunger affecting the agricultural natives and jungle tribes, though the hunters and herdsmen would seem to do well enough without.[3] The same authority points out how natives in Africa obtain chlorate of potash from wood-ashes, and use this as a substitute for sodium chloride: the chlorine used for breaking down the proteins in the stomach being thus, apparently, more important than the sodium required at a further stage to counteract acidity in the gut. It becomes, thus, an interesting question how far sodium may, by certain races at least, be substituted for other substances such, perhaps, as calcium and potassium. This point is discussed at length in the next chapter.

Finally, in regard to iodine, we find, as might be expected, that, with the exception of a single goitre-area in the Northern Territories of the Gold Coast, no regions of deficiency have been reported.[4] There are some extensive Cretaceous formations in this last region extending over the greater part of the area drained by the Niger and Volta rivers. The northern parts of the Continent, including the hinterlands of

[1] Orr: *Minerals in Pastures*, p. 74.

[2] Theiler, du Toit & Green: *J. Dep. Agric. S. Afr.*, 1924, VIII, 460–504; cft. Orr: *Min. in Past.*, p. 77.

[3] Lapicque, L.: "Sur l'Alimentation Minérale," *L'Anthropologie*, 1896; cft. Bunge, C.: "Ethnologisher Nachtrag zur Abhandlung über die Bedeutung des Kochsalzes," *Zeitschrift. für Biologie*, XIII, 1874.

[4] Orr: *Min. in Past.*, p. 83.

Oran, Algiers, Tunis and Tripoli are also Cretaceous, the line of exposures running WSW. to the coast of Morocco, but excluding Tangier. A further big area extends S. and SW. from Tripoli, being broken between the 25th and 20th parallels, to reappear in the goitre-area previously described. If, then, the Sahara was ever well watered and thickly populated, it seems probable that it also contained goitre-areas.

OTHER AREAS OF DEFICIENCY

Before concluding this brief survey of mineral-deficiencies we will glance along the line of the Quaternary Equator drawn from our interpretation of Wegener's theory. Ceylon, still close to the Equator and surrounded by sea, seems unlikely to have experienced any large variation in climate ; so that one would expect its soil to be deficient. We may remember the small size of the human indigenous population, the Veddas ; and also that the elephants fail to develop tusks. Burma and Malaya, too, will have been denuded of lime and phosphorus, if we are correct. Rice would appear to be the staple diet of the people, and timber the principal export. Neither contains or requires much phosphorus. I am informed, moreover, by an official of the Burma Teak Co., that elephants working timber on a diet of sugar-cane frequently get run-down, and may be greatly benefited by the feeding of calcium lactate. The imported Indian coolies would appear to obtain additional mineral from the eating of rotten fish ; while the native Burmese may be considered to conserve supplies by their somewhat lethargic mode of life. It is in this region that we find two distinct types of pygmy, the Semang and Sakai, the one of Negroid and the other of quasi-Caucasian appearance.

In China, most of the population is concentrated in the alluvium of the river valleys, and in an area that is even now of high rainfall; though the precipitation may be expected to have been greater still if the Equator can ever have run NE. along the China coast.

On the assumption that frequent flooding is liable to cause an iodine-deficiency, we might expect goitre to exist ; though beyond the statement of Janney (1924), quoted by Orr, which I have been unable to check in the original, we can find little direct evidence of this.[1]

Huntington mentions the crowding out of domestic animals by human beings in China. This is a fact well capable of interpretation in terms of mineral-deficiency, when we reflect that human milk, and so too presumably an adequate human diet, contains only 3·7 gms. of mineral ash per 1000 calories, as compared with the figures 10·5, 10·9 and 15 in the cases of faster-growing animals such as the cow, the pig and the rabbit respectively.[2] Moreover, as early as 1881 it was noted that Cochin China hay was very deficient in calcium.[3] There is, likewise,

[1] Orr : *Iod. in Nut.* ; cft. Janney (1924), *Endocrinology and Metabolism*, 1, 441.
[2] Orr : *Min. in Past.*, p. 51.
[3] Ibid., p. 18.

ample evidence that osteomalacia and rickets among human beings are common in China, and can be cured by the administration of calcium and cod-liver oil. The disease would seem to be more common in the rest of China than in the neighbourhood of Peking.[1]

Finally, we come to Japan, which, besides being once within our presumed Quaternary equatorial region, seems doubly liable to deficiency owing to the volcanic nature of much of the country. Unfortunately, I have found no data with regard to the effect of Japanese soil on animal nutrition. With regard to the human population, however, the observations of Huntington are of very great interest.[2] Besides remarking upon the conspicuous lack of domestic animals, similar to that referred to in the case of China, he points out that milk is regarded as a very great luxury. Elsewhere he stresses a certain lack of physical vigour due to "anæmia and other minor ailments." Can the anæmia be from lack of iron, as in the other volcanic areas? He goes on: "Few people can realize the extent to which the capacity of the nation is tied up with the number of illnesses and the death-rate. Even in June an inordinate number of the Japanese, especially the children, suffer from colds and running noses. Among civilized races few have so high a death-rate as Japan. The average there, since 1900, has been above twenty per thousand, practically all of the time." In considering the main reasons for this lack of health and the high death-rate, we can agree with him in attributing it, firstly, to the unbalanced diet—rice; secondly, to the density of the population; and lastly, to the unfavourable summer climate. Regarding the latter, it would seem that the autumns are very wet, and it is then that the health of the population suffers. Thus in June (when it is dry) the rate of live conceptions of children per day is at its height of 574 and the death-rate at its lowest: 233. In the wet September, on the other hand, live conceptions fall to 311, and deaths rise to 317.

The above facts are at least consistent with a theory that human health is in this case closely bound up with some soluble mineral-content of the soil. One would suggest calcium. The thick population would seem to deny a phenomenally low phosphorus-content of the soil; and it is here suggested that the volume of the human population, while being roughly adjusted to the phosphorus-value both in numbers and in the quality of the vegetation on which they subsist, must be wont to ebb and flow mainly at the dictate of the soluble mineral supply. Of course, in generalizing to this rather extreme extent, we must not forget the international fame of the Japanese as fishermen. Nor is it surprising that, for the inhabitants of this impoverished land, sea-gained phosphorus, lime, and vitamin should stand in such high regard.

This theory of a northern migration of the Equator during the

[1] Maxwell, J. P.: "Further Studies in Osteomalacia," *Proc. R. Soc. Med.*, XXIII, 639 (1930).

[2] Huntington, E.: *The Human Habitat*, London, 1928.

Quaternary is accepted by Davidson Black, although the maps he has published do not correspond very closely with my own.[1] In explaining the origin of the Mongolian loëss he points out that " a great weight of palæontological evidence has been accumulated by workers in the Orient pointing to the conclusion that throughout Quaternary time until its close, while Europe and North America were subjected to successive glaciations, the climate along the present East coast of Asia, from Kamchatka to the tropics, had been progressively warmer than at present. As far back as 1911, Yokoyama was forced to the conclusion, from the evidence then at his disposal, that the temperature of Central Japan had gradually increased since the early Pliocene to reach a maximum at the close of the Pleistocene, from which time to the present it had decreased."[2] Nevertheless, we must also consider the evidence of glaciations in North China recently obtained by Mr. Lee.[3] Perhaps the European Polar approach corresponds with the red clay which intervenes between the two strata of boulders. If so, and considering that the lowest of these overlies sandstones of Eocene and Oligocene date, whereas the upper underlies Sinanthropus, the polar shift in question would appear to have been earlier than Wegener has suggested.

CONCLUSION (CHAPTERS II AND III)

The last two chapters represent an attempt to formulate and justify the principles upon which the mineral hypothesis of animal and human evolution must be based. Heavy rainfall is deemed to have depleted the soil of its calcium, and with it of the sodium and, may be, of the phosphorus as well. Only occasionally, as in the case of volcanic soils, would iron or iodine appear to be lost through this cause. Nevertheless, the fact that some soils and regions may be rich in all minerals, while others are poor, must be borne in mind. On the whole, however, aridity, by concentrating calcium and sodium, will inhibit an abundance of iodine and iron, and under extreme conditions will prevent phosphorus from finding its way into the plant and the grazing animal. Possibly it is of more value to think in terms of constantly changing conditions. A long period of aridity may be expected to have accumulated calcium, and the latter may in its turn have collected phosphorus; while the iodine supply will be low. A change to pluvial conditions would quickly wash away all calcium that was not combined with phosphorus, and with it might go some of the already rare iodine. Following upon this, soil acidity would slowly accumulate new stocks of iodine, while the phosphorus would gradually be lost.

[1] Davidson Black: " Palæogeography and Polar Shift," Reprint, *Bulletin of the Geological Society of China*, Vol. X, Peking, 1930.
[2] Yokoyama, M.: " Climatic changes in Japan, etc.," *J. C. Col. Sci. Tokyo Imp. Univ.*, Vol. 32, 1911.
[3] Lecture recently delivered in Oxford.

CHAPTER IV

SODIUM, POTASSIUM, AND PIGMENTATION

Drought and the Animal: Drought and the Plant: Water versus Salt Economy: Pigmentation in Man: Sodium, Pigmentation and the Endocrines: Sex and the Adrenal-cortex: Stature and Colour: Sodium, Protective Colouring and the Negro: Drought, Protective Colouring and the Bushman: Bushman, Negro, and Nilote: Table of Conclusions.

IN THIS AND THE NEXT CHAPTER IT IS PROPOSED TO CONSIDER SOME of the physiological data bearing upon the mineral metabolism of plants and animals. Any complete review of the subject would, however, be too unwieldy, even were I competent to undertake it. All that it is proposed to do here is to specify some of the experimental facts that will be used in the theories to be presently developed. At the same time, however, it will be necessary to make some mention of the theories for which the evidence is needed.

As we have already examined the distribution of the three important elements, calcium, phosphorus, and iodine, and given some brief account of their functions, further discussion concerning them can be delayed. They will be dealt with at the end of the next chapter, in which brief note will also be taken of various other rare elements whose deficiencies might sometimes occur so as to influence animal evolution. Something must at once be said about the importance of water as a substance whose economy has governed natural selection. This perforce introduces the subject of sodium, its partner chlorine, and its possible substitute potassium. Moreover, since the question of skin colour is here involved, a theory of Negroid evolution has been inserted at this point.

DROUGHT AND THE ANIMAL

Now in most studies of the higher animals it has long been recognized that an ability to conserve moisture has been one of the main criteria of success. It may be argued, therefore, that this insistence upon the importance of minerals in general reflects, partially at least, only a new aspect of an old view, namely that the ratio of dry matter to water tends to increase with each ascending step of that evolutionary ladder whereby the vertebrate has hoisted itself clear of its native element. In attempting, therefore, to distinguish orders and species in terms of their relative requirements in the matter of specific substances, one must also be on the look out for perhaps even greater differences in the ratio maintained between the total amounts of all these potential solids and the volume of water which is needed for their utilization. This has already been suggested by MacAuliffe.[1] Davenport, too, distinguishes between an early " imbibatory " stage in the tadpole, and a later phase when the proportion of dry matter increases from 4 per cent to 20 per cent. In Man this proportion rises to about 40 per cent.[2] It is conceivable, then, that inter-racial and inter-sexual differences, correlated with a greater or less degree of adult-like or child-like development, might influence the final ratio between the water and salts in the body.[3]

We may now go one stage further, however ; for we have already found good reason to suppose that it is in the damp regions of the earth that acidity, and so an abundance of iodine, may be expected. Conversely, therefore, any racial reaction to a dry environment should normally be linked with a necessity for conserving iodine. Thus, if this law is given a sufficient width of application, one might expect an economy in the matter of the number of adaptational devices, and hence the utilization of a single means for dealing with either aspect of a frequent kind of change. Thus, as pointed out in the first chapter, we may expect a lack of iodine to produce the reaction that is also typical of drought irrespective of the moisture actually available, and vice versa. Moreover it will be clear as we proceed how this suggestion, namely, that there may be an economy of possible effects leading to the elaboration of a few complex reactive mechanisms, for each of which more than a single cause may be accountable, seems borne out by observation. To be more definite, even at the cost of anticipating our conclusions, the similarity between certain physical characters, often pathologically associated with thyroid-deficiency, linking the Bushmen and the Mongoloid peoples of Asia, must otherwise seem puzzling; especially since there is no reason for assuming a lack of iodine in Africa, though this, rather than drought, seemed the outstanding kind of selective agent likely to have operated in the mountain regions of Asia. In this connection it becomes plain that the exceptional features, namely the developed steatopygy and pronounced lumbar curvature of the Bushmen, if, as suggested by Hooton and others, they are an evolved means of overcoming drought,[4] may be

[1] MacAuliffe : *Les Mechanismes Intimes de la Vie*, Paris, 1925 ; " Constitution et Sécrétion Interne," Bull. 1 & 2 Soc. d'Etude Forme Hum., Paris, 1925 ; quoted by E. Miller : *Types of Mind and Body*, London, 1926, p. 34.

[2] Davenport, C. B. : " The rôle of water in growth," *Proc. Boston Soc. nat. Hist.*, 28, 73–84.

[3] See also review by Adolph, E. A. : " The Metabolism and Distribution of Water in Body and Tissues," *Physiological Reviews*, Vol. XIII, No. 3, Baltimore, 1933.

[4] Hooton, E. A. : *Drawings of Hottentot Women*—Harvard African Studies, Vol. II, pp. 91–3. Smuts, J. C. : " Climate and Man in Africa," *S.Afr. J. Sci.*, Vol. XXIX, pp. 98–131, July, 1932.

regarded as the secondary specializations of a character always to some extent present in all hereditary examples of relative achondroplasia, whether in man or the animals. Achondroplasia in turn seems an attempt to economize mineral, mainly perhaps iodine, and is undoubtedly associated with a strong tendency to accumulate liquid and to achieve brachycephaly.[1] The latter effect, indeed, might well be regarded largely as an intermediate condition leading to the hydrocephaly often found in the more extreme cases; the majority of which, in cattle, are apt to be further complicated at birth by the over-development of another liquid-storing tendency, namely, hydramnios, and may thus be doubly lethal. It is suggested, however, that the genes responsible for such a condition have at some earlier time, and in other associations, served to confer survival-value on the vertebrate. Their simplex occurrence is still considered desirable in the Dexter cow.

DROUGHT AND THE PLANT

Regarding the plant's reaction to drought, it would appear that the calcium and potassium intake of a plant or pasture must diminish much slower than its phosphorus intake. This is what one might expect on the view that lime and potash are soluble and, having risen in the soil-capillaries in response to drought, may then be expected to enter the plant in amounts largely in excess of any minimum requirements; their internal concentration depending thus mainly on that of the water adhering to the soil particles. This may be demonstrated by the following example, quoted by Orr, for the composition of oat straw grown on the same land in years of heavy and of low rainfall:[2]

Year	P_2O_5	CaO	Rainfall
1902	·372	·541	275·7—Wet.
1904	·222	·784	118·3—Dry.

This shows also how, during drought, the phosphorus intake of the plant tends to drop; and also how the drought tends to raise the calcium-content. Similarly, irrigation may be shown considerably to increase phosphorus, accompanied by a much smaller rise in potash, and by a slight fall in calcium and sodium.[3] Phosphorus, then, may be regarded, with water, as the most common regulator of vegetative growth. The reactions of the plant to the soil seem to be such that an abundance of either tends to encourage a concentration of the other. Orr points out that pastures rich in phosphorus are better able to withstand drought. This immobile element would thus, within limits, seem capable of attracting water to itself where life demands it. The distinction should, however, become clear-cut when drought rather

[1] Crew, F. A. E.: "The Significance of an Achondroplasia-like condition in Cattle," *Proc. roy. Soc. Lond.* Ser. B, XCV, 1923, pp. 228–255.
[2] Orr: *Min. in Past.*, p. 42.
[3] Ibid., p. 44.

than lack of phosphorus dictates the bulk of life that may exist throughout an area.

Before disposing of the mineral metabolism of plants suffering from drought, we must once more mention the high mineral-content of plants specialized for a desert or semi-desert environment. The salt bushes of Australia, according to Orr, " are known to have a marked beneficial effect upon the health of stock."[1] Similarly, in the deserts and hot steppes of Asia, the camel and fat-tailed sheep are particularly fond of the salt-rich bushes which alone seem able to survive the drought, and to tolerate the often brackish supplies of soil-water. A comparison of the mineral-contents of these bushes with those of some normal pastures is thus of interest :[2]

	Kochia pyramidata Australian " Grey Bush."	Atriplex mummularia " Old Man Salt-Bush."	Swiss Meadows. Irrigated.	Swiss Meadows. Dry.	Scotch Hills. Eaten.	Scotch Hills. Not Eaten.
K_2O	4·62	4·91	3·306	2·895	2·60	1·61
Na_2O	12·83	9·25	—	—	0·41	0·17
NaCl	9·93	9·47	—	—	(Cl)0·60	0·33
CaO	3·26	2·71	0·943	1·002	0·56	0·30
MgO	2·72	2·12	0·474	0·381		
P_2O_5	1·48	1·28	0·729	0·457	0·60	0·37

Sodium and Chlorine, then, may normally be expected to abound in lands which have at some past time stood below the level of the sea. To bring them to the surface, however, they will require a dry climate. But they would appear to be present in greater quantity, and also to be required in larger amounts, in the hot steppe than in the cold arid regions.

WATER VERSUS SALT ECONOMY

In common with the other electrolytes sodium chloride would appear to perform most of its physiological functions through the separate agencies of its individual anion and cation. In this connection the preservation of excitability in living tissue, dependent as it is on a delicate adjustment not only of the mere CO_2 and hydrogen ion concentration, but on the presence and interaction of specific ions of calcium, sodium, potassium, and to a lesser degree magnesium, and chlorine, is of considerable interest. The absence of chlorine has been shown to bring about a tetany or paralysis of the central nervous system similar to that produced also by a shortage of calcium.[3] Chlorine is perhaps equally important from another point of view. It is required to maintain the acid reaction of the stomach necessary for the proper function of pepsin in the reduction of protein, and in the killing of ingested bacteria. There would seem to be no other substance usable by the vertebrate in its absence.[4]

From the ecological view-point, one might thus be tempted to class

[1] Orr : *Min. in Past.*, p. 93. [2] Ibid., pp. 93, 44, 15.
[3] Bayliss, p. 218. [4] Ibid., p. 374.

chlorine with phosphorus as a substance so necessary to the animal, even if not to plant life, that methods of economising it are unlikely to have met with much success.

This attitude, however, is dangerous. The possibility must not be forgotten that some races and species may normally possess a higher salt-concentration of the body or blood than others. In addition, reserve supplies might always be held in readiness by any hereditary character making for an increase in the capacity of the capillary system, which is very variable, and normally contains the largest portion of the whole blood volume. The capacity of the capillaries is enlarged by the action of the drug histamine, or by the toxic metabolites of wound shock, and to some extent by small amounts of adrenaline.[1] They seem to be contracted, and ordinarily to be maintained in tone, on the other hand, by the secretion of the post-pituitary.[2] The post-pituitary indeed, might be said to regulate the volume of the blood. The salt-concentration of the blood is normally maintained by a re-absorption taking place through the tubules of the kidney ; and it might be significant that the loss of fluid through the kidney can be temporally inhibited by the posterior-pituitary extract.[3] Despite this, however, chlorine derived from the body tissues is actively excreted.[4] The anterior-lobe, on the other hand, seems to encourage both the intake and outflow of water.[5] The urine, moreover, has different maximum concentrations in different animals.[6] Besides, though excretory products such as urea, foreign salts, foreign crystalloids, etc. are refused absorption by the cells of the tubules, the useful part, corresponding to the non-colloidal portion of the blood, is accepted at a " threshold " concentration. When, as shown by Cushny, the kidney is caused to secrete under an increased pressure in the ureter, so that the filtrate remains longer in contact with the tubules, an increased amount of sodium chloride, but not of sulphates or urea, is absorbed.[7] It seems quite possible, then, that in Man racial differences in the matter of salt economy may exist. If so, they probably involve differences in the activity of the adrenal-cortex, the action of which has recently been shown to encourage the retention of sodium. In any case, according to Bayliss, if an animal receives no sodium chloride in the food for several days, the serum still contains nearly the whole of its normal amount, but the urine practically none. Very nearly the whole of that filtered through in the glomeruli must be re-absorbed in the tubules.[8]

[1] Bayliss, pp. 706–719.
[2] Krogh, A. : *The Anatomy and Physiology of the Capillaries*, Yale, 1922.
[3] Bayliss, p. 359.
[4] Trendlenburg, P. : *Die Hormone*, Berlin, 1929, pp. 166–167.
[5] Gaebler, O. H. : *J. exp. Med.*, LVII (1933), p. 349.
[6] Bayliss, 356, cft. Cushny, R. : (1901) " On Diuresis and the Permeability of the Renal Cells," *J. Physiol.*, 27, 429–450. Same author (1902). " On Saline Diuresis," *J. Physiol.*, 28, 431–449.
[7] Ibid.
[8] Ibid., p. 354.

Sodium, like chlorine, seems indispensable as an ion necessary to maintain the excitability of tissue. It was shown by Overton that frogs' muscle immersed in isotonic cane-sugar loses its excitability, and that restoration can be brought about by a sodium salt, or in a less degree by a lithium salt.[1] The two substances seem thus to some extent interchangeable. At the same time, it would appear capable of being toxic, but to a less extent than the ions of potassium to be described presently. Nevertheless, sodium and potassium seem able to annul the toxic effect of each other on the fish Fundulus ; while in all cases the presence of the bivalent ion of calcium appears also to be necessary for prolonged activity. Indeed, calcium has a much more powerful effect than sodium in neutralizing the toxic properties of potassium. Sodium ions seem also capable of annulling the toxic action of acids ; though here again the calcium ions are more powerful.[2] Ringer found sodium bicarbonate useful in his solution for overcoming the acid produced in the contractions of the heart-muscle.[3] St. John (1928), working on rats, showed that a ration containing less than 0·3 per cent of sodium inhibited growth.[4]

It is clear, then, that a lack of sodium could have influenced natural selection. The other, and perhaps no less important, possibility which must be borne in mind is that an excess of sodium may sometimes have been experienced also. A defensive mechanism may even have been evolved.

It was pointed out by Lapicque, and is now well known, that many African and other tropical agriculturists use wood ash, which contains a high proportion of potassium chloride, as a substitute for the sodium chloride more usually consumed by vegetarian men and animals. This ash, however, also contains some sodium.[5] Thus it is not quite clear whether the practice arises primarily through a demand for chlorine or for sodium. It seems almost certain that an excess of potash must thereby be consumed ; and it is not impossible that an active excretion of excess chlorine might likewise become necessary. Now, as previously stated, extracts from the posterior-pituitary encourage the discharge of chlorine from the tissue cells.[6] Thus one might argue that an hereditary activity of that organ could be of value to the Negro in protecting him from a chloride excess. It will later be argued that this same posterior-lobe activity is likewise of assistance in

[1] Bayliss, p. 217, cft. Overton, E. (1904) : " Studien über die Wirkung der Alkali und Erdalkalisalze auf Skelettmuskeln und Nerven " ; *Pflüger's Arch.*, 105, 176–290.
[2] Ibid., p. 213.
[3] Bayliss, p. 208.
[4] St. John, J. L. (1928) : " Growth on a synthetic ration containing small amounts of sodium," *J. biol. Chem.*, 77, 27.
[5] Lapicque, L. : " Sur L'alimentation Minérale," *Anthropologie*, 1896.
[6] Trendlenburg, P. : loc. cit., p. 167, cf. t. Miura, Y. : *Arch. exp. Path. Pharmak.*, 107, I (1925).

encouraging a tissue storage of the often rare element sodium, and for discharging an embarrassing excess of potash.

In comparison with potassium, the sodium ion has more water molecules associated with it ; and for this reason, apparently, its rate of ionic migration is slower. Most of the sodium of the body remains in the blood-plasma, in contradistinction to the potassium which enters cells such as the red corpuscles. The high sodium content of desert-plants seems explicable by the affinity of sodium for water. Whether the desert type of animal and Man have likewise a higher sodium content or requirement is, therefore, a question that might deserve further investigation. There seems little doubt that the desert environment tends normally to cater for such a demand ; for sodium chloride, like the lime salts, rises in the soil-capillaries in response to drought. Water, though normally regarded as being chemically inert, enters into violent reaction with sodium.[1]

Potassium, like phosphorus, is a substance so necessary to plant-life that its lack must often constitute a limiting factor to vegetative growth. Since it is released from the huge surface area of the colloidal and other small particles constituting clay soils, the lack of it, as most farmers know, is frequently met with on light, sandy land of coarse texture. In nature, then, a lack of potassium must be expected, firstly in sandy deserts, and, secondly, in the more heavily podsolized and therefore sandy soils of the more rainy temperate regions. Under agricultural conditions in Europe, at all events, it is the dry sandy lands which seem to respond best to dressings of potash. Used as an artificial fertilizer it is useful in assisting crops to withstand drought. A lack of potash is often indicated by a yellow tinge in the green leaf.

There seems no evidence that a lack of potassium in the food has ever been a limiting factor governing animal development. Indeed, considering the comparatively large quantities of this substance used in the building of the rigid cell wall of the vegetable, and the relatively small amount contained in the animal body, it seems hard to believe that any animal, except just possibly a complete carnivore, could ever suffer from a deficiency of this substance.

As an alternative to a deficiency, however, it seems quite possible that sometimes—in Africa for instance—an excess of potassium might have been responsible for some racial reaction. Before believing this, however, it would first have to be proved that such excess had been disadvantageous, and had thus influenced selection ; and this I am unable to do. As regards the areas where an excess of potash is likely to have found its way into the diet, I would suggest that in regions often subject to forest fires—park-lands, but not tropical rain-forest—the animals would make up for some considerable portion of their important chlorine requirement by the ingestion of wood-ash, consisting largely of

[1] Bayliss, p. 240.

chlorate of potash. In the case of Man in the French Congo, an elaboration of this natural behaviour has, as reported by Lapicque, led to the invention of a process whereby this substance—in company, however, with a small amount of sodium chloride—is obtained in a relatively pure form. Potash, then, seems to some extent able to be substituted for sodium. Moreover, such an arrangement would seem to have assisted the survival of animals and Man in areas where sodium tends to be lost by seasonal rains, and potash is returned to the soil-surface in the form of wood-ash. In the rain-belt itself a lack of calcium might similarly be believed to result in an excess of potash. Indeed, the observations of Reed and Haas, together with those of Godden, show a reverse relationship between calcium and potassium.[1] Thus, an excess of potash, which I believe to be associated with black pigmentation in Man, tends probably to extend from the edge of the park-land to the Equator.

It was these observations of Lapicque which stimulated Gérard to experiment on dogs fed with a high potassium and low sodium ration. He found that, while the additional potassium left the blood composition practically unaltered, the tissue cells, on the other hand, lost sodium, which was to some extent replaced by potassium.[2]

These somewhat unexpected results would seem to suggest that selection may already have evolved a mechanism whereby the powerful and rapid physiological action of potassium may be controlled by its maintenance at an unaltered blood-concentration; for, as shown by Overton, the actions of potassium and sodium on muscle are on the surface only.[3]

Potassium is slightly radio-active.[4] This may possibly account for the high speeds at which its ions migrate. In comparison with those of sodium their affinity for water is small. Potassium tends to paralyze nerves, nerve-endings, and heart-muscle, while it excites plain muscle of all kinds.[5] Indeed, it seems probable that the well-known power of the vagus nerve to inhibit heart-action is brought about through the agency of potassium. Howell and Duke found that an increase of potassium could be detected in a small amount of Ringer Locke solution which has passed repeatedly through a mammalian heart under vagus inhibition.[6] Ringer demonstrated the action of potassium in

[1] Orr: *Min. in Past.*, pp. 21, 22.

[2] Bayliss, p. 126, cft. Gérard, P.: (1912) "Influence de l'alimentation sur la teneur en potassium et en sodium d'un chien," *Comptes Rendus Acad.*, France, 154, 1305–1307.

[3] Bayliss, 142, cft. Overton, E.: (1904) "Studien über die Wirkung der Alkali und Erdalkalisalze auf Skelettmuskeln und Nerven," *Pflüg. Arch. ges. Physiol.*, 105, 176–290.

[4] Bayliss, p. 214.

[5] Ibid., p. 217.

[6] Ibid., p. 217, cft. Howell, W. H., and Duke, W. W.: (1908) *Amer. J. Physiol.*, 21, 51–63.

abolishing the tonic action of calcium on the heart, without depriving it of the power of neutralizing the injurious effects of pure sodium chloride. He showed that an increase in the potassium concentration could lower the diastolic blood pressure.[1] This suggests an inhibition of posterior-lobe activity such as is later deemed to follow from an over-activity of the adrenal-cortex. The latter guards the escape of sodium through the kidney, and may thus be stimulated either by a sodium deficiency or a potassium excess. Finally, in concluding the physiological data which might just conceivably have some application to anthropology, we must again mention the action of potassium in contracting the pigment in the black chromatophores in the skin of the fish Fundulus ; the expansion of this black pigment, accompanied by the contraction of the yellow pigment of other cells, being a response to an environment containing more sodium.[2] Some fishes, cephalopods, for instance, have red as well as yellow and black pigment and cells, and so probably represent a stage closer to the ancestral stem leading to the skin of Man.

PIGMENTATION IN MAN

Now the behaviour of the chromatophores of Fundulus runs exactly counter to what might have been expected, were it assumed, firstly, that there was an unmodified hereditary connection between the direction, if not the speed, of pigment-migration in the skin-cells of Man and of the fish ; and, secondly, that an excess of sodium or potassium in the external environment would be communicated directly to the cells in each case. For the purpose of the remainder of this argument, then, it will be assumed—though without any experimental proof—that, in the case of the higher organism, Man, a direct reversal of the primitive system has been developed : that is to say, that in the tissues, if not actually in the blood, of the black races there is an abnormally low concentration of potassium, while the bodies of the yellow peoples tend to be deficient in sodium. Possibly the point has been investigated, but if so, I am unaware of the results.

To give credit where it is due, attention must be drawn to the book by Armitage. In a comparison between the sodium-contents of the diets of peoples representative of the three colours, he arrives at the conclusion that a sodium-abundance of the diet is correlated with a lack of melanotic pigmentation. Moreover, he draws attention to a theory, elsewhere confirmed, that an abundance of potash will deprive the body of sodium.[3]

Where it seems unsafe to follow him blindly is in his suggestion that the bodies of the people specialized for a sodium-abundant diet will contain more sodium. This does not fit in with the evidence from

[1] Bayliss, p. 207, 8.
[2] Bayliss, p. 215, cft. Spaeth, R.A. : (1913) " The physiology of the Chromatophores of Fishes," *J. exp. Zool.*, 15, 527.
[3] Armitage, F. B. : *Diet and Race*, London, 1922.

Fundulus, for whatever it is worth, since here sodium produces black and potash yellow. I propose, therefore, to try and interpret these facts, making due allowance for a process of natural selection, and so almost reversing the more simple theory that an abundance in the external environment is necessarily reflected in the adapted organism and vice versa. For it seems at least equally possible that the organism will react so as actively to resist a single new factor in its environment, and thus maintain the rest of its adjustments unchanged. I suggest, therefore, that the pigment-cells of the Negro, and probably all other tissues, and possibly the blood as well, tend to contain an excess rather than a deficiency of sodium. From this it would follow that the skin-cells of the yellow race, which is presumed to be adapted to arid conditions, would contain a low concentration of sodium. Thus, when evaporation had removed an excess of water the content of the yellow skin would achieve the normal of the human race. Similarly, if the Negro was subjected to a very severe sodium-deficiency in the food, the blood might withdraw some reserve of sodium from the body-tissues. Either Armitage's theory or my own could claim survival-value for the mechanisms postulated in either case. Supposing Man to turn yellow as a result of long exposure to sodium-rich foods, he would thereby achieve protective coloration together with the drought-defying capacity of the yellow type of skin. Actually, however, I strongly suspect that there is a limited and accidental ontogenetic reaction to sodium-abundance, but that it encourages black and not yellow skin-colour. Rawlings draws attention to the very dark colour of the coastal peoples of New Guinea, and to the fact that they disliked salt or salted food. Inland the lighter-coloured peoples showed the usual salt-hunger common to other tropical agriculturists.[1] This fact is, of course, inconclusive, since we have no assurance here of racial homogeneity. Indeed, difference of colour would normally be regarded as proof of such hereditary difference. It would be interesting to know whether the habitat of the equally "stove-black" Nilotes supplies them with an abundance of sodium. In their case, however, a difference of stature and culture clearly divides these people from the remaining populations of Africa; and we are confronted with a difference of heredity probably affecting the endocrines.

SODIUM, PIGMENTATION AND THE ENDOCRINES

Two of the endocrines, the posterior-pituitary and the adrenal-cortex are somehow concerned with pigmentation. Moreover, the latter maintains the sodium-concentration of the blood by preventing its loss—or encouraging its re-absorption—by the kidney. Destruction of the adrenal-cortex by disease leads to a lowering of the sodium-concentration of the blood, followed by a remarkable pigmentation of

[1] Rawlings, C. G.: *The Land of the New Guinea Pygmies*, London, 1913, pp. 181 and 186.

the skin. The condition is known as Addison's disease.[1] On the face of this evidence one is again tempted to abandon the hypothesis that a high, rather than a low, sodium-concentration within the skin-cells is responsible for melanotic pigmentation. Since, however, a good many pieces of the puzzle are missing, I propose to adhere to my original theory. The phenomenon of Addison's disease could still be explained on the assumption that the posterior-lobe and the adrenal-cortex each encourage the passage of the sodium ion through certain classes of cells : the former affecting the tissues of the body as a whole, and the skin in particular ; the latter furthering the re-absorption of the sodium ion through the cells of the tubules in the kidney. In addition to this it is necessary to suppose that the hormone of each gland inhibits secretion by the other. On this view the pigmentation in Addison's disease would be due to a compensatory hypersecretion of the posterior-lobe allowed by the failure of the adrenal-cortex. It would result in a storage of sodium in the tissues, despite the loss of sodium from the blood. This would be of some survival-value.

Extracts from the posterior-pituitary of mammals have been found to affect the pigment cells of fish and amphibia, though substances from the pars-intermedia of the pituitary—a structure which seems to be absent in the case of Man—produce a much greater effect. Not only does this melanophore hormone expand the black pigment within the cells, but it can likewise result in the growth of large numbers of black cells ; and at the same time it inhibits both the growth and display of the yellow chromatophores.[2] I suggest, therefore, that the posterior-lobe, which we know to encourage the water-storage and chlorine excretion by the body tissues, acts by allowing the passage of the sodium ion into the pigment and other body cells. Thus, if the hormone of the adrenal-cortex is of a similar nature, so that the two are to some extent interchangeable, it becomes necessary to assume that this also acts by increasing rather than by inhibiting the sodium-permeability of some kidney-cells. Since the kidney acts by re-absorbing a few required substances from a filtrate, it therefore seems reasonable to suggest that the adrenal-cortex encourages the re-absorption of sodium by the tubules of the kidney.

A scrap of evidence favouring the view that suprarenal failure affects the sodium, and so the potassium, content of all tissues is afforded the experiments of Loeb and his co-workers. They found that the potassium-concentration of the blood rises as a result of removing the suprarenals, but that the body does not lose potassium. This suggests that the tissues have been encouraged to yield the less valuable potassium to make room for the extra stocks of sodium they are enabled to store.[3]

[1] Loeb, R. F. : *Science* (1932), 76/420 : also *J. exp. Med.*, LVII (1933), p. 775 : also Harrop and Weinstein : *J. exp. Med.*, LVII (1933), p. 305.

[2] Huxley, J. S., and de Beer, G. R. : *The Elements of Experimental Embryology*, Cambridge, 1934, p. 425.

[3] Loeb *et al.* : *J. exp. Med.*, LVII (1933), p. 775 *et seq.*

This view of the posterior-pituitary acting as a sentry to guard the more valuable constituents of the blood is further borne out by the work of Heller and Smirk. They have shown that in rats pituitrin (from the posterior-lobe) increases the water-storage of the skin and muscles; and they quote Priestly, who showed that the storage of water in the tissues is accompanied by a withdrawal of electrolytes from the blood.[1] If the posterior-lobe does increase the sodium-content of the cells, we might expect water to accompany it, rather than the potassium ion which it is here supposed to replace.

Some mention must finally be made of the influence of the pituitary upon the kidney, which, as we have seen, is also governed by its neighbour, the adrenal-cortex. The immediate effect of the administration of pituitrin is to inhibit diuresis and cause water, but not chloride, to be retained. This is explicable on the theory that the posterior-lobe, like the adrenal-cortex, promotes the return of sodium and water through the tubules of the kidney, while leaving the excretion of chlorides by the glomerule unaffected. Again, fasting blood has been found to contain more of the posterior-lobe melanophore hormone than when water had been given. Under fasting conditions the blood and tissues might be expected to contain an excess of sodium; but, since the surface concentration of the former is of greater physiological importance than the internal contents of the latter, any agency able to accumulate the surplus sodium in the less important cells, so maintaining a constant blood-concentration, would be of value. I suggest, therefore, that a high sodium-concentration of the blood results in a hypersecretion of the posterior-lobe; and that this, firstly, encourages a storage of sodium in the skin and muscles, and, secondly, inhibits diuresis and so prevents a further rise in the sodium-concentration: so that, finally, it becomes necessary to postulate an inhibition of the adrenal-cortex. This could allow a loss of sodium through the kidney, while retaining part of the water to which it had formerly been bound. Such mutual inhibition by the adrenal-cortex and the posterior-lobe would then account for the postulated activity of the latter at a time when the sodium-concentration in Addison's disease was low rather than high.

SEX AND THE ADRENAL-CORTEX

Before we dismiss the question of the adrenal-cortex, attention must be drawn to the curious case reported by Holmes in which a pathological over-activity of this gland was responsible for the development of secondary male characters and instincts in a woman. After removal of the tumour there was a return to normal.[2] This suggests that the male is normally characterized by a greater activity of the adrenal-cortex than the female; and that in his case the activity of the posterior-lobe would be repressed unless it also received a similar autosomal

[1] Heller, H., and Smirk, F. H.: "Tissue Hydration and Diuresis," *J. Physiol.*, 76, 37 (1932).
[2] Holmes, G.: *Quart. J. Med.*, Vol. 18, Oxford, 1924.

encouragement. A further fact which supports the same view is that the anterior-lobe is known to encourage the growth of the adrenal-cortex; for there is good reason to assume that the superior skeletal size of the male indicates a greater activity of the anterior-lobe and so of the other endocrines and organs whose growth seems directly dependent thereon.[1] Now it is often noticed in animals that melanism or dark colouring is both a male and a gerontomorphic character, developing after puberty. It seems probable, therefore, that the posterior-lobe activity of the female and adolescent is lower. This might be of value in allowing a larger liquid and sodium reserve owing to the greater bore of the capillaries, made possible by the weaker "pressor" stimulus of the pituitary.

From the evolutionary point of view this fact is not easy to fit in with the general theory. One might have assumed that, since femininity encourages lime-economy, it should also have encouraged sodium-economy, and hence an activity of the adrenal-cortex; for sodium- and lime-deficiencies are encountered together. It seems possible, however, that, whereas the genes for sodium-economy are very old, and, if ever sex-linked, became autosomal at the time of the evolution of the homogametic female, the genes for lime-economy, on the other hand, may have evolved later upon the new sex-chromosomes.

Indeed, if we imagine lactation to have been first developed as a means of economizing fluid under conditions of soil-acidity and sodium abundance, it can be understood that the female's need to consume greater quantities of food and drinking water would probably entail a need to excrete greater quantities of sodium than before. Moreover, supposing the next change of environment to have demanded a physiological economy of calcium—since in the meantime the latter had become necessary to accelerate a hardening of the offspring's skeleton—it could follow that the retention of an environmentally imposed acidity, due to a simultaneously imposed deficiency of sodium, would be of value. Such an acidity could not only assist the bio-chemical absorption of the more necessary calcium through the wall of the intestine, but, as will be explained later, it could limit the growth of cartilage and so restrict the skeletal development. The retention and secondary intensification of such an externally and momentarily imposed condition could be secured through the natural selection of sex-linked modifiers restricting the activities of both parts of the pituitary gland. A limitation of the posterior-lobe activity would increase the chlorine-content, and probably lower the sodium-content of the body tissues; thus increasing their acidity and power of attracting calcium. At the same time, less activity of the anterior-lobe would result in a reduced development and activity of the adrenal-cortex[2]; and this would facilitate the loss of sodium through the

[1] Trendlenburg, P.: *Die Hormone, Ihre Physiologie und Pharmakologie*, Berlin, 1929, p. 176.
[2] Trendlenburg, P.: loc. cit., p. 176.

kidney. Of course, the reduced activity of the anterior-lobe would also directly inhibit the skeletal development, and its influence would thus co-operate with the alteration of electrolyte balance produced by the inhibition of the posterior-lobe.

The application of this theory to the evolution of Man is important, since it suggests that, whereas a selection for calcium-economy will encourage femininity, a selection for sodium-economy may tend to reverse certain aspects of this process.

I attribute certain characters of the Negro, particularly the strength and activity of the Negro woman, to an inhibition of femininity caused by a selection of sodium-economy. This would require an activity of the adrenal-cortex and of the posterior-lobe.[1] Almost diametrically opposite conditions are seen in the Bushman, whose steatopygia, greatly exaggerated in the women, suggests a weakness of the posterior-lobe encouraged by a sex-linked character. Whether the adrenal-cortex is also below normal activity must remain uncertain. We may reflect, however, that a capacity to lose sodium through the kidney might be a blessing when the drink was brackish, as it would be in desert water-holes. If so, a sex-linked inhibition of cortical activity would be fraught with positive survival-value.

STATURE AND COLOUR

So far we have taken for granted the existence of black and yellow skin-cells. It is interesting, however, to note that the black melanin seems but to be the complete product, whereas yellow and red pigments seem to represent stages in its synthesis. Raper and Wormall show that the action of more than one enzyme on tryosine is to form a red substance by direct oxidation. On the acid side of neutrality, and at the neutral point, this red substance oxidizes to the black pigment melanin ; but on the alkaline side this occurs at a much greater rate.[2]

In amphibia and other low organisms, pigment is formed most easily in positions of high metabolic activity and growth-rate.[3] It is at these points that oxidation takes place most rapidly. These regions of high growth-rate have been shown to be electro-negative to others in the external circuit.[4] This again shows an alkalinity, due to the positively charged hydroxyl ions.

If, then, human pigmentation is connected with the state of the internal environment, we might expect races with the most alkaline blood-reactions and highest metabolic rates to be blackest. Actually, when we consider Africa, it is the very tall peoples who show the

[1] *N.B.* Since each tends to inhibit the action of the other the selective process would involve the strengthening of both.

[2] Bayliss, p. 586, cft. Raper, S., and Wormall, A. : (1923) *Bio-chem. J.*, 17,454.

[3] Huxley and de Beer : loc. cit.

[4] de Beer, G. R. : *Elements of Experimental Embryology*, p. 63 *et seq.*

greatest intensity of pigmentation. It might thus be suspected that their great height, as also their colour, was due to the same cause, namely, to a great activity of the bone-growth hormone of the anterior-pituitary.

Now extracts of the anterior-lobe have been found not only to raise the metabolic rate, but also the serum-calcium.[1] Possibly, indeed probably, the parathyroids and the thyroid are both stimulated at the same time. In any case, both the high metabolic rate and the high calcium might be expected to reduce acidity; and the raised metabolism might favour pigmentation in some other way besides. Incidentally, it is worth mentioning that the mere influence of heat might also be expected to assist the reaction towards alkalinity. This is due to the fact that the electrolytic dissociation of water rises more rapidly in accordance with temperature than can that of sodium bicarbonate.[2] This suggests that in the adaptation of tropical forms less reliance will have been placed on the buffering action of the mineral-fixed base, and more upon that of the blood corpuscles. This accords with the theory that hot periods have been humid and deficient in soil-salts.

To return, however, to the tall black races of Africa, attention must here be drawn to the theory of Balint and Weiss, who consider that cartilage proliferation, and so speed of bone-growth, are encouraged by alkalinity.[3] This suggests that the peoples in question have an active anterior-lobe, a high basal metabolism, and high serum-calcium, and that the stove-black colour is the result of these conditions. As for the evolutionary significance of this, it would not be impossible for a sexual selection for black colour thus to encourage stature; or for a sexual selection for stature to encourage blackness. The main point, however, would be that one could not expect the survival of these giant types, except with a diet rich in calcium and sodium salts. Since they are now pastorals this is provided. It would be rash, however, to assume that the culture had produced the man. Doubtless there may be a mutual interaction, but it seems more probable that adoption of milk and blood food arose as a means of maintaining a relatively wasteful kind of physiology, which had developed as an accident of peculiar environmental and hereditary associations. Cultural adaptation probably involves the changing of relatively few genes in order that the survival of the remainder may be further secured. These questions will be more fully discussed later.

SODIUM, PROTECTIVE COLOURING, AND THE NEGRO

It has been argued that the extreme blackness of the Nilote is the product of peculiar conditions which have modified the heredity of a

[1] Frei, W., and Emmerson, M. A.: *Biochem. Z.*, 226, 355 (1930).
[2] Bayliss, p. 202.
[3] Balint and Weiss: *Tissue Proliferation and Acid-Base Equilibrium*, London, 1932.

more normal Negroid physiology. The latter may be considered to have been adjusted to heat, and to calcium- and sodium-deficiency—conditions which may be expected in the equatorial region and have probably been more widely distributed, and more intense, during times of increased solar heat. Potassium, being abundant, has been used as a partial substitute for sodium; and water, being likewise plentiful, has involved no need for an evolved economy.

Looking, then, to the endocrinology of the man evolved for the tropical forest, we may expect a high activity of the adrenal-cortex to economize sodium. The posterior-lobe must be active enough to encourage a tissue storage of sodium, without inhibiting the adrenal-cortex so as to allow a loss through the kidney. This will reduce the bore of the capillaries, and the fluid reserve will be small. Stature, the presumed product of the bone-growth anterior-pituitary hormone, must be reduced if calcium and phosphorus are to be economized. Iodine, being plentiful, will demand no great activity of the thyrotropic hormone of the anterior-lobe; and it seems probable that no special activity of the parathyroids will be required either. Parathyroid extracts encourage a loss of calcium.[1] At the same time, a very low parathyroid activity might fail to mobilize sufficient calcium from the often poorly nourished skeleton; and, if the parathyroids serve to inhibit skeletal development, their activity during the growing period would be all to the good. On the whole, then, we can find no need for an active anterior-lobe, while an active posterior-lobe is definitely required. If, therefore, as seems probable, the two halves of the pituitary inhibit each other's effects,[2] the posterior-lobe may be believed to have got the upper hand.

Genetically, it seems possible that this inhibition of pituitary activity may have been secured, firstly, by an increase of mammalian sex-linked predominance leading to a relatively great secretion of the female-determining substances. In the second place, however, the great activity of the adrenal-cortex must be set down to the predominance of autosomal factors, and may thus tend to inhibit the expression of full femininity. It seems probable that the blackness of the tropical man is correlated or linked with the autosomal characters favouring sodium-economy. This would be useful, firstly, as a means of concealment in the shade of trees. Secondly, if used as a mark of sexual attraction, it would serve to encourage the mating of those individuals whose hereditary sodium-economy was best; and whose sodium reserves at the moment happened to stand in least need of replenishment. I suggest, therefore, that, whereas protective coloration through melanism was evolved in a lower animal, in Man it has served as a mark of a particular type of physiology, and has therefore been valuable in the evolving of the Negroid race through sexual as well as through natural selection.

[1] These matters are dealt with in the next chapter.
[2] Cf. Hogben, L. T.: *Proc. roy. Soc. B.*, 94, 1922, p. 204.

DROUGHT, PROTECTIVE COLOURING, AND THE BUSHMAN

I regard the Bushman as the one form of man specialized for desert conditions. His environment, besides being hot in the sun, probably provides him with an excess of sodium ; while it imposes the need to economize water. Calcium will probably be abundant, but drought might inhibit the intake of phosphorus by the plants. In the primitive vertebrate, it was supposed, drought was countered by large size ; so that we are left with the difficulty how to explain the dwarf stature of the Bushman. As for the yellow skin colour, this could serve both to provide protective colouring and to act as the sexual advertisement of a specialized desert form of physiology ; for, besides blending with its surroundings, it will probably be found to possess independent physico-chemical advantages. The yellow colour of the desert soil is itself the result of pigment-excreting bacteria, which are thus probably enabled to absorb some radiations and to reflect others.[1]

If we turn, however, to the possible endocrine relationships operating at the twofold dictate of the heredity and the environment, it seems fair, first of all, to postulate a considerable activity of the sex-linked female-determining genes. The steatopygia was much greater in the females of this remarkable, and now virtually extinct, race than in the males. It is clearly a sex-linked character and was probably intensified by sexual selection. It is suggested, therefore, that large amounts of female-determining substances have served to inhibit the normal capillary constrictor-effect of the posterior-lobe, at all events in so far as these influences affect the capillaries of the buttock. Doubtless there has been a specialization as well as a mere intensifying in the somatic expression of pre-existing characters. The fat-deposits of the Bushman differ in kind as well as in degree from those of other races.

It seems probable that there is a greater posterior-lobe activity in the males of all mammals, leading to greater capillary constriction and tonus, and so to greater strength and reduced vulnerability. If so, an intensification of the condition found in the average female would lead to the evolution of a greater fluid reserve. Indeed, it is hard to think of a single endocrine, except possibly the sex-glands, in which a lowering of activity would not confer survival-value in a hot desert in which iodine was not rare. Under conditions of cold and aridity, of course, large size and anterior-lobe activity are required to economize heat.

As for the anterior-lobe of the dwarf Bushman, then, we must assume an inhibition of the bone-growth influence, and may attribute it to the greater femininity. We may recall Gaebler's observation that anterior-lobe extracts encourage the intake and loss of water, and the breakdown of proteins.[2] It seems probable that, when drinks were few and

[1] The loss and redevelopment of human pigmentation is discussed in Chapter XI.

[2] Gaebler, loc. cit.

far apart, water intake would look after itself, and that a reduced anterior-lobe activity would serve to check diuresis. Similarly, a reduced activity of the adrenal-cortex might allow the drinking of saline water, since the body would have a tendency to lose sodium. As for the reduced capacity to deal with nitrogenous food, a low anterior-lobe activity might explain why the Bushman, although a hunter, retained, and may even have developed, the probably older habit of vegetable feeding. He either invented, or more probably adopted, the weighted digging-stick. This would provide him with food of a wider carbo-hydrate to protein ratio. It may be concluded, then, that the whole pituitary is of reduced activity ; and that this has been caused by a sexual selection for increased racial femininity, and has resulted in a relatively useless, or positively disadvantageous, reduction of stature.

BUSHMAN, NEGRO, AND NILOTE

The relationship of the Bushman to the Negro will be dealt with later. Let it here suffice to state, however, that the similarity of the type of head-hair is regarded as a mark of close relationship. The Bushman could, perhaps, represent the ancestral stem ; while the enlarged Negro might be a Bushman in whom a greater masculinity and dark colouring had been developed in response to a selection for sodium-economy. Finally, the Pygmy and the Nilote could represent specialized forms of the Negro, the former selected for calcium as well as for sodium-economy, and the latter enlarging his stature by indulgence in an abundance of those two substances.

Actually, this theory has been discarded for another ; but it must be remembered that the mineral hypothesis seeks mainly to determine the survival-values of existing types, and can throw but the most indirect light upon their ultimate ancestry. In the chapter dealing with the probable relationships of the different modern races the hypothesis of a pygmy origin for the whole Neanthropic stem has been adopted. The Negro is then explained as an enlargement from an ultra-feminine pygmy adapted to calcium and potassium abundance and for sodium-deficiency. An increase of masculinity is supposed to have been secured through polygyny and selection through the males. This could have secured the predominance of the autosomal inheritance, and have thereby strengthened the originally sex-linked, and now translocated, genes of the proto-mammal, assumed to have been evolved for the purpose of fluid economy. These are believed to have utilized a retention of sodium as a means towards this end.

The Bushman is here considered as a specialized, and refeminized, offshoot from the Negroid stem. A sodium-abundance in the desert environment could turn the autosomal sodium-economy of the Negro into a positive disadvantage and danger. What would be required must be the capacity to withstand drought, and to permit the evaporation of the fluid reserve, without allowing the sodium-concentration to rise to any toxic amount. This must have been a special risk to the lactating female forced to live under desert conditions. The young require milk, but would be harmed by any excess of sodium such as might cause œdema. In all arid environments, therefore, the lactating female will be tempted to drink saline waters; and her capacity to do so without harm to herself or her offspring will depend upon her capacity to excrete salt through the kidney. Hence the autosomal masculinity encouraging an activity of the adrenal-cortex will need to be inhibited by the sex-linked inheritance. Thus the feminization of the Negro would result in an improved capacity to maintain life in an environment where water was scarce and sodium over-abundant. It would incidentally result in small size, and in calcium and phosphorus-economy. Besides economizing phosphorus, small size might likewise help to combat heat.

ERRATUM

Page 97, paragraph 3, line 21.

For "The Nilotes, at all events, sometimes display a modified steatopygia and a 'mongoloid' cast of countenance, both of them suggestive of a line of Bushman ancestry,"

read

"Individuals showing mongoloid facial features, but no steatopygia, have been observed among the Bari and Madi of Mongalla on the Nile-Congo watershed. This, as suggested by Dr. Joseph Weninger, may indicate a Bushman admixture."

the Pleistocene or even before. Whatever may be the historical pedigree of the Pygmy, there can be little doubt that his evolution has been directed by a need to economize all the soluble soil-salts. The analogy of dwarfed domesticated animals affords a safe parallel.

Dealing lastly, then, with the "stove-black" Nilotic giants, one can suspect a sodium sufficiency, or abundance, without water shortage to have characterized their cradle-land. At all events, I assume this description to hold good of their present habitat, though the supposition needs to be checked by observation. Much of their present grazing land is subject to flooding by salt-rich waters from the surrounding highlands. The evaporation which must also take place may be suspected of lowering the iodine-contents of some of these soils. This, too, however, at present amounts to speculation, and goitre—as far as I know—has never been reported from this area. Did it exist, iodine-deficiency might have encouraged a compensatory hyper-secretion of

[1] Seligman, C. G., and B. Z.: *Pagan Tribes of the Nilotic Sudan*, London, 1932.

AFRICAN RACES AND ENVIRONMENTS

Race.	Environment.	Heredity.	Endocrine Relationships and Physiology.
Pygmy	*Tropical Forest* Deficiency of Calcium Sodium Potassium Chlorine Abundance of Iodine	Ultra-feminine Probably sex-linked repression translocated to the autosomes	Repressed Anterior-pituitary. Repressed Posterior-pituitary. Active Adrenal-cortex. Economy of all structural substances.
Negro	*Park-Lands* Deficiency of Sodium Over-abundance of Potassium and Chlorine Abundance of Calcium and Iodine	Masculine variant of ancestral Pygmy (as above)	Active Anterior-pituitary. Active Posterior-pituitary. Active Adrenal-cortex High Sodium and low Chlorine and Potassium content of tissue cells. Active excretion of Chlorine and Potassium.
Bushman	*Hot Desert* Deficiency of Water and Phosphorus Over-abundance of Sodium Abundance of Calcium and Iodine	Feminine and specialized variant of Negro or proto-Negro	Repressed Anterior-pituitary. Repressed Posterior-pituitary. Repressed Adrenal-cortex. Low sodium-content of tissue cells. Large fluid reserve.
Nilote	*Tropical Grass Land and Flood Area* Pastoral Possible deficiency of Iodine Over-abundance of Sodium and Chlorine Abundance of Calcium	Negro-Bushman hybrid selected for masculinity, and sexually selected for stature and black skin colour	Active Anterior-pituitary. Active Posterior-pituitary. Tissues abnormally sensitive in their reactions to the pituitary hormones. Repressed Adrenal-cortex due to abnormal reaction to an inhibitory influence of the posterior-lobe.

the anterior-lobe. Alternatively, the tall stature may be the result of sexual selection.

The tall stature and its immediate cause, namely, the activity of the anterior-lobe, could have been encouraged also by a racial reaction to an improved supply of sodium. In the Negro the two opposing " sodium endocrines," the posterior-lobe and the adrenal-cortex, were assumed to have both reached a maximum activity—the former in order to prohibit a loss of sodium through the kidney, and the latter so as to permit its storage by the tissues. Now for the Nilote this economy of sodium will no longer be so important. Thus a weakening of the adrenal-cortex could be permitted, and might even be of some positive value. This would allow the posterior-lobe to gain the upper hand : a fact I take to be indicated by the darker colour. The high activity of the posterior-lobe would in its turn probably tend to inhibit the activity of the anterior-lobe.[1] For some reason, then, it is necessary to imagine a compensatory selection for tall stature and anterior-lobe activity as being brought about by the useless, and perhaps positively disadvantageous, decrease of stature otherwise liable to follow from this accommodation to the sodium-abundant habitat. Alternatively, or in addition, it is possible that the Nilote has developed a useful capacity to excrete sodium by further developing an activity of the whole pituitary through sexual selection ; though the true object of this process would have been to increase the posterior-lobe activity and so inhibit that of the adrenal-cortex. By way of initiation to some such process it seems probable that the pituitary activity of the Negro became combined with the later evolved lack of cortical activity characterizing the Bushman. The former would have served to utilize the still abundant supply of calcium, and would have been further encouraged by polygyny and male sexual selection. The Bushman feature of weak sodium-retention would also have been of use when dealing with the larger sodium supply. At the same time the probably sensitive reaction of the Bushman's tissues could have been acted on by the high concentration of the Negroid pituitary hormones.[2] These conclusions are summarized in the tabular form appended.

[1] Cf. Hogben, loc. cit.
[2] Cf. Chapter I, " Racial Mixture."

CHAPTER V

MINERAL METABOLISM AND THE ENDOCRINES

Bromine : Fluorine : Fluorine Cachexia an Acquired Hereditary Character ? : Manganese : Sulphur : Boron : Silicon : Lithium, Cæsium, and Rubidium : Magnesium : Beryllium, Strontium, and Barium : Cobalt, Nickel, Zinc, Lead, Silver, Aluminium, Tin, and Arsenic : Iron and Copper : Iron and the Hereditary Blood Groups : Calcium, Iodine, and the Endocrines : Calcium- and Phosphorus-Economy versus Excretion : Iodine and the Thyroid : Environment and Exophthalmic Goitre : Heredity and the Thyroid : Thyroid, Anterior-lobe, and Compensation for Ultra-femininity : Primary and Secondary Sex Characters : Conclusion.

THE LAST CHAPTER DEALT WITH AN EVOLUTIONARY THEORY connecting the elements sodium, potassium, and chlorine with certain ideal physiological types. In the course of this inquiry it was necessary to deal with many of the main data concerning the endocrines, and upon these further theories will also be built. It remains now to make some mention of the ascertained functions of certain of the perhaps less important substances ; and, in doing so, I shall draw not only upon Orr,[1] but also upon a recent valuable summary by Sheldon.[2] My idea is to proceed, not strictly according to the chemical classification of these elements, but roughly in what is assumed to be their probable inverse order of importance in the evolution of Man. Thus it is proposed to end with the sections concerning calcium and iodine metabolism ; the environmental and physiological associations of these two most important substances being used as a frame within which the still more important inter-relationship of the endocrines with each other and their subservient tissues can then be pictured.

BROMINE

Taking the halogens, then, chlorine has already been dealt with, and a discussion of iodine must wait. Bromine can probably be classified with the two former substances as an element continually present in all animal tissues ; and it is found in high concentrations in the pituitary. Blood bromine is lowered to half its normal figure in

[1] Orr : *Min. in Past.* ; *Iod. in Nut.*

[2] Sheldon, J. H. : " The Mineral Basis of Life," *Brit. med. J.*, Jan. 13th, 1934, p. 47.

manic-depressive psychosis.[1] The amounts drop considerably with age.[2] Crookshank's observation that the manic-depressive type is more common among the Mongoloid physical types, which are here regarded as the result of a hereditary over-economy of iodine, suggests that the metabolisms of the two elements may be synergistic rather than antagonistic. I suspect that bromine strengthens the strata of dissociation of which the existence is postulated in chapter XV.

FLUORINE

Fluorine, the remaining member of the halogens, may well have played some important part in vertebrate evolution, since it is said to occur in blood and milk,[3] and forms an important constituent of bone and the enamel of teeth. On the whole, however, such evidence as exists points to excess quantities of fluorine exerting a toxic influence, and so perhaps requiring the evolution of some protective mechanism.[4] Only in the case of plants have deficiencies been shown to exert a limiting influence on growth.[5] This could possibly be explained by the normal association of fluorine and phosphorus in rocks. If the former was to be allowed to stimulate growth, increased amounts of the latter would at least need to be tolerated, and could eventually become requisite in order to satisfy the whole of the organism's growth-reaction to its environment.

Feeding with fluorine causes overgrowth of the upper incisors accompanied by a defective development of the enamel.[6] It may be worth noting that the tooth enamel of Sinanthopus is particularly thick.[7]

FLUORINE CACHEXIA AN ACQUIRED HEREDITARY CHARACTER

In Algeria a disease known as " darmous " occurs in Man and animals, the symptoms being general cachexia in addition to dental distrophy.[8] It is stated also to occur at Maldon, in Essex.[9] In each case the cause has been attributed to an excess of fluorine in the drinking water ; the safe limit having, in the latter case, been determined as 1·5 parts per million.

[1] Sheldon, loc. cit., cft. Zondec, H., and Bier, A. : *Klin. Wschr.*, 1932, XI, 633.
[2] Ibid., cft. Zondec, H., and Bier, A. : *Klin. Wschr.*, 1932, XI, 759.
[3] Ibid., cft. McClure, F. J. : *Physiol. Rev.*, 1933, XII, 277.
[4] McClure, F. J. : " A Review of Fluorine and its Physiological Effects," *Physiol. Rev.*, XIII, 3, 1933, p. 217.
[5] Orr : *Min. in Past.*, pp. 28–29.
[6] Sheldon, loc. cit., cft. Pachaly, W. : *Arch. exp. Path. Pharmak.*, 1932, CLXVI, 1.
[7] Davidson Black : *Philos. Trans. B.*, 223, 57 (1934).
[8] Sheldon, loc. cit., Pachaly, W. : *Arch. exp. Path. Pharmak*, 1932, CLXVI, 1.
[9] Sheldon, loc. cit., Ainsworth, N. J. : *Brit. dent. J.*, 1933, IV, 233.

Now the interesting fact in connection with this is that a case of cachexia or hairlessness was discovered at Ohio among a group of rats that were being artificially subjected to an excess of fluorine in their diet. It was regarded as a mutant, and, after genetic analysis with descendants reared on a normal diet, was shown to behave as a simple Mendelian recessive.[1] The point arises, therefore, whether there was any causal connection between the excess fluorine of the diet and the occurrence of the mutation. The authors think it " best to consider the fluorine diet and the advent of the new type as coincident and not showing any causal relation."

As a less orthodox explanation it might be suggested that an abnormal amount of fluorine may have served to alter the genetic predominance of the factors controlling the form of the skin. This increased fluorine-concentration might favour the expression of some primitive and long-repressed character, while at the same time hindering the action of the more modern genes selected at a time when fluorine-poisoning was less to be feared.

Haldane, discussing the causes of mutation, points to Goldschmidt's (1929) results with *Drosophila*, when heat was shown to result in a comparatively regular production of two particular types of feature (one a dark body and the other an abnormally veined wing). This was quite different from the mere acceleration of the normal rate of non-specific mutation obtained by the use of X-rays and radium. This, too, may well possess an evolutionary significance. Heat is probably more regularly distributed in nature than the more penetrating short-wave radiations. If so, an ability to develop differently in response to heat and cold would have survival-value.

Haldane also quotes Harrison (1928), who reported the induction of melanism in moths by feeding with lead and maganese salts. The melanism, after it had appeared, behaved in a Mendelian manner. Subsequent repetition failed, however, to repeat the results. Referring elsewhere (p. 154) to the same experiments he writes, " A decisive step from animal to human mentality may have occurred by mutation, though only a very convinced disciple of Harrison would nowadays ascribe such a mutation to changed diet."[2] To this charge I cannot altogether plead innocent. Indeed, in dealing with the next relatively unimportant substance, manganese, it must be pointed out that it is believed to encourage the process of oxidation, and that melanin is an oxidation-product. On the theory of selective dominance, the original induction of melanism in Harrison's moths could be due to an environmental assistance of a gene promoting a higher metabolic rate. This, having once been achieved, could then become permanent,

[1] Wilder, W., *et al.* : " A Hairless Mutation in the Rat," *J. of Hered.*, Vol. XXIII, No. 12, 1932, p. 481.

[2] Haldane, op. cit., p. 58, cft. Harrison (1928) : *Proc. roy. Soc. B.*, 102, p. 347.

possibly through the assistance of manganese acting in direct co-operation with the gene in question.

MANGANESE

To continue, then, with some facts concerning Manganese, let it be stated at once that large amounts have been found in the suprarenals of some individuals; the liver and pancreas being the other two richest organs. Here again, remembering the pigmentation in Addison's disease, we are entitled to suspect that manganese may somehow be concerned with the production of melanism; while its presence in the pancreas, which governs the oxidation of glucose, confirms, to some small extent, the belief that here also it is concerned with the synthesis of the catabolic substance insulin.[1] The meconium, too, contains a quite remarkable amount.[2] Sheldon considers that there is no doubt that the human fœtus is normally provided with an excess, as in the case of its store of iron and copper. He suggests, therefore, that manganese, being a general stimulant of the oxidation process, tends to counteract any tendency towards an oxygen-deficiency of the fœtal blood due to the comparative inefficiency of the placenta in its capacity as a lung. In the vertebrate it seems to play no part in the synthesis of hæmoglobin. In the Lamellibranch *Pinna squamosa*, however, it is used as the basis of a respiratory pigment. In the mammal manganese-deficiency leads to atrophy of the testes, and inhibits the female's instinct to suckle her young.[3]

In regard to the distribution of Manganese in relation to the environment of the animal, it is found in leaves roughly in proportion to their greenness,[4] with high concentrations at the growing point.[5] This may be associated with the fact that herbivorous animals, such as the guinea-pig, have high values for their tissues when compared with Man.[6] Manganese has already been mentioned in connection with the soils of New Zealand, where its ability to replace iron in the plant, but not in the animal, was suggested. It occurs in every part of the plant, and is concentrated, like phosphorus, especially in the seeds. It is believed to have functions in connection with the germination and early development of the plant, as also with the photosynthetic process, and the formation of chlorophyl. A disease called "grey

[1] Sheldon, loc. cit., cft. Sheldon, J. H., and Ramage, H.: *Bio-chem. J.*, 1931, XXV, 1608.

[2] Sheldon, loc. cit., cft. 41 Sheldon, J. H., and Ramage, H.: *Bio-chem. J.*, 1933, XXVII, 674.

[3] Sheldon, loc. cit., cft. Pryde, J.: *Recent Advances in Biochemistry*, 1931, 3rd edn.

[4] Sheldon, loc. cit., cft. Bertrand, G., and Rosemble, H. M.: *Acad. des Sci.*, 1932, CXCIV, 1405.

[5] Sheldon, loc. cit., cft. Bishop, W. B. S.: *Aust. J. exp. Biol. med. Sci.*, 1928, V, 125.

[6] Sheldon, loc. cit., cft. Sheldon, J. H., and Ramage, H.: *Bio-chem. J.*, 1931, XXV, 1608.

speck " in oats, occurring in parts of Europe and Australia, is due to a deficiency of manganese in the soil.[1] McCarrison believes it to be connected with the vitamins. Wheat and fruit are rich, and rice is poor.[2] As happens with other minerals, a deficiency seems capable of communicating itself to the nervous system with the usual results of " depraved," or, better, abnormal, appetite. Since it seems to occur more in the protein-rich leguminosæ than in the grasses, it may probably be considered as necessary for building up the nitrogenous substances. Without more data it seems hard to include manganese among the elements here claimed to be important as having, by their deficiency or abundance, modified the form or physiology of Man or his ancestors. It cannot, however, be considered entirely free from some suspicion of having played a part in the evolution of pigmentation.

This substance seems to be relatively immobile in the soil and hence liable to form black bands at old soil-surfaces.[3] It may thus be concentrated—like iodine—by the vegetation. It is suspected, indeed, that manganese may have been " selected " by life to play its part as an oxidizing agent owing to some physical law whereby it tended to accumulate in the hotter and so, incidentally, wetter portions of the earth's crust. Provisionally, it may be classified with iodine and iron as a substance probably more plentifully supplied to animal life in humid habitats. In this it can probably be regarded as distinct from calcium and its companions phosphorus and fluorine. The toxic action of manganese on the plant can be inhibited by calcium.[4]

SULPHUR

Sulphur, which, as already mentioned, is a constituent of all protoplasm, is another element of which the deficiencies, if they occur at all, must be rare and so, from an evolutionary point of view, unimportant. The sulphur-content of good and bad pasture is about the same ; though, like manganese, sulphur occurs more in the leguminosæ. Wool is relatively rich in it.[5] It is a main constituent of keratin which forms on epithelial cells as a result of vitamin A deficiency.[6]

BORON

Boron, on the other hand, is perhaps of rather greater interest, since, for the proper growth of legumes at all events, the application of amounts greater than those already present has been shown to encourage growth. Concentrations of more than 1 in 100,000 were found

[1] Orr : *Min. in Past.*, pp. 25–26.
[2] McCarrison, R. (1927) : " The Effect of Manganese on Growth," *Indian J. med. Res.*, 14, 641.
[3] Keith, A. : *The Antiquity of Man*, Vol. I, p. 268.
[4] Sheldon, loc. cit., cft. Bishop, loc. cit.
[5] Orr : *Min. in Past.*, p. 267.
[6] *Vitamins*, Spec. Rep. Ser. med. Res. Coun. Lond. No. 167 (1932), p. 33.

to be harmful. It has been suggested that boron plays some essential rôle, possibly catalytic, in the cell.[1] At all events, it occurs in small amounts in many, if not all, plants and animals.[2] In its absence the nodule bacteria of leguminosæ become parasitic on the plant, which in its absence is unable to assimilate calcium. It exists both in the blood[3] and in milk.[4]

SILICON

Silicon seems also comparatively unimportant, though it has been shown that the amount of phosphorus taken up by the plant depends on the amount of water-soluble silicate in the soil.[5] This may possibly account for the low phosphorus-content of dry pastures that has been noted elsewhere. The percentage of silica appears to increase with the growth of the plant, and probably constitutes one of the main factors rendering old dry herbage hard, unpalatable, and innutritious.[6] It has been suggested, however, that a high silica-content of pastures is a factor in preventing tuberculosis.[7] In this connection it may be remarked that another equally common substance, potassium alum, which when injected into the blood stream acts as a poison, seems nevertheless capable of stimulating the antigenic faculty of horses when the latter are used for the manufacture of diphtheria toxin.[8] It is perhaps worth noting that colloidal silica is itself capable of bringing about anaphylactic shock.[9]

It is faintly possible, therefore, that the animal's ingestion of silica may be bound with that of phosphorus and calcium. If so, part of the increased susceptibility to disease resulting from these shortages might involve deficiencies of silicates as well.

LITHIUM, CÆSIUM, AND RUBIDIUM

Turning now to the Alkali Metals, the most important of which, sodium and potassium, have already been dealt with, we are left with lithium, cæsium, and rubidium. Lithium is of sporadic occurrence in Man, but is more common in marine animals.[10] Lithium chloride

1 Orr : *Min. in Past.*, p. 29.
2 Sheldon : loc. cit., cft. 14 ; Barton-Wright, E. C. : *Recent Advances in Plant Physiology*, 2nd edn., 1933.
3 Sheldon : loc. cit., cft. 15 ; Bertrand, G., and Agulhon, H. : *Bull. Soc. Chim.*, XIII, 395.
4 Sheldon : loc. cit., cft. 27 ; Blumberg, H., and Rask, O. S. : *Jl. of Nutrition*, 1933, VI, 285.
5 Sheldon : loc. cit., cft. 14 ; Barton-Wright, loc. cit.
6 Orr : *Min. in Past.*, pp. 27–28.
7 Aston, B. C. : *N.Z. J. Agric.*, 1927, XXXV, 96–101.
8 Glenny, A. T. : *Brit. med. J.*, No. 3624, 244 (1930).
9 Bayliss, p. 738.
10 Sheldon, loc. cit., cft. Sheldon and Ramage : *Bio-chem. J.*, 1931, XXV, 1608 ; also Fox, H. M., and Ramage, H. : *Proc. roy. Soc. B.*, 1931, CVIII, 157.

prevents the neural folds of the frog from closing over.[1] It decreases the amount of ectoderm produced by the Echinoderms, and increases the amount of endoderm.[2] Cæsium is almost universally absent from animal tissues, though it is readily absorbed. Rubidium seems especially important to fungi, and its amount varies in snails from different localities. It is probably important to growth. Like manganese, it is present in higher concentrations at the growing point of the plant (e.g., in oats) than elsewhere.

MAGNESIUM

Of the Alkaline Earths, Magnesium seems physiologically of much the greatest importance. Like potassium and silica it is a degeneration-product of clay, and is present in vegetable matter in amounts varying from 0·24 to 0·51 per cent. The figure 0·709 has been reported from a sample of alfalfa hay. Orr considers the amounts of magnesium present in pastures as probably in all cases sufficient for the requirements of grazing animals.[3] It does not seem so certain, however, that carnivorous and specialized hunting races, who had not learned to utilize milk, would be able to obtain redundant supplies.

As mentioned previously, the magnesium-content of sea-water is much greater than that of the blood, despite the correspondence of the ratios of sodium to calcium and potassium. If this increase of magnesium has occurred as a result of continental drift, it could follow that the mechanism of magnesium-exclusion may have been evolved at a comparatively late date, even in vertebrate history.[4]

Magnesium plays some part in the function of the chloroplast. It has been suggested that it serves to attract CO_2 to within the reach of the green chlorophyl.[5] Its presence or absence might thus possibly have played some part in the evolution of pigmentation in the animal. It may be regarded as assisting calcium in the chemical sense that it can annul acidity. Physiologically, however, the actions of these two cations are violently opposed. Its injection into the blood causes anæsthesia and paralysis, and assists the action of the other anæsthetics. Magnesium-anæsthesia can, however, be counteracted by calcium chloride.[6]

Haag and Palmer (1928) show that, with rats, high Mg is a disturbing factor in the diet requiring a balance of calcium, phosphorus, and vitamin D.[7] As pointed out elsewhere (Chapter VI) magnesium seems to predispose towards a pathological calcification of certain

[1] De Beer, C. R.: *An Introduction to Experimental Embryology*, Oxford, 1926, p. 58.
[2] Huxley and de Beer, loc. cit., p. 334.
[3] Orr: *Min. in Past.*, p. 29.
[4] Bayliss, pp. 209–210. Also Chapter VI.
[5] Ibid., p. 565.
[6] Ibid., p. 217.
[7] Haag, J. R., and Palmer, L. S. (1928): *J. biol. Chem.*, 76, 367.

tissues. This may be the overdevelopment of a defensive mechanism. In common with alcohol, chloroform, and ether, magnesium chloride produces a cyclopic eye when applied to embryos of the fish Fundulus. It is not impossible, therefore, that it may play some part in the human reaction to environment.[1] The question would seem to turn upon whether such changes are purely fortuitous, or are the result of a genetic reaction to a former type of environment. In the rat magnesium-deficiency causes marked vaso-dilation and tetany,[2] while there is also renal damage.[3]

BERYLLIUM, STRONTIUM, AND BARIUM

The remaining alkaline earths, with the notable exception of calcium, seem quite unimportant. Beryllium, however, can cause severe rickets when fed to animals. Strontium occurs sporadically in animals and plants, passing through the placenta and being present in the eye. Barium is less frequent than strontium, and has been found in the eyes of cattle (but not in those of other animals) in amounts which increase with age.[4] This may be evidence of a degenerated mechanism of exclusion that has been allowed to survive owing to the protection of the domesticated animal by man.

COBALT, NICKEL, ZINC, LEAD, SILVER, ALUMINIUM, TIN, AND ARSENIC

Of these substances, dealt with by Sheldon, Cobalt does not appear to exist in vertebrate tissues. Nickel is more widely distributed. It is more common in tropical plants than in others, and in the body occurs chiefly in the pancreas. This suggests a connection with the mechanism of oxidation ; and the metal may be placed in the same category as iodine and manganese. Zinc, too, is present in relatively high concentration in the thyroid and genitals. Elsewhere it is found in the cells rather than in the blood. The fact that it is specially plentiful in the colostrum suggests that it has some important part to play. It is regarded as probably essential for reproduction (in the rat), though not for growth. Lead is present both in sea-water and in the body of the vertebrate. Nevertheless, its physiological importance is doubtful. Silver is more important. It is probably not universally present in plants—a fact which suggests that deficiencies, even in the minimal quantities required by the lower forms of life, may have affected natural selection. It stimulates the growth of watercress ; and influences the tobacco-plant by inhibiting root-growth, while the secretion of nicotine is encouraged. This almost suggests the action of

[1] De Beer, C. R. : *Introduction to Experimental Embryology*, p. 58, Oxford, 1926.
[2] Sheldon, loc. cit., cft. Krause, H. D., Orent, E. R., and McCollum, E. V. : *J. biol. Chem.*, 1932, XCVI, 519.
[3] Sheldon, loc. cit., cft. Cramer, W. : *Lancet*, 1932, ii, 174.
[4] Sheldon, loc. cit.

a plant-hormone. It is found in the blood and in all organs, the amounts in the thyroid and tonsil being particularly high. Aluminium has no known function, though it is absorbed and excreted in amounts of about 12 mg. per day. Tin seems to be a special constituent of the mucous membrane of the tongue, and occurs also in the brain, spleen, and thyroid. The connection between the thyroid and so many of the inorganic substances—iodine, zinc, silver, and tin—is interesting. Arsenic is, perhaps, more important. The average amount in human blood is $63 \cdot 8\gamma$ per 100 c.c. At menstruation this amount rises to $92 \cdot 5\gamma$, and in the fifth and sixth months of pregnancy achieves a maximum of 220γ. Similar high values have also been found in carcinoma; and arsenic has consequently been considered as a substance concerned with cell-proliferation.[1]

It seems probable that research into the geographical and climatological distribution of these rare substances, bearing in mind the classes of plant, and so the class of habitat, in which each was liable to be abundant or deficient, would throw important light, not only on the evolutionary importance of the substances in question, but also, as a consequence, on their functions within the animal and plant organisms.

IRON AND COPPER

Last of these perhaps less important substances we may mention iron on account of its function in the building of hæmoglobin; and with it must be mentioned copper, which in some lower forms of life, such as shell-fish, would seem to be used as an alternative and less satisfactory building material for a blood pigment (hæmocyanin). Indeed, it seems very possible that in some human subjects, if not all, a lack of copper no less than one of iron may result in a failure of proper hæmoglobin-synthesis. A study of the heredity and blood-grouping of anæmia patients responding to copper-therapy would be of interest in this latter connection.

Sheldon has shown that close correlations exist between the iron, calcium and copper contents of the liver, so that a shortage of one could lead to a deficiency of the others as well.[2]

Iron must be soluble before it is absorbed by the plant, and so by the animal. It seems possible that the presence of soil-calcium may, as has been already suggested (p. 72), largely inhibit its bacterial liberation and consequent ingestion. Outside the body, then, soluble iron may be regarded as usually accompanying iodine; and, what from an evolutionary point of view is more important, shortages of each are liable to occur together. Thus, in view of the theory of the economy of mechanism, it is not perhaps surprising to find iron concerned with the distribution of oxygen, while iodine controls the basal metabolism, and so the rate at which the latter is combined with the blood sugar.

[1] Sheldon, loc. cit.
[2] Ibid.

Also, iodine is required for the full growth of the red blood-corpuscles.[1] Have we not here a key to the old distinction between "sanguine" and "lymphatic" types of humanity? The race adapted for life in the iron- and iodine-deficient surroundings might be expected to require either an increased power of iron, and iodine, ingestion; or, at least, a reduced consumption, and possibly also an additional storage capacity. It will be argued later that the Mongoloid peoples seem on the whole to come under this category. On Sheldon's theory of an iron and calcium synergy they might be expected to make use of the lime-abundance that may be expected in arid regions.

The function of iron in hæmoglobin synthesis seems to be inhibited by some other substance contained in the ashes of lettuce, beef, liver, and yellow corn.[2] As regards the toxic effects of large quantities of iron, these apparently may be overcome by the addition of vitamin D.[3] They would seem, therefore, to be counterbalanced by the calcium or phosphorus concentration, and might thus be expected to occur in a calcium- or phosphorus-deficient environment. This fact would seem to bear some relation to the cause of the survival of menstruation, and the habits of blood-letting by primitive people to be discussed later. Since all the iron is bound with the hæmoglobin, while most of the calcium phosphate is in the bones and not in the blood, a loss of blood would lower the iron reserves of the body, while leaving the calcium phosphate almost intact.

The mother, as already stated, supplies the child with enough iron and copper before birth to last until weaning; for milk is very poor in these two elements.[4] Females, then, must normally be regarded as demanding more iron than males, since among the primates they lose blood at menstruation; while in placental mammals, at all events, they supply iron to the young. Iron is stored in the liver of new-born animals, and the total amount present in the body does not seem materially to increase until after weaning. It would appear that, among the poorer inhabitants of London, anæmia due to iron shortage in the food was formerly very common among women and young girls.[5] In the light of Sheldon's discovery, however, this may actually have been due to a shortage of lime and vitamin D.

It seems faintly possible that the cicatrization, circumcision, and many other forms of blood-letting, practised almost, though not quite, exclusively by males, and especially by those of the negroid races, may owe part of its popularity and "survival-value" to some dimly

[1] Orr: *Iodine in Nutrition*, p. 54.
[2] Waddel, J., Elvenhjem, C. A., Steenbock, H., and Hart, E. B.: (1928) *J. biol. Chem.*, 77, 777.
[3] Waltner, K.: (1929) "Über die Wirkung grosser Mengen Eisens," etc., *Biochem. Z.*, Vol. 205, p. 467.
[4] Mackay, H.: "Nutritional Anæmia in Infancy, the influence of Iron deficiency on Health;" Med. Res. Council, Special Report, No. 157.
[5] Sherman, C.: *Chemistry of Food and Nutrition*, 1933.

felt need for lowering the iron-concentration within the body. Indeed, menstruation itself, when both calcium phosphate and iron are lost, need hardly be expected to have survived among the members of a single order had it been actively disadvantageous to the race. Can it be that we have here an example of an evolved "safety valve," useful to the primates, perhaps as fructivores—since fruits are relatively rich in iron[1]—when they lived in a tropical and therefore iron-abundant habitat? It is perhaps significant that in pathological mongolism menstruation is often delayed or absent.[2] Is this loss of iron in blood comparable to the annual ejection of calcium-phosphate that occurs when the reindeer shed their antlers? In the latter case the main reaction is to a cold, arid, and therefore phosphorus- and calcium-rich environment. It should not be forgotten, moreover, that the antlers of one male deer, may, for good or evil, be regarded as lancets for the bleeding of his rivals. Is ceremonial blood-letting a physiological—and so, perhaps, a psychological—substitute for the wounds formerly obtained in a seasonal fighting for wives?

Such a hypothesis might be reconciled with the apparent anomaly of the Australians, who may be suspected of employing red ochre to supplement an iron-deficiency of the soil, while at the same time bleeding themselves on ceremonial occasions. For if the practice of blood-letting can be believed to have evolved in the iron-rich and calcium-deficient tropics, the use of red ochre must correspondingly have begun in an arid and calcareous, or, just possibly, in a volcanic, region. Its presence in Australia in association with a partially negroid race must, on this hypothesis, be considered as a product of culture-contact and racial mixture between peoples of the tropics and those of the steppe or tundra. Indeed, in view of the theoretical likelihood of iron- and iodine-deficiencies occurring side by side, might we not regard the use of red ochre as having arisen in response to some of the same environmental conditions as were responsible for selecting the ancestors of the Mongoloid stock? Unlike the bigger races of the hot and cold belts, the Pygmies are remarkable in that they do not either mutilate or bedaub their bodies.

IRON AND THE HEREDITARY BLOOD GROUPS

I have been unable to see any clear connection between the iron or other mineral constituents of the soil and the distribution of the genes responsible for Jansky's hereditary blood-groups. Nevertheless, the assumption that different classes of habitat may have encouraged the survival of the different genes might offer a hopeful line of attack upon the evolutionary significance of the facts. Further, it is even possible that the genetic dominance of the alternative hereditary conditions could be affected by environment.

[1] Sherman, C.: *Chemistry of Food Nutrition*, 1933.
[2] Crookshank, F. C.: *The Mongol in our Midst*, London, 1924, p. 78.

It has been suggested that the numerical superiority of the recessive condition (R), when both agglutinogens are absent, which is found in Australia, Iceland, and among the American Indians, is due to isolation. To this one can agree. What is less certain, however, is that the absence of the dominant conditions (A and B) is due to their having arisen by mutation at a time subsequent to the colonization of Iceland by the Norsemen. Surely, it is more reasonable to suppose that isolation has led to in-breeding, and that the latter has served to eliminate the older dominant conditions owing to some greater survival-value of the recessive mutant (R).

This survival-value, I suggest, may lie in a more efficient utilization of iron, or possibly of its assistants in oxidation, iodine, or manganese. Iron, like iodine, is believed to be deficient in the North. It is also deficient on volcanic soils, which may well have provided a temporary habitat for the Australoids at a time of Indonesian submergence. The further question how far the peculiar soil-bacteria of Australasia serve to liberate soluble iron has already been mentioned.

So far as America is concerned, such a theory would postulate a relatively early and "once for all" colonization by a single in-breeding group. It would thus run counter to any suggestions of an ethnic stratification resulting from the continuous ingress of different Old World types. Rather would it explain the phenotypic variation of the American Indian as a result of the in-breeding of a heterozygous, if once anatomically uniform, group: the present diversity being due to the survival and genetic predominance of different pure-bred types in the various types of habitat offered by the new continents.

CALCIUM, IODINE, AND THE ENDOCRINES

It would be foolish, in the space of half a chapter, to attempt much more than a mere mention of the main classes of phenomena involving the behaviour of these last two substances, and of the endocrines whereby their concentrations in the blood stream are controlled. Much of the evidence comes from the study of disease. Rickets, now that it is explained, has furnished a knowledge of the inter-relationship of calcium, and vitamin D with the growth of bone; while the action of the parathyroids in mobilizing calcium from the bones, thereby rendering it available for the use of other tissues as well, is beginning to be understood.[1] The importance of the calcium ion in maintaining the proper excitability of isolated tissues has been known for some time, and its value in helping to maintain the acid-base equilibrium has also been noted. The difficulties of applying this knowledge have lain in the often incalculable behaviour of the whole organism, now recognized to be due to the action of vitamins and the endocrine system; and the latter still offers a host of unsolved problems.

[1] Thompson, D. L., and Collip, J. B.: "Parathyroid Glands," *Physiological Reviews*, Vol. XII, No. 3, July, 1932.

In the same way, knowledge of iodine and of the normal function of the thyroid have been obtained from a study of thyroid disease, with two puzzling aspects, myxœdema and simple goitre on the one hand, and the nervous or toxic goitre, known as Graves' disease, on the other. Iodine-deficiency, coupled with various other factors, some of them certainly of an environmental, and others possibly also of an hereditary, nature, seems able to produce either phase of the trouble.

The metabolisms of calcium and iodine can properly be discussed together. Not only does the secretion of the thyroid and the parathyroid appear to be controlled by the same master endocrine, the pituitary, but in the two sorts of goitre it is significant that a striking difference in the level of blood-calcium exists. In Graves' disease it is low—thus probably contributing to the nervous symptoms ; whereas in simple goitre the lethargy of the myxœdemous subjects may be partially attributed to the high calcium-concentration that occurs. As regards the pituitary's control of the thyroid and the parathyroid, it is probable that the pressor hormone of the posterior-lobe would tend to constrict the blood-supply to both organs, which are anatomically related. The anterior-lobe, on the other hand, seems able to encourage the secretion of both. If so, here, as also in the matter of amphibian metamorphosis, the two halves of the gland would appear to oppose each other. Each half of the pituitary, however, probably secretes two or more distinct hormones.

Indeed, the pituitary is beginning to be regarded as the central point of the endocrine system ; though this concept of an endocrine monarchy is far from unassailable, the rival republican theory having also a good deal to be said in its favour. In these pages it will be regarded as the centre of sensitivity to differences in the levels of inorganic iodine and calcium, and probably of glucose and other substances as well. This view accords perfectly with its probable ancestral function as an excretory organ ; and the undoubted connection between the anterior-lobe and the growth of bone supports a view that the latter originated as a waste product.

CALCIUM AND PHOSPHORUS ECONOMY VERSUS EXCRETION

Now although goitre may have drawn attention to the iodine-deficiency of human food, while the study of rickets has similarly emphasized the lack of calcium or vitamin D, it by no means follows that either of these two pathological conditions is directly associated with the inheritance of defects likely to be weeded out by a natural selection imposed by the shortage in question. Rather, indeed, might the reverse be true. Goitre may indicate an hereditary ability to counteract iodine-deficiency. Similarly, rickets might indicate the inheritance of a mechanism of bone-growth which, under emergency conditions, was able to sacrifice material for the still more important function of maintaining the calcium and phosphorus level of the internal environment at a height sufficient for the maintenance of vitality in the soft tissues.

Besides curing rickets, calcium-therapy has been recommended in cases of tetany, œdema, hæmorrhage, imbalance of the autonomic nervous system, hæmophilia, dermatoses, and alleric conditions. Or, again, to move from the field of human pathology to that of veterinary experience, it has recently been shown that injections of calcium gluconate can achieve dramatic and instantaneous cures of so-called milk fever—a common, and once fatal, form of tetany. It is often assumed, moreover, that calcium- and phosphorus-deficiency are responsible for sterility ; and, indeed, as Orr points out, complaints of reduced fertility usually come from areas where these minerals are scarce. I know of no observations, however, proving that the level of blood-calcium in sterile animals is on an average lower than that of the remainder, though one might expect it to be the case.

In regard to the intake of calcium and phosphorus, Kramer and Howland, after a critical review of the literature, point to their own experiments as showing how a low vitamin D content of the ration results in considerable variations in the ratio of calcium to phosphorus. With more vitamin D, the blood analysis is less variable. With large amounts of calcium in the diet, and minimum amounts of phosphorus, much of the phosphorus is precipitated as insoluble phosphate, and is then very gradually re-absorbed, or else excreted in the fæces. Similarly, on diets low in calcium and high in phosphorus, it is considered that the excess phosphorus, unable to combine with calcium to form insoluble calcium-phosphate, will remain as HPO_4 and H_2PO_4 and their salts ; and that these will be absorbed, and will raise the serum phosphorus concentration above the normal level.[1] Similarly, Bulger, Dixon and Barr note the essential independence of the absorption of calcium and phosphorus from the intestines in cases of hyperparathyroidism.[2] These views are important, since it is sometimes assumed that the mechanism of calcium- and phosphorus-absorption is indivisible. The exact methods whereby the intake and excretion of these two substances are achieved are far from clear, and must await a better understanding of the nature and physiological action of vitamins.

Grahams and Morris point out that the absorption of calcium is promoted by any condition producing a more acid reaction of the small intestine. Under such circumstances the insoluble calcium phosphate, carbonate, and soaps are changed into soluble calcium salts. In view of the fact that calcium helps to counteract acidity in the body, this arrangement is of obvious use. Similarly, these authors explain that in the blood-serum itself calcium may be, firstly, bound to proteins ; secondly, dialysable but not ionised ; or, thirdly, ionised ; and that acidosis leads to an increase both of the total and of the ionised

[1] Kramer, B., and Howland, J. : *J. Nutrit.*, New York, Vol. 5, No. 1 (1932).

[2] Bulger, Dixon and Barr : *Jl. clin. Invest.*, 9, 143 (1930).

fraction.[1] Conditions liable to cause acidosis are defective carbohydrate metabolism, leading to the accumulation of ketone bodies, or any strong acids such as those derived from protein food. The elimination of strong acids places a tax upon the alkaline reserves. Weak acids can be excreted in the urine without needing to be accompanied by portions of this "fixed base," as the sodium, calcium, potassium, and magnesium is called. Under certain pathological conditions the kidney's ability to retain calcium seems to be lost, and there results a form of rickets which cannot be cured by vitamin D.[2]

The body's power of eliminating an excess of calcium does not seem to have been studied with the same attention as has its absorption of this substance. However, as is well known, calcification of the soft tissues represents a permanent danger. Indeed, although the skin-reception of ultra-violet radiation seems now mainly to be used as a means of ionising and absorbing calcium, it seems possible that the mechanism was originally developed rather with a view to excreting it. On this view, the growth of hard structures such as shell or bone, and even the mineral in milk, may be regarded as a secondary utilization of an otherwise embarrassing excess. Somewhat on these lines, then, may one explain the otherwise puzzling fact that a substance often so common as calcium seems yet to be so slowly absorbed even under conditions when the need for it is causing severe disadvantages to the organism.

Now the parathyroid glands serve to raise or maintain the level of the blood's calcium-concentration. In like manner, however, injections of anterior-lobe extract have been found to produce this result. Moreover, since there is evidence that the anterior-lobe also encourages thyroid activity, it seems fair to assume—though it is not proved—that the raising of the serum-calcium by anterior-lobe injections is achieved by stimulating an increased secretion of the parathyroids. One result of raising the serum calcium by parathormone is to increase the excretion of calcium by the intestine and kidney, and it seems probable that the same thing happens when the serum calcium is raised by means of the anterior-lobe. Indeed, extracts of the latter gland encourage the excretion of water, and this increase of membrane-permeability is at least suggestive of a corresponding failure to retain calcium.[3] Moreover, in pituitary cachexia, due to sub-normal anterior-lobe activity, calcium together with nitrogen and water is retained, while basal metabolism drops.[4]

This arrangement can hardly be understood as a method designed solely to regulate the growth of bone, or even to supply extra material at the time when the latter is required. There is one hormone of the anterior-lobe which encourages growth at epiphyses, and thus tends to

[1] Graham, S. G., and Morris, N.: *Acidosis and Alkalosis*, Edinburgh, 1933, p. 178.
[2] *The Vitamins*, p. 64.
[3] Gaebler, loc. cit.
[4] Curshmann, H.: *Endocrine Disorders*, Oxford, 1929, p. 97.

reduce the calcium-concentration of the blood by providing more cartilage to be eventually calcified. As we have seen, however, either this same hormone, or another emanating from the same structure, must also be strongly suspected of stimulating the parathyroid, and so encouraging a loss of calcium through the kidney and intestine. Further, in speaking of this loss, it may be pointed out that the anterior-lobe also encourages an increased nitrogen-metabolism, which in its turn must tax the fixed base. On this view, one can best explain the evolutionary significance of the whole mechanism—including bone growth—in terms of calcium-excretion. From the more practical and intimate standpoint of human evolution, we may infer that the tall races, using more calcium phosphate for their skeletons, will also tend to be more wasteful of calcium passed through their digestive tracts. Thus, in so far as an economy of calcium has been achieved by a process of natural selection, we may expect an inhibition of anterior-lobe activity, and a consequent lowering of thyroid and parathyroid activity, to have been favoured. Moreover, since it has been argued that the female has more need for calcium economy than the male, one may expect her extra sex-chromosome to exert a direct effect in inhibiting anterior-lobe activity.

Actually both the male and the female sex-hormones are believed to inhibit the activity of the pituitary ; probably by means of a sex-centre in the brain.[1] I suggest, therefore, that the female-determining secretions have developed a stronger inhibitory influence than those responsible for sex-determination in the male. Both male and female sex-hormones are probably present in the bodies of both sexes, and presumably in differing ratios of concentration. This fact, if true, is of great importance in supporting the view that sex is essentially a matter of degree rather than of kind. I have avoided any detailed discussion of the sex-hormones. Unlike the anterior-lobe and thyroid secretions which stimulate the gonad, they contain no rare substances.

IODINE AND THE THYROID

The relationship of the pituitary to the thyroid must now be discussed. A very large amount of information concerning iodine, and the effect of a deficiency of it, resulting in goitre, has been dealt with by Orr, and I shall quote largely from him throughout the whole of the following section.[2]

As regards plants it is interesting to note that, while an excess of iodine is definitely toxic, a deficiency inhibits growth. Moreover, different species would seem to be characterized by very wide variations of optimum requirement. Plants descended from ancestors specialized for a coastal habitat, such as the beets, would seem to have a much

[1] Schoeller, W. : *Lancet*, Jan. 7th, 1933 ; cft. Hohlweg, W., and Junkerman, K., *Klin. Wschr.* (1932), XI, 32.

[2] Orr, J. B. : "Iodine in Nutrition," *Spec. Rep. Ser. med. Res. Coun.* Lond. No. 123, 1929.

higher iodine tolerance and requirement than inland forms such as the Gramineæ.[1] This is interesting in view of our inclination towards the theory that the calcium-rich Tchernozems, the natural grass lands of the world, are likely thus to have evolved a vegetation, and so perhaps a fauna, whose iodine requirement is low.

In this connection it is of great interest to find that Stocklasa[2] has investigated the iodine-requirement of *Azotobacter*, the soil-organism responsible for the nitrogen-fixation in these areas.[3] He finds, that whereas the toxic concentration is comparatively low, the administration of amounts up to 0·0005 gm. per litre gave significant increases in the nitrogen fixed by the soil-organism. Iodine was also found to encourage the fixation of nitrogen by the nodule-bacteria of leguminosæ.

As regards the function of iodine within the plant, it would seem, again in the light of the researches of Stocklasa, that dressings of iodine salts increase the rate of oxygen-consumption, and also reduce acidity in the leaf, and to a lesser extent in the root sap. This would seem to be associated with a more rapid breakdown of organic acids, which, if allowed to accumulate, depress enzyme activity, and lead to the destruction of chlorophyl.

The iodine requirement of animals, like their demand for all other necessary minerals, would appear roughly to vary with the rate of growth and development. As in the case of plants, too large an amount of iodine would appear sometimes to inhibit growth no less than too little of it; though, whereas the effects of deficiencies are common and marked, the toxic effects of a natural superabundance are difficult to detect. Calves seem to benefit from amounts up to, but not greatly in excess of, 0·05 gm. per day. I have myself, however, administered totals of 16 oz. of potassium iodide in half-ounce doses per head each day to a herd of fourteen Jersey cows suffering from mastitis, and found no harmful effects to follow. Extensive scurfing of the skin was the only noticeable effect. In pigs, too, amounts of as much as 1 gm. (potassium iodide) per day had no toxic effect. These latter amounts are so enormously in excess of the normal iodine-contents of a natural ration, that the effect of iodine excess on selection need not seriously be considered. In human beings toxic effects seem sometimes to have followed the administration of iodine to adult women in goitre areas; though seldom if ever in the case of men or children.[4]

The normal function of iodine within the animal and human body can best be studied, not in the effects of over-dosage, but by an enquiry into the ætiology of goitre, with which we will now proceed. This subject in its turn is naturally bound up with the physiology of the thyroid gland.

The thyroid gland, according to Gaskell, is derived ancestrally from

[1] Stocklasa: (1926) *Biochem. Z.*, 176, 38.
[2] Ibid.
[3] Hall: *The Soil*, p. 216.
[4] Orr: *Iodine in Nutrition*, p. 77.

the uterus of the original non-vertebrate palæostracan.[1] Commenting on this, Bayliss remarks that it is not unlikely that remains of the internal secretion may have continued when its original function ceased.[2] For the purposes of this enquiry, then, setting out as it does to investigate a problem which from the first has been suspected of being intimately connected with the evolution of sex, this suggestion appears to be of considerable importance. Moreover, in relation to live stock and human beings, there is a mass of evidence showing that the iodine requirement of the female, as measured by goitre incidence, is normally much greater than that of the male.[3] Thus, if our original supposition be at all correct, namely, that the evolution of the mammal has resulted in a selection in favour of ultra-femininity, dictated mainly by deficiencies of calcium and phosphorus, we might expect that the demand for iodine will have tended to increase. Thus, in discussing the apparent reactions of Man and the animals to environments in which shortage of iodine would seem to be a salient selective feature, we must be on watch to discover how far iodine-deficiency has served merely to inhibit the further development of femininity, in contrast to the question of the degree in which altogether new devices for its conservation, such as an increased utilization of calcium, may have been perfected. We should enquire which aspects of femininity demand iodine, and must thus often be held in check; and which of them may be developed to a fuller degree.

On the whole, assuming that iodine will be abundant just in those very areas of heavy rainfall where calcium is deficient, we may expect to find a full development of femininity in the pluvial habitats, no less than in the pluvial epochs. The condition will doubtless have been initiated by a selection imposed by the unfavourable condition, namely, the lime- and perhaps phosphorus-deficiency. The abundance of iodine, however, may be regarded as a permissive condition without which the reaction towards femininity could not have taken place.

Goitre would seem to be essentially an over-development of a natural tendency. The thyroid gland not only varies in size between health and disease, but to a lesser degree its size varies likewise in accordance with the demands of growth, and with those of the sexual rhythm. Simple goitre, which is the condition usually found in young people is characterized, firstly, by an increase in the size of the gland; and, secondly, by the storage of colloid—which is allied to the thyroxin isolated by Kendall (1919) and synthesized by Harrington (1926)—in structures known as adenomata. Webster, working on simple goitres in rabbits, states that, following the injection of even minute quantities of iodine, the so-called "chief" cell-type of Langendorff, characterized

[1] Gaskell, W. H. (1908): *The Origin of Vertebrates*, London, Chapter V.
[2] Bayliss, p. 726.
[3] *N.B.* In cattle the thyroids of females and castrates contain more iodine than those of adult males. Orr: *Iod. in Nut.*; cft. Fenge (1913), *J. biol. Chem.*, 14, 397.

by large vesicular nuclei and reticular protoplasm, is changed into the acinar cells of the colloid structures.[1] This colloid storage may proceed to such a degree that these distended follicles, or adenomata, become small cysts. The adenomata would appear to form the basis of most malignant tumours of the thyroid;[2] and in this connection we may note, not only that the goitre-incidence and cancer-incidence have been shown by Stocks[3] to correspond; but also that the connection between sex and the thyroid is here faintly suggested by the fact that the cells of cancer-tissue are often characterized by a haploid or single chromosome outfit similar to that of an ovum or spermatozoon.[4]

Speaking very generally the symptoms associated with simple adenomatous or colloid goitre would seem to be cretinism, mongolism, small stature, and various failures of normal growth and development. On the other hand, we have the exophthalmic or nervous type of goitre, which seems probably, though by no means certainly, due solely to thyroid abnormality. As contrasted with the colloid or adenomatous type, its incidence increases, instead of decreasing, with age.[5] Histologically, it is characterized by a diffuse, parenchymatous structure. Colloid is scanty or absent, though in contrast with the adenomatous type, the total iodine-content of the blood is raised; but whether the organic to colloid ratio remains constant does not seem to have been investigated. One would expect an excess of the latter. The gland has been described as "fixed in the secreting phase."

ENVIRONMENT AND EXOPHTHALMIC GOITRE

The fact that the incidence of simple and exophthalmic goitre are correlated both in England and America would seem to confirm the theory that exophthalmic goitre is, like simple goitre, a direct product of iodine deficiency. In Switzerland, however, exophthalmic goitre seems relatively infrequent.[6] Stocks, reviewing the whole question of goitre-incidence in Switzerland, England, and America, points out that, whereas in Switzerland simple goitre is common and exophthalmic

[1] Webster, B.: *Endocrinology*, Vol. 16, No. 6, p. 622, 1932.
[2] Orr: *Iodine in Nutrition*, p. 64.
[3] Stocks, P.: "Cancer and Goitre," *Biometrika*, XVI, 1924, p. 391.
[4] *N.B.* Note also that thyroid proliferation is encouraged by the secretion of the anterior-lobe, which is identical or similar to vitamin E, and that tar extracts, which also contain substances allied to this vitamin, cause cancer. Incidentally Roussy and Oberling (*Presse Medicale*, Nov. 18th, 1933) find that 10 per cent of all subjects show adenomatous foci of the anterior-lobe, though most of these are microscopic. This suggests that the process is non-pathological and represents the mechanism whereby hormone concentrations are regulated. (See *B.M.J.*, Feb. 3rd, 1934, p. 200.)
[5] McCarrison, R.: *The Etiology of Simple Goitre*, London, 1928.
[6] Stocks, P.: "Some further notes on Cancer and Goitre Distribution," *Biometrika*, XVII, 1905, p. 156.

goitre rare, in England, where the relative death-rate is much lower, exactly the opposite is found. In America the two sets of symptoms seem to occur side by side. He then postulates for the development of exophthalmic goitre, firstly, a (common) goitre-producing factor—probably lack of iodine ; secondly, another factor probably of nervous origin, which is only present to a slight degree in Switzerland, but is more pronounced in the U.S.A., and almost universally present in England and Wales.

I find that, as already pointed out, rainfall is positively correlated with the incidence of exophthalmic goitre in England and the United States, whereas it is negatively correlated with the incidence of simple goitre in the States of U.S.A. Taken together these facts suggest a connection between a lime-deficiency of the soil and food with the onset of exophthalmic goitre. Considerations tending to support this view are, firstly, that the lime-content of the blood is known to be low in exophthalmic goitre ; so that the condition of the body seems to reflect that of the environment. Secondly, calcium is considered to conserve the stability of colloidal systems, and in exophthalmic goitre colloid is scanty or absent. Lastly, it does not seem impossible that calcium-deficiency might itself encourage thyroid activity. The parathyroids are closely associated with the thyroid, and both seem to secrete in response to the stimulus of the anterior-lobe of the pituitary. Now if the calcium was rendered abnormally low owing to faults of nutrition, it is probable that the concentration of blood calcium would drop, and would thus—in some way—encourage a hypersecretion of the parathyroids. The latter would encourage the withdrawal of calcium from the bones, until the more easily withdrawn reserves had been used up. After this, if the blood-calcium still remained low, they would continue to hypersecrete as before. If, then, the anterior-lobe is the organ normally responsible for encouraging or inhibiting secretion on the part of the thyroid and the parathyroid, it could follow that the low lime-concentration would itself promote thyroid as well as parathyroid activity as the result of a hypersecretion of the anterior-lobe.

The correlations on which this theory is based are as follows :

Correlation between the Ratio of Exophthalmic to Simple Goitre in the various States of the U.S.A. with Rainfall.	$R = +0{\cdot}40 \pm{\cdot}01$

Goitre—Males per 1000. Rainfall ins. per year.

Correlation between deaths from Exophthalmic Goitre in Counties of England and Rainfall in ins. per year.	$R = +\,0{\cdot}52 \pm.02$

The relationship of exophthalmic goitre to iodine-deficiency is probably, to some extent, indicated by the correlation between simple and exophthalmic goitre for the various States of U.S.A. This is $+\,0{\cdot}61 \pm{\cdot}01$. As for the relationship of drought to goitre-incidence, and so, presumably, to iodine-deficiency, this is indicated by the negative correlations between the U.S.A. goitre-incidences and rainfall. Thus :

Simple Goitre to Rainfall (U.S.A. States) $R = -0{\cdot}43 \pm {\cdot}02$.
Total Goitre to Rainfall (U.S.A. States) $R = -0{\cdot}45 \pm {\cdot}001$.

Of course, rainfall provides only a very rough way of judging the probable calcium-intake of food grown in various regions ; and in any case it does not follow that the whole of the correlation that we have noted is due to nutrition. It is not unlikely, for instance, that humidity may discourage tissue-hydration by some direct or indirect action upon the skin or lungs, and this in its turn might possibly affect the behaviour of the endocrines.

HEREDITY AND THE THYROID

Of course, it is quite possible that heredity as well as environment might influence the nature of the thyroid disease common in a given kind of habitat.

The population of Switzerland is brachycephalic, the type that I have all along suspected of having evolved in response to a diet deficient in iodine. The English population, on the other hand, though not a pure example of a dolichocephalic race, is, considering the probable differences in its ancestral components, now remarkably uniform in respect to its mesocephalic head-form. The influence of such Alpine or other brachycephalic characters as have contributed towards it seem now seldom able to reassert themselves. In comparison with England, however, we may regard the United States as a racial melting-pot in which the constituent elements have as yet had insufficient time to combine. Moreover, whereas in Switzerland, and the U.S.A., the goitre-incidence is not only severe but very widespread, in England the incidence is much less, and can thus hardly be considered seriously as a selective agent.

As evidence that liability to goitre does depend on race as well as on environment, we may point to its lower incidence among New York negresses as compared with white girls. The percentage incidences are 13·6 as compared with 20·3, the size of the groups being 9978 and 1106 respectively—large enough to make the racial differences significant.[1] The fact that the thyroids of Negroes are smaller than those of Whites might, of course, have helped to conceal some of the milder cases, and so to affect the statistics.[2] On the other hand, this fact is also capable of being interpreted so as to show that the Negro is less adapted to iodine-deficiency than the White. On this view the enlargement of the thyroid in simple goitre would be considered as an evolved reaction conferring survival-value. A further possibility, again, is that the Negro may be better adapted to calcium-deficiency than the White, and that the hereditary economy of the one substance automatically

[1] Goldberger and Aldinger (1925), quoted by Orr : *Iodine in Nutrition.*
[2] Loth, E. : *Anthropologie des Parties Molles*, Paris, 1931.

results in a lower requirement of all others. This, however, seems unlikely. Economy of iodine, if achieved by slow growth, may be expected to confer calcium-economy, but not vice versa.

There is a little direct experimental evidence to prove that over- and under-activity of the thyroid can indeed be hereditary. Thus, Riddle was enabled to establish high and low thyroid strains among pigeons, using artificial selection, and achieving results independently of the ontogenetic influence of environment.[1] In addition, however, ontogenetic development has been shown to be affected by the heat of the habitat ; and the results run strikingly parallel with the phylogenetic effects, postulated on *a priori* grounds in the first chapter, and observed in the case of the differences between the thyroid-sizes of the Negro and the White. It is pointed out by de Beer that, for any given temperature, there is a definite relationship between the size of the thyroid and the size of the body ; and that, until the thyroid has achieved its proper relative size in regard to the temperature, metamorphosis in the bull-frog will not take place.[2] Further, it has been found that different geographical races of the same species of frog have different rates of development of their thyroid glands ; those from cold climates having larger thyroids than have warm-climate races when developed at the same temperature.[3] Experiments have also shown that frog tadpoles, developed in the cold, not only grow to a larger size than normal before undergoing metamorphosis, but also have larger thyroids. The evolutionary significance of this becomes clear if we can assume the efficiency of the thyroid to vary with its size, and regard the cold environment not only as throwing a greater strain upon the basal metabolism, but also as tending to supply lower concentrations of iodine in the food. Applying this to Man, we may thus suppose the White races to be possessed of an heredity making for a larger thyroid. Also, it would not seem unreasonable to expect on the part of the enlarged glands a superior power of expanding still further in response either to cold or to iodine-deficiency or to both.

As for the allied question of the receptivity of the tissues to iodine, it is known that in myxœdema, where the blood iodine is low, the rise of basal metabolism to a standard dose of thyroxin is higher than in the case of a normal individual.[4] The same holds good of parathormone and insulin. The results are greatest in cases of calcium-tetany and diabetes respectively. It would be interesting to know, however, whether the response to an endocrine stimulus depends solely upon the

[1] Huxley and de Beer : p. 436 ; cft. Riddle, O. : *Amer. Nat.*, LXIII, 1929, p. 385.

[2] De Beer, G. R. : *An Introduction to Experimental Embryology* ; cft. Swingle, W. W. : *J. exp. Zool.*, 43 (1926), p. 151 ; Swingle, W. W. : *Anat. Rec.*, 23 (1922), pp. 41, 100, 106 ; Uhlenhuth, E. : *J. gen. Physiol.*, I (1919), p. 473.

[3] Ibid., cft. Adler, L. : *Pflüg. Arch. ges. Physiol.*, 164, 1916, p. 1.

[4] Boothby *et al.* (1925) : *Trans. Ass. Amer. Phys.*, 40, 195.

low level of the particular hormone. If it were also dependent upon separately hereditable genes it might be possible to explain some cases of extreme endocrine peculiarity, such as giants and dwarfs, in terms of strong endocrine-stimulus inherited with great tissue-sensitivity, or vice versa. Ontogenetically, however, it seems clear that high endocrine-activity produces a relative lack of response, and it seems probable that in the case of pure races the same will hold good of phylogeny.

The mere measurement of basal metabolism cannot, of course, distinguish between the two possible genetic factors responsible for its intensity. This work, however, has already produced some very interesting results which, while still unexplained, indicate a possibility of interpreting differences of racial psychology in material terms. For instance, Wardlaw and Laurence find that the basal metabolism of the Australian aborigines is capable of falling to a lower level than that of Whites.[1] The extent to which factors affecting the heredity, physical environment, and social environment severally contribute towards such a result remains obscure. The influence of hereditary or ecological influences could not be considered proved until the possible ontogenetic effect of education in increasing the nervous irritability, and so the degree of endocrine activity, had been already ascertained.

As evidence that differences of iodine-metabolism are indeed hereditary in Man we may quote the observations of Walsh (1907),[2] who on clinical evidence considers frontal-band alopecia, and patchy baldness, to be hereditary, and as such associated with both myxœdema and Graves' disease. In this connection, the more frequent occurrence of baldness in brachycephalic men than in those with longer heads has been remarked upon,[3] and is of particular interest in its bearing on the theory that brachycephaly itself may be a racial reaction to iodine-deficiency. The inheritance of mongolism or goitre does not seem ever to have been made a special genetical study. Next best, however, are some accounts of hereditary goitre from California reported by Janney and Henderson (1920).[4] From a study of these it can be seen that a tendency both to myxœdemous and to exophthalmic goitre tends to run in a family, though exophthalmic cases are liable to occur in families where the main tendency seems to be towards the myxœdemous type. Secondly, a case is quoted where a man can be believed to have handed on a tendency to goitre to his son, thus showing that the inheritance of goitre is probably not sex-linked, even though its higher incidence in the female does show it to be sex-limited. This, perhaps, might have been expected, since we have already suggested that the probable reaction to iodine-deficiency might be to inhibit, rather than to encourage, the domination of the autosomes by the sex-inheritance.

[1] Wardlaw, H., and Laurence, W. J.: *Aust. J. Exp. Biol. med. Sci.*, X, III (1932).
[2] Walsh: (1907) *Lancet*, II, 1080.
[3] Crookshank: *The Mongol in our Midst.*
[4] Janney, N. W., and Henderson, M. D.: (1920) *Arch. intern. Med.*, 26, 297.

The tendency towards simple goitre, then, may be regarded as an over-development of a (sometimes) beneficial character, evolved and still present, in the autosomes. It would be interesting to know whether, on the contrary, there may be any sex-linked characters that, although useful perhaps for some other purpose, are liable in a goitre-area to induce the dangerous exophthalmic phase of thyroid trouble.

THYROID, ANTERIOR-LOBE, AND COMPENSATION FOR ULTRA-FEMININITY

As regards the direct ontogenetic endocrine relation between the action of thyroid and the organs of sex, there would again seem to be direct antagonism. Reviewing the experimental data, Orr concludes that, whereas thyroid is necessary for the normal growth and functioning of the sex organs, excess of thyroid interferes with the sexual development and activity.[1] In the frog, we may note, one region of the epidermis will proliferate, and another degenerate, under the influence of thyroid.[2] As regards the mammary gland, atrophy of the breasts would seem to accompany hyperthyroidism ; while in the case of a non-pregnant rabbit thyroidectomy was followed by a great growth of mammary tissues overflowing with milk.[3] This, perhaps, is surprising. One might have expected the ultra-feminine types, derived from the iodine-rich areas, to demand the greatest amount of thyroid for their growth. We find, on the other hand, that this iodine, at all events after its mobilization in colloidal form, tends to inhibit the development of the very sex-mechanism itself. The development of the genital organs seems likewise to be inhibited by the intraperitoneal injection of vitamin E (the sex vitamin), and also by an extract of the anterior-pituitary. Indeed, Verzár, who discovered this, regards vitamin E as necessary for the production of the anterior-lobe hormone, and as even possibly identical with it.[4]

The question how far the inhibitory effect of the anterior-lobe on the primary sex-mechanism is likewise secured by way of the thyroid secretion is of vital importance, and will now be discussed. Hogben used injections of anterior-lobe substance to complete metamorphosis in Axolotls from which the thyroid glands had been totally removed.[5] This opens up the question whether the anterior-lobe acts by influencing membrane-permeability to iodine, or whether the similar influences of the anterior-lobe and the thyroid are achieved by quite separate mechanisms. In view, however, of the close functional relationship

[1] Orr : *Iodine in Nutrition*, pp. 58–60.

[2] Huxley and de Beer : op. cit., p. 427 ; cft. Champy, C. : (1922) *Arch. Morph. gén. exp.*, IV, p. 1.

[3] Orr : *Iodine in Nutrition*, p. 60 ; cft. Koranyi : (1913) *Proc. 17th Inter. Conf. Med.*, p. 53.

[4] Verzár, F. : (1931) *Pflüg. Arch. ges. Physiol.*, 227, 499. Quoted Med. Resch. Council Special Report, No. 167, *The Vitamins*, 1932, p. 109.

[5] Hogben, L. T. : *Proc. roy. Soc. B.*, 94, 1922, p. 204.

of the two organs in the normal animal, it seems, at this juncture, safer to adopt the provisional hypothesis that the anterior-lobe must obtain at least part of its results with the assistance of iodine. For, in the absence of the thyroid, there is a strong probability that other less specialized structures could mobilize iodine in its stead. Indeed, in the trout removal of the thyroid does not prevent development; whereas, when the hypophysis is removed, this no longer occurs.[1] The pituitary of the trout may thus be suspected of manufacturing the thyroid hormone. Similarly, iodine alone will induce slow metamorphosis in a frog tadpole whose thyroids have been removed; while in Axolotl this does not occur, though the metabolism of the thyroid is accelerated.[2] Nor does it take place in the frog tadpole if the hypophysis has been removed, so that no pituitary gland is formed.[3] Hogben's experiments with Axolotls, whose pituitaries were intact, and whose diet—raw meat—could have supplied iodine, do not thus disprove the possibility that the anterior-lobe acts by way of facilitating the passage of iodine through cell membranes in the pituitary, so that it there undergoes transformation into thyroxin.

Incidentally, it is worth noting that he found that even small amounts of posterior-lobe substance inhibited metamorphosis. Since the latter acts on the blood vessels as a " pressor " substance, it may be regarded as an inhibitor of membrane-permeability. Thus, the two halves of the gland may be regarded as being in some senses physiologically opposed to each other. The same would probably hold good of the substances they mobilize, convert, and secrete. Is then the vitamin E, used by the anterior-lobe, usually in opposition to some other vitamins A or B or C, that serve the *pars nervosa* or posterior-lobe? This discussion has been somewhat lengthy, since it is desired to investigate the possibility of some other substance acting as a complete substitute for iodine. The experiment of Hogben renders this interpretation possible—though it does not prove it. If such were the case, most of the arguments here made to rest on the assumption that iodine economy has been a fundamental selective agency would require drastic qualification. As matters stand, however, it will be taken for granted that, although a surplus of vitamin E, mobilized by the pituitary, may be enabled to make a small amount of iodine achieve a large effect, nevertheless, the latter is a fundamental requirement without which growth and development cannot take place.

As noted already, it seems probable that vitamin E will be more plentiful in habitats subject to extremes of climate where plants are forced to die and refertilize each year. In the tropics, on the other hand, iodine will be more plentiful owing to heavy rainfall and soil-acidity, whereas pollen might be less plentiful because of the greater

[1] Orr: *Iod. in Nut.*; cft. Swingle: (1926) *Proc. Soc. exp. Biol.*, 24, 205.
[2] Huxley, J. S., and Hogben, L. T.: *Proc. roy. Soc. B.*, 93, 1922, p. 36.
[3] Swingle, W. W.: *J. exp. Zool.*, 27, 1919, p. 397.

tendency towards vegetative and asexual reproduction. These considerations could incidentally offer an ecological explanation of the probable synergism between the hormone of the anterior-lobe and the growth of bone. If the vitamin responsible for the former is more plentiful in arid regions, it would be there that the most abundant calcium-supplies would also be available.

PRIMARY AND SECONDARY SEX CHARACTERS

Now it seems important to try and understand this curious inhibition by the thyroid and anterior-lobe upon the development of the reproductive mechanism. Moreover, it seems possible to see in it a method whereby the phylogenetic factor of sex may have been allowed to exert an influence upon such secondary sexual characters as size, while leaving the still more important development of the primary sex-mechanism unaffected. The thyroid and pituitary almost certainly have a direct influence upon the sex gland or gonad. And the sex-linked inheritance is responsible for moulding the latter into a testicle or ovary, which in either case will elaborate two or more sex hormones : the first, or *corpus luteum* secretion, perhaps identical with the male-determining substance ; and the second, the follicular, being possibly a female-determining substance. In the male the former will exist in relatively high concentration, while, vice versa, in the female the latter is relatively abundant.

Now what may be expected to result from a phylogenetic change involving more or less activity on the part of the sex-linked inheritance ? Suppose an increase in femininity, with a corresponding increase in the secretion of the female sex-hormone. One would look for an over-development of the female genitalia, just as a reduction of activity on the part of the X chromosome might have been expected to leave them half finished. If such were the rule all variation in the degree of racial sexuality would be disadvantageous, and as a regular way of adapting body-size to food-supply the method would need to be either abandoned or improved. It is suggested, then, that the direct action of the thyroid and the anterior-lobe in inhibiting the development of the primary sex-mechanism was evolved as a means of balancing the positive effect that those same two endocrines would otherwise be bound to produce by way of the gonad. In an ultra-feminine race, evolved for an iodine-rich habitat, the influence of the gonad would be strong ; but the direct inhibitory influence of the thyroxin would be strong also. In a more masculine race, the direct inhibiting stimulus of the iodine would be less, but the activity of the gonad must, for the same reason, be reduced. As regards the actual mechanism whereby these effects are possibly achieved, one may point to the high iodine-content of the genital organs, which would appear to be second only to that of the thyroid itself. It seems improbable, therefore, that they would react positively to different external levels of a substance in which they themselves were already rich.

CONCLUSION

So much for the physiological data upon which it is proposed to try and erect a theory of human evolution. It is hoped that attention has been drawn to the close relationship that appears to exist between the distribution of the body's structural substances outside and that within itself. If this relationship of physiology to environment is brought home, it seems a minor matter if some of the evolutionary corollaries are later proved to be wrong. In the tracing of each of them facts were missing, and it was necessary to guess. So too, then, although it is now proposed to try out the mineral hypothesis in its direct application to human evolution, lack of exact knowledge must at many points weaken our confidence in the lasting value of the result. If, however, the theories in question serve only to stimulate further research, especially in regard to the inheritance of various associated conditions of high and low endocrine-activity, and the relationship of those states to the metabolism of the minerals, this study will not have been undertaken in vain.

CHAPTER VI

THE ORIGIN OF MAN

The Mechanism of Cranial Expansion : Iodine and Cranial Expansion : Growth and Behaviour : Primary and Secondary Reaction : The Relation of Man to the Great Apes : Conclusion.

MY ARGUMENT WILL BE THAT THE FIRST HOMINIDÆ WERE developed out of large anthropoid apes which had in their turn developed from a similar but smaller animal ; and also that the Anthropoidea were developed from a more primitive four-legged form. Indeed, it accords with a single hypothesis to attribute the evolution of anthropoid brachiation to a food-deficiency causing a hypotrophy of the hind legs ; and, likewise, to relate the human power of walking erect to a subsequent, but similar, withering of the then elongated and specialized anthropoid arms. In each case the acquired physiological change, involving an anatomical defect, is deemed, on balance, to have nevertheless conferred an immediate survival-value. In addition, it initiated a process of secondary mechanical adaptation. These influences upon the limbs are discussed in the next chapter.

Not only the evolution of the erect attitude, but also the expansion of the brain and skull, and the loss of body hair, are all viewed as the results of atavistic, and probably rapid, reactions to mineral-deficiency. A single relatively short period of severe iodine-shortage is thought to have precipitated the large anatomical change from ape to man. A returned predominance of genes, previously evolved and perfected during two or more similar, but earlier, phases of mammalian and anthropoid development, is held responsible. Such a reaction as is imagined would, if observed among ourselves, or in one of our domesticated live stock, be considered definitely pathological. Except under very exceptional circumstances, those subject to it could never survive. Exceptional circumstances are, however, given credit both for the change and for its survival. Some aspects of it may thus have been more favourable to the new type than to the old. It is suggested, then, that the evolution, or creation, of the first human being occurred in response to the rising of the heads of the Tertiary limestone mountain-system above the hitherto unbroken carpet of forest with which it was formerly covered. This introduced a completely new kind of habitat to which physiological efficiency was the sole test of entry. Here, I imagine a hairless, hydrocephalic, achondroplasic, and therefore in most senses degenerate, variety of the big Dryopithecus to have sought asylum. Nevertheless, both in the matter of mineral economy and in cerebral capacity, this first proto-hominid was greatly superior to his predecessors.

The most important human character is the size of the brain. This I attribute to a series of three or more major cranial expansions each recapitulated in the development of the child, and representing times when the absolute size of the body was reduced owing to severe selection and in-breeding caused by mineral-deficiency. By selecting in favour

Index of Cephalization. Diagram showing the variations in the index of cephalization at different stages in the development of the child. Also suggestions of past environmental influences held responsible for selecting the unit hereditary characters believed to influence this aspect of individual growth.

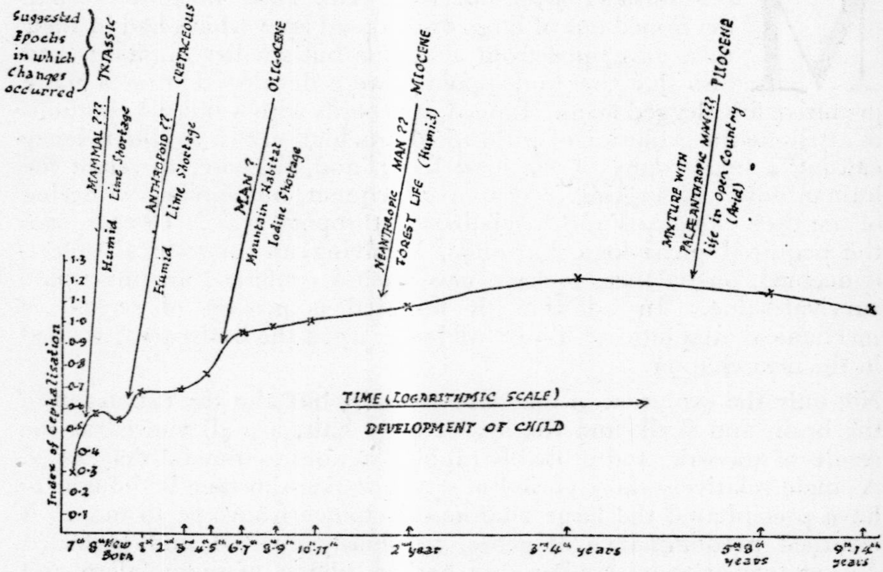

After Anthony and Coupin ; quoted by Kappers, A : Phil. Trans. Roy. Soc. Lond. B., 221 (1932).

of an animal with a small and physiologically efficient form of body, the same changes are considered to have encouraged a relative expansion of the brain. These ontogenetic changes, together with the inferences that it is proposed to draw from them, are shown in the diagram.

THE MECHANISM OF CRANIAL EXPANSION

Now, just as the vertebrate endocrine system would appear to have become adapted in response to the needs of constant environmental change, so does the mechanism of mammalian neurocranial expansion seem to have evolved a design whereby every large reduction in the size of the body confers at least a sufficiency of extra brain-tissue. This relative increase in the size of the brain is necessary if the originally evolved behaviour is even to be kept intact. Moreover, it will become of still greater use after a positive increment in the ratio of body-size to brain has made possible elaborations of behaviour, such as those developed by small social mammals which are thereby enabled to compensate for their individual weakness in competition with their independent and stronger, but less economical, relatives.

This important relationship between the minimum cranial requirements of animals of like behaviour but differing widely in size is expressed by Dubois' important formula $K=\frac{E}{S^{\frac{5}{9}}}$. E represents the weight of the brain and S the weight of the body (in gms.). K is the coefficient of cephalization which is found usually to remain constant for animals of the same order or general type of organization. This holds good for birds and fishes as well as for mammals. When K does vary between two allied species, the difference is very great: so much so as to suggest a sudden increment of cranial capacity due to the bipartition of brain-cells. The expansions appear to take place by geometrical progression. For instance, K is nearly constant for all the four living anthropoids, despite the enormous difference in body size between the gibbon and the gorilla. Nevertheless, when the common and the pygmy hippopotamus are compared it is found that the cephalization of the latter is almost exactly a degree above that of its larger and, I suspect, more primitive relation. The same holds good of the llama whose brain is twice the size of its extinct and similar-sized relative procamelus. In this case we have no knowledge of an intermediate pygmy form, but, for reasons that will be developed later, these gaps in our typological series are explicable. Mineral-deficiency not only reduces numbers, but also encourages the dissolution of bone. Professor Dubois points out that the human index of cephalization shows a double geometrical increment above that of the anthropoid apes. Moreover, calculating the body weight of Pithecanthropus from the femoral size, and utilizing the directly estimated cranial capacity, he places his famous "missing link" into the vacant position which is thereby inferred.[1]

All this fits in with my general hypothesis that anatomical evolution occurs in waves and that the causes of the temporary retreat and simplification are quite as important as those governing the slower and more easily traced advances. It remains, however, to try and understand the genetical and physiological mechanism whereby these changes of external circumstances are so regularly enabled to produce almost identical effects in widely differing hereditary stocks. It implies a mechanism that was developed before animals now as distinct as the

[1] Dubois, E.: "Phylogenetic Cerebral Growth," Compte Rendu. Congrès Internat des Sciences Anthropol. et Ethnol. I, London, 1934, pp. 71–75.

hippopotamus and the anthropoids had diverged. I suggest, therefore, that the capacity to expand the brain in rapid response to a reduction in the size of the body was first evolved by the root-stock of the mammals at the time when they first developed their ability to diminish the size of the body in response to calcium and other mineral shortages. If so, it dates from the first selection of sex-linked size-reducing mutations, when these first appeared upon the newly doubled sex-chromosome of the homogametic mammalian female.

Now mineral-deficiency may not only adapt the outside of the organism to its food supply ; it can also be responsible for happenings inside the body. Not only does the food seem to have regulated the size of the body as a whole, but the reactions of the various parts seem to have been drilled to answer to a similar set of commands. It is well known that a lowering of the salt- or glucose-concentration in the fluid surrounding an animal cell will cause the flexible and semi-permeable membrane to expand until the imbibition of water and the exclusion of bombarding ions have permitted an equal or isotonic concentration of electrolytes on either side.[1] But this capacity to expand and contract varies in the different cells of the body, and has been retained to a high degree by those of the brain. Moreover, this is a special feature of the lower and more rudimentary parts of the brain, and is especially marked in the case of young animals.[2] All this suggests the harnessing of an old and very primitive character into the new and highly complex mammalian system whereby the single influence—mineral-deficiency—is required to inhibit growth at one point and to favour it at another. The body has become so adjusted that, when it contracts, the brain automatically expands. It is true that growth, which implies cellular proliferation, as opposed to mere expansion through hydration, need not necessarily follow. The latter, however, is probably an important prerequisite of the former.

Of course the endocrines are almost sure to play an important part in any such regulation of physiological activity. Indeed, if we assume them to work as the turnkeys permitting or barring the passage of specific substances, and especially of electrolytes, through the cell membranes, it is no wonder if we find other lines of more direct evidence pointing to the pituitary—the master endocrine—as chiefly responsible for the failure of bodily development, and for the almost invariably associated cephalic expansion seen in the pathological dwarfed condition known as achondroplasia. Further details in regard to this abnormal development will be discussed in a later chapter concerned with the changes that may overtake the growth of the skull.[3] Let it here be mentioned, however, that achondroplastic conditions, as observed in cattle and dogs as well as in human beings, are found to

[1] Cf. Bayliss, p. 162.
[2] Haldi, J. A., Rauth, J. W., Larkin, J., and Wright, D. : (1927) *Amer. J. Physiol.*, 80, 631–638.
[3] Chapter IX.

involve defects of the limbs, often coupled with an extreme expansion of the head. In the so-called " bull-dog " calves, which arise through in-breeding the already normally short-legged Dexter cattle, Crew found the two halves of the pituitary to be defective, and attributed the generally water-logged condition of the tissues to a notable failure of the posterior-lobe. This endocrine is concerned with constricting the bore of the capillaries. Its physiological efficiency can be tested by its power to expand the black pigment-cells of the marine fish, Fundulus. He also noted a premature closure of the skull-sutures, though this did not prevent one case of pronounced hydrocephalus. The skulls, like those of human beings, were almost spherical with a cephalic index of 100.[1] Growth at the skull-sutures, and indeed all cartilage proliferation, is probably dependent upon the bone-growth hormone of the anterior-lobe. In the cases here cited the vascularity of that organ was below normal, while its histological structure was atypical. The anterior-lobe probably affects the growth of bone in another way also. If—as is probable—it excites the parathyroid, as it does the thyroid, its activity would indirectly inhibit ossification, while also directly stimulating cartilage proliferation.[2] A failure of the achondroplastic parathyroids might thus account for much of the premature synostosis. It was observed that the thyroids were badly developed ; so it is probable that the parathyroid tissue was likewise defective.

I suggest, then, that achondroplasia may be looked upon as the accidental release of a mechanism of which the original purpose has been to adapt the development of the body, brain and skull to a change of diet during periods of severe mineral-deficiency. To put this in another way, the failure of the pituitary hormones, from whatever cause, may have allowed the renewed activity of some very old genes, originally selected at a time of extreme mineral-deficiency. During the more favourable intervening periods, their activity has been sternly held in check.

I suspect that an original sex-linked repression of pituitary activity occurred in response to calcium-shortage at the time of mammalian evolution. In the reptile, the double sex-chromosome of the male has been presumed to stimulate masculine development, and to permit the attainment of greater size ; though this last matter needs experimental verification. If the reptiles evolved an increased sexuality as a response to drought and iodine shortage, it follows that the original sex-chromosomes also encouraged fluid-economy as well. This could have been secured through a comparative diminution of the salt-concentration of the male blood ; and the same capacity would have been useful to

[1] Crew, F. A. E. : " The Significance of an Achondroplasia-like condition in cattle," *Proc. royal Soc. B.*, XCV, 228–255.

[2] Cf. Chapter V. Anterior-lobe extracts raise the serum calcium probably by activating the parathyroid. The latter acts by inhibiting the absorbtion of calcium phosphate by the bone cells. Cf. Frei and Emmerson, loc. cit. ; also Thompson, D. L., Collip, J. B., loc. cit.

the female, following upon the hypothetical sex-reversal when the old reptilian sex-chromosomes became autosomes.[1] It would be during this period of reversed sex-dimorphism, when the drought-defying female was larger than the male, that the new sex-linked factors must be held to have developed the power of encouraging a loss of sodium, while at the same time also favouring an energetic excretion of calcium, together with a liberal development of cartilage. For, under arid conditions, there would always be an abundance of the calcium necessary to consolidate this precursor of bone. During this phylogenetic experience of drought, the water-holding capacity of the cells would be encouraged by a high activity of the posterior-lobe, whereby sodium would be allowed entry ; while at the same time an escape of salt through the kidney, due to a consequent relaxing of activity on the part of the adrenal-cortex, would encourage complete cellular hydration, owing to the lowered ionic concentration outside the cell-membranes of the tissues.[2]

Now the very reverse of these conditions would be required if the proto-mammal had to adapt itself to a pluvial and mineral-deficient habitat. The growth of cartilage would need to be inhibited, and a capacity for rapid ossification would be an advantage. I suggest, therefore, that at this point the female sex-genes and ovarian secretions became adapted so as to be able to inhibit, instead of encouraging, the activity of the pituitary. They are believed to do this through a " sex centre " in the brain.[3] Perhaps a mere intensification of the internal secretion automatically turned a nerve-stimulation into an inhibition. Whatever the gene-influences may have been, one can argue that, as far as the hormones are concerned, an inhibition of the anterior-lobe would prevent an undue skeletal development, and so economize lime. The influence of a corresponding weakness of the posterior-lobe is less easy to foresee except in so far as we know that it would allow a dilation of the capillaries, and might thus mechanically expand the tissues through which they pass. This dilation may be partly due to the indirect influence of a posterior-lobe failure permitting a hypersecretion of the adrenal-cortex and a corresponding rise in the sodium content of the blood and body-fluids. Since sodium has a close affinity for water, this would encourage an extra-cellular hydration, and would tend to counteract the initial failure of the posterior-lobe, which might otherwise permit a greater loss of sodium by the tissue cells.

In short, the evolution of the true mammal in response to the conditions

1 *N.B.* The dependence of desert animals on salt probably indicates a capacity to excrete sodium chloride to balance water lost through evaporation. They will be wasteful of these elements in which their environment abounds.

2 See Chapter IV for argument in favour of this mutual inhibition of the posterior-lobe and adrenal-cortex.

3 Schoeller, W. : " New Work on Hormones," *Lancet*, Jan. 7th (1933), pp. 38–42 ; cft. Hohlweg and Junkermann : *Klin. Wschr.* (1932), XI, 32.

of a pluvial habitat probably involved an inhibition of activity on the part of the whole pituitary. Calcium would be deficient and iodine abundant, so that with an inhibition of the bone-growth, thyrotropic and "parathyrotropic" influences of the anterior-lobe would be permitted if not actively demanded. Similarly, sodium shortage would demand an increased activity of the adrenal-cortex, such as could best be secured by an inhibition of the posterior-lobe. This would result in a tendency towards œdema; which could be usefully retained, and indeed encouraged, in the case of the brain, since it would serve as the basis for a necessary mechanism whereby cranial expansion would ever afterwards follow, as a result of selection or other circumstances encouraging pituitary repression and small size. Incidentally, this tendency to expand the skull, and at the same time economize in the production of hard parts, helps to explain the inverse relationship of palatal to cranial development, which has long been of interest to students of human evolution.

IODINE AND CRANIAL EXPANSION

Now, if the mechanism of cranial expansion was first constructed as a reply to calcium-shortage at the dawn of mammalian evolution, it is not altogether easy to see how the almost opposite environmental condition, iodine-deficiency, could serve also to throw it into gear. Nevertheless, I believe, this to have occurred at least once in the course of human evolution, and perhaps on a previous occasion when the anthropoids were being developed. I have adopted the hypothesis that the three cranial expansions and increments in the index of cephalization represent the evolution of the mammal, the anthropoid, and Man respectively. Alternatively, it would be possible to consider anthropoid evolution as recapitulated in the first of these, and then to place a being allied to Pithecanthropus in the middle position, while postulating a third period of severe deficiency as responsible for the final development of Neanthropic man. All this can be discussed later, the need of the moment being to outline a reasonable physiological hypothesis; and many considerations favour the inclusion of iodine-shortage as one possible cause of what will later be called the primary achondroplasic reaction. Of the two, a shortage of iodine, not of calcium, is by far the most probable deficiency responsible for the hairless condition of the human race. It is known to produce this effect in domesticated animals kept in goitre-areas, and it is thus convenient to consider a loss of hair as being one result of a pituitary failure brought about by iodine-shortage. Moreover, whatever theoretical difficulties may stand in the way, it has been often observed that dwarfism tends to be associated with cretinism, which is due to thyroid underfunctioning and could thus result from iodine-deficiency. For instance, in a recent paper to the International Congress, a writer complains that certain psychotic forms of dwarfism encountered in Alpine valleys are wrongly confused with the non-pathological characters of the normal Alpine race.[1] More certain evidence, however, comes from Max Schmidt, who records the almost universal occurrence of goitre in all the individuals composing several communities in Central Brazil. He noted that a large number of these people were hydrocephalic dwarfs. Moreover, he found that they had a song in which the possession of a goitre was held up to admiration.[2] Now, thyroid-deficiency is often associated with an accumulation of fluid in the body—myxœdema—and in such cases the administration of thyroxin serves to encourage diuresis.[3]

Calcium and iodine assist each other in counteracting acidity, and it seems probable that the mechanism used as a reaction to the shortage of the one has become closely bound up with that adapted to economize the other.

It has been suggested that the original reptilian sex-genes encouraged iodine-economy, just as they are also supposed to have favoured a loss of sodium. Indeed the acidity caused by the latter escape would have favoured iodine retention. If then the mechanisms became transposed, so that in the new mammal small size needed to be coupled with a deficiency of fixed base, some of the genes for iodine economy might desert their now autosomal partners and side with the new sex-linked inheritance. If the new small-sized homogametic mammal was already adjusted to an economical borderline diet of sodium, the individuals possessing the best capacity to economize iodine would be those in which basal metabolism was lowest, while the general acidity of the body—such as favours early synostosis—was extreme. This is consistent with the general position adopted throughout this enquiry, namely, that the male tends most strongly to retain sodium, and is thus more alkaline; whereas the female is more acid, and so attracts iodine and calcium, and economizes the latter by an early ossification also due partly to this same acidity.

If this view be correct, the catabolic anterior-lobe hormone must be regarded as wasteful both of iodine and calcium, since it excites the thyroid, and probably the parathyroid, and in any case raises the serum calcium, which last, when experimentally produced by the use of parathormone, leads to a more active calcium-excretion. Similarly, there can be little doubt that an active thyroid secretion, instead of encouraging colloid storage, will tend to waste iodine. It will follow, therefore, than any circumstance tending to inhibit the activity of the anterior-lobe will encourage the economy of either or both of the two substances whose shortages are held to have played the most important part in vertebrate evolution. I consider, therefore, that, whenever there is a tendency towards any mineral-deficiency, the

[1] Krauss, W. W.: Congrès Internat des Sci. Anthropol. et Ethnol., I, London (1934), p. 164.

[2] Schmidt, Max: *Indianerstudien in Zentralbrasilien*, Berlin, 1905, pp. 29, 34.

[3] Loeb, L.: *Edema*, Baltimore (1923); cft. Eppinger.

mammal's first reaction will be in the direction of small size and a compensatory expansion of the neuro-cranium. Only if iodine-deficiency be coupled with calcium abundance and cold need one expect a slow secondary reversal of this process subsequently to take place. Remnants of the old reptilian mechanism may still be within recall upon the autosomes, but if these are to be uncovered the process will have to be gradual. Heat and iodine might both be economized by an increase of size, but I suspect that in the modern mammal a natural selection for strength, or for reach, or else a sexual selection for fighting efficiency, has been mainly responsible for the slow increments of size that are assumed to have punctuated several probably shorter periods of size-reduction and cranial expansion.

A further argument favouring the view that iodine-deficiency could select for any faculty of inhibiting the primitive instincts might be based on the fact that excitement in a child was shown by V. Fellenberg to result in the excretion of three times the normal amount of iodine.[1] Thus, long residence in an area of deficiency would encourage a control of the motor and emotional centres by the higher parts of the brain. Thought, as opposed to blind trial-and-error action, would pave the way towards the evolution of a considered behaviour.

GROWTH AND BEHAVIOUR

The ebb and flow of bodily development may be believed to have been accompanied by a corresponding inherent tendency towards the manifestation of two general and contradictory types of behaviour, as associates of each of the alternating phases of anatomical and physiological development. This might be traced back to the remote aquatic origin of the vertebrate, and probably pre-dates even that stage of relatively high organization. Even the members of a cell-aggregate must be considered to have developed the rudiments of co-operation and communication, as compared with independent protozoa. I propose to associate mineral-deficiency with the co-operative tendency, and at the aquatic stage to consider fresh water as the nurse of the large anabolic and now female ovum ; whereas the salt water, with its iodine-rich vegetation, will be held to encourage small size and catabolic activity. Incidentally, it could be argued that the monthly rhythm of sex was thus evolved in an estuarine environment, and that the early representatives of the independent male gametes were carried out to sea. Conversely, the more highly developed and sessile cell-aggregates were stimulated to expand, and finally to divide, under the stimulus of almost salt-free, but calcium-rich, river-water, which would lower the ionic concentration of sodium chloride imposed by their environment during the ebb of spring tides. At the opposite lunar phases the less extreme variations of neap-tides would cause a mere rhythmic expansion and contraction of the semi-permeable and increasingly complex cell-membrane. In

[1] Orr : *Iodine in Nut.*

this way food could be allowed ingress during the expansions on the ebb, while its oxidized remnants could be excreted during the diuretic contraction following the return of the salt-water. The sessile, and incipiently female, cells would thus tend to contain less sodium and more calcium than the smaller marine males. If any of the latter were left behind after the retreat of the salt-water at the spring-tide ebb, they would be devoured by the salt-starved and already expanded females, whose fission would thus be precipitated.

To move a vast distance further along the evolutionary path, it may be pointed out that true fish are believed to have evolved in the rivers, and only later to have re-invaded the sea ; and, similarly, that the emergence of the vertebrates on to the land was almost certainly from fresh and not from salt-water. Some intermediate form allied to the lung-fish developed the power to breathe pure undissolved air, and achieved the first stages of fluid-economy as a passive response to drought, before an active and inherent terrestrial mobility became habitual. If this all happened in response to aridity, it must have accompanied an increasing concentration of salts in the food of the newly emerged land-animal. Correspondingly, it can be argued that the earlier " tadpole " stage would have been associated with a lower concentration of electrolytes within the body, such as still holds good to-day.

To return, then, to the question of behaviour, it must be pointed out that the emergence of the vertebrate on to dry land must almost certainly have been a solitary pilgrimage. Competition would be one of " all against all " ; and physiology, rather than anatomy, would provide the weapons, until the rivalry of other species could favour mechanical co-operation. At the previous aquatic stage, however, circumstances may well have been very different. One species would already have begun to prey upon others, and the young may well have been forced to guard themselves from the cannibalistic tendencies of their parents. The aquatic form of defence is the school, or convoy. This requires two types of instinctive reaction, namely, gregariousness and suggestibility. The most gregarious individuals will secure the best protection, owing to their tendency to congregate towards the centre of the group. At the same time, they must possess the capacity to imitate the behaviour of their more independent relatives upon the flanks. When the latter turn inward to secure protection by flight, all must blindly follow suit, or otherwise the whole company will meet with disaster. The ideal arrangement will be for the older individuals, and especially for the less expensive males, to guard the flanks, while the young and the females occupy the safety-zone at the centre. Even at this stage delayed maturity will pay, while precocious independence is punished.

It must be the young, therefore, who will need the strongest " feminine " instincts. Thus, as the ratio of solids to water in the body rises with the approach of maturity or of terrestrial independence, as it does in the tadpole, these two instinctive tendencies will tend to fade. A fish will then leave the shoal, and may even help to discipline its own offspring by attacking the school of which it has ceased to be a member. Indeed, this last consideration introduces us to what is later to be developed into an important theory of sexual selection. The liability of the young to stand in danger of attack by the old is made to account for an ever-increasing complexity of safety-reaction involving a long continuation of immature and femininely orientated behaviour. This process undergoes a marked acceleration as soon as intra-specific competition through male sexual selection demands a capacity for sexual combat on the part of the adult male, and thus puts the adolescent in increased danger of death ere ever his full genetic potentialities can be developed and put to the test.

It is arguable that much human behaviour, as well as many somatic characters, will be found to correspond with the youthful stages of development in other animals. The gregarious instinct seems to have been a character common to almost all young vertebrates, though but occasionally retained by the adults of the more social animals. It implies an ancestry in which multiple births were the rule. It is interesting, therefore, to note that twinning is not uncommon in human beings, and has probably been checked by social rather than by physiological factors. There is no placental leak such as prevents the fertility of the bovine free-martin, and so helps to prevent the numerical increase of twin-breeding stocks. In later chapters it is suggested that certain social phenomena are explicable on the assumption that an increased racial sexuality results in greater fecundity.

I suggest, then, that in all vertebrates the young, and also the female, will tend to be gregarious and suggestible. Conversely, an independent behaviour will characterize the adult and the male. Thus, if independence be regarded as more primitive than co-operation, we may treat even the school-behaviour of tadpoles and young fish as a reversal of a previous independent phase, and very possibly as based on a recapitulation of a still earlier co-operative behaviour. In each case the co-operative tendency seems to involve an inhibition of a more primitive activity. It may be noted also that this inhibition would appear to be associated with a low concentration of electrolytes both within and without the body. It is of interest, therefore, to recall Macdonald's theory of nervous inhibition. Here a low ionic concentration is held responsible for the greater adsorption of electrolytes to the increased surface of uncoagulated colloids in the nerve cells. Correspondingly, since the presence of these electrolytes at the synaptic membrane is considered essential to excitation, a high concentration will favour coagulation and the release of surface energy.[1] Either phase thus tends to be unstable. But the inhibitory behaviour might be encouraged by a low environmental concen-

[1] Bayliss, p. 426 ; cft. Macdonald, J. S. : "The Structure and Function of Nerve Fibres," *Proc. roy. Soc. B.*, 76, 322–350, 1905.

tration. Nevertheless, it must be pointed out that excitation appears to be associated with membrane permeability. Thus inhibition will be assisted by ions, such as calcium, whose action is to inhibit permeability, and whose importance within the cell is probably less than that of either potassium or sodium. All this, so far as it goes, favours the view that the hypothetically high sodium-to-calcium ratio of the male body, as well as its higher absolute electrolyte concentration, must be associated with nervous excitation ; as also, correspondingly, that absolute deficiency and relative calcium abundance must be associated with inhibition. Moreover, it suggests that inhibition may be the precursor of excitation. Some members of the hypothetical cell-aggregate might become specialized for the sole purpose of preventing reproductive mitosis at times when the electrolyte concentrations were low. This would encourage the continuation of an anabolic food-collection until these inhibitory influences could be usefully annulled.

These speculations represent an attempt to extend Rivers' hypothesis concerning the origin of mental dissociation. At the same time the opportunity has been taken to carry forward his later theory of social suggestibility beyond the already early stage of amphibian metamorphosis which he considered responsible for the evolution of forgetfulness.[1] I have attempted to relate the opposite types of racial and individual behaviour to each other ; and to account for each in terms of the alternative expression of two mutually opposed tendencies towards masculinity and femininity respectively. These rhythmic alternations in the behaviour of an initial hermaphrodite ancestor are deemed to have been slowed down in phylogeny. In another respect, however, they have been accelerated, so as to be reflected not only in the ontogenetic development of the individual, but in his moment-to-moment behaviour as well. In later chapters it will be argued that the nervous system, together with the mind, is stratified in successive layers, each of which represents the recapitulation of an opposite phase of emotional response, which has had survival value in the past. Thus, the higher organisms and especially Man, are to some extent, free to choose between various and warring tendencies, half of which spur them to an independent individualism, while the rest restrain them in the interests of the group. I have tried to illustrate this theory in a diagram whereby alternations in the sex-bias are held responsible for the basic changes of phylogeny and ontogeny alike.

It is time, however, to return to a consideration of human cranial evolution and development. It is clear that the evolved mechanism, whereby the mammal manages to increase the development of brain-tissues, at times when the size of the body is reduced, will have a profound influence upon the nature of the various layers of nerve-cells as these are progressively evolved and recapitulated in the development of the individual. If the big and sudden increments of neuro-

[1] Rivers, W. H. R. : *Instinct and the Unconscious,* Cambridge, 1920.

Relationships of Phylogenetic and Ontogenetic Stages of Behaviour as Determined by the Temporary Sex-bias of the Race and Individual.

(*Read from bottom upwards.*)

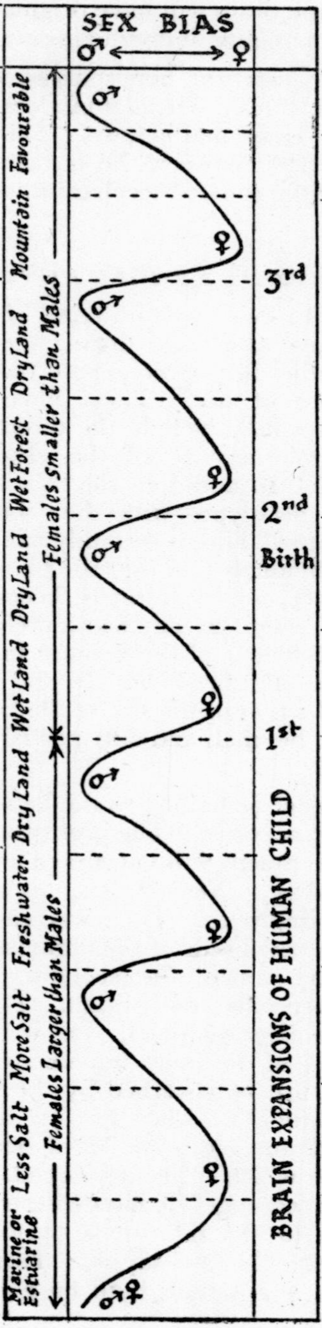

PHYLOGENY.	STAGES OF MENTAL DEVELOPMENT.	ONTOGENY.
INDIVIDUALISED HUMAN	Release of more Super Ego aggression.	ADULT MAN
	Release of some Super Ego aggression.	ADULT WOMAN
SMALL SOCIAL PROTO-HOMINID	Formation of Ego and charging of Super Ego during narcissistic phase of emotional development.	ADOLESCENT CHILD
ENLARGED AGGRESSIVE ANTHROPOID	Formation of Super Ego by release of aggression from memory patterns in the Id.	INFANT
SMALL SOCIAL ANTHROPOID	Inhibition of voluntary movement with formation of memory images by the Id.	
ENLARGED INDEPENDENT MAMMAL	Release of involuntary muscular movement for breathing and sucking. (Decerebrate rigidity ? ?)	FŒTUS
SMALL SOCIAL MAMMAL	Inhibition of earlier tendency towards bodily activity. (Plastic tonus ?)	
INDEPENDENT TERRESTRIAL PROTO-MAMMAL / AMPHIBIAN	Tendency to catabolic activity which must be inhibited to prevent premature (seven months) birth.	
TADPOLE / FRESH WATER SCHOOL-FISH	Anabolic phase. Tissue-hydration and growth of embryo.	EMBRYO
MOBILE MARINE ORGANISM	Catabolic phase. Independent mobility of embryonic cells in search of suitable somatic environments. Mosaic stage.	
SESSILE FRESH WATER CELL AGGREGATE	Anabolic phase. Evolution of first inter-cellular communication. (Gastrulation.)	ZYGOTE
ESTUARINE HERMAPHRODITE	Alternation of food storage and reproductive activity.	GERM CELL

cranial expansion take place at periods of mineral-deficiency, and in conjunction with the evolution of an arrested bodily development, it must follow that these parts of the brain will have originated as inhibitors of the previous phases of masculine individualistic activity.

Actually, it is known that the cerebral hemispheres, which are so greatly developed in the human brain, act as inhibitors of the lower and more primitive motor and emotional centres. This is consistent with the view that the differences between the human and animal brain are due to the working of the evolved mechanism of mammalian size-reduction.

PRIMARY AND SECONDARY REACTIONS

I have distinguished between the two opposite types of phylogenetic change that are believed to have alternated during the evolution of Man. Mineral-deficiency, if sufficiently severe, could result in a series of relatively sudden reductions of size. These have been called primary reactions. Their causes may include the direct influence of mineral-deficiency upon the relationships of the genes with each other : though this is doubtful. In addition, the relationship of the whole gene organization—the genotype—with the food supply and other aspects of the environment will almost certainly affect the growth of each of a related series of individuals ; so that the phenotype will in any case be altered. Moreover, as has already been argued, the alteration will tend to be in a direction already found useful in the past. This will consequently select in favour of the greatest possible degree of ontogenetic plasticity in the one direction. In the mammal the primary reaction involves a reduction in the size of the body, together with a tendency for the limbs to be small and only partially developed, and for the head to be enlarged.

Secondary reactions will take place according to the better recognized process of random mutation and selection. The process will be slower, since the more favourable environment will encourage large numbers, and will thus inhibit in-breeding. Nevertheless, opportunities for sexual selection will thereby be improved. Thus, whereas the primary reaction will be directed by the new needs of the organism as dictated by the physical factors of its environment, the secondary reactions will be guided by inter- and intra-specific competition. This point will receive further consideration in later chapters. Let it here be mentioned, however, that the nature of the more intense rivalry between related individuals must in its turn be governed by the final requirements of the species in its relation to other species, whether prey, enemies, or parasites. A disadvantageous system of sexual selection will soon wipe out the group in which it has developed. Thus inter- and intra-group rivalry both encourage an increasing complexity of organization. This is pushed to the full limits permitted by the nature and amount of the available food-supply. Forms of sexual selection will be constructed as adaptations built on a framework of older instincts recapitulated from earlier stages of phylogenetic expansion in the past. In the same way the primary reactions towards small size and inhibited aggressiveness will also be recalled by each primary reaction, after having once been developed at the dawn of mammalian evolution. Both primary and secondary reactions to environment are thus recapitulations of formerly evolved characters.

To some extent, then, the primary and secondary reactions will tend to annul each other's effects. On balance, however, each will leave a residue of credit such as can be utilized by the race. I have tried to represent my theory of human evolution in a diagram.[1] In this what are held to be the minimum possible number of primary reactions have been represented. The ascent from the amphibian to a large-sized lactating proto-mammal is shown as a single upward slope; which becomes increasingly steep as sexual selection develops as a method of enlarging size, and thereby economizing fluid and iodine. The evolution of the homogametic female makes relatively little difference, except that this process is thereby considered to have been assisted. The first small mammals are found in Triassic deposits. This was probably a period of climatic extremes—dry and warm in the North, but wet and warm in the South. The previous age, the Permian, shows evidence of glaciations, such as might be expected to encourage an increase in size and demand an increment of basal metabolism. It is to the Triassic, therefore, that we are bound to attribute the increased rainfall responsible for the first reduction in the size of the body. During this age, too, hair might well have evolved. After its evolution, on the other hand, a migration to an arid and iodine-deficient habitat must be held responsible for the first abolition of the hair-coverings; for later it will be necessary to postulate the returned activity of hair-suppressing genes. The fact that these act only on the parts covered by hair in a quadrupedal animal justifies the assumption that hair was evolved, lost, redeveloped, and lost again.[2] Alternatively, it is possible that the first loss occurred as a result of racial mixture with an enlarged and hairless type, in which size had never been so reduced as to make a hair covering necessary as a means of conserving heat.[3]

It has been necessary to postulate as a minimum three primary reactions involving size-reduction and cranial expansions; while a fourth, marking the separation of Neanthropic from Palæanthropic man, seems sufficiently probable to deserve inclusion in the series. Of course the exact nature of the adverse condition responsible for each change must remain a matter of extreme doubt. As a working hypothesis I propose the following scheme. Firstly, in regard to the reduction in size of the first proto-mammal, deficiency in lime rather than in iodine seems the more probable cause; for it is at this period that hair is held to have evolved, and there is a good deal of rather indirect evidence

[1] See over-leaf. [2] See Chapter VIII.

[3] For the sake of simplicity this last assumption is adopted in the diagram.

suggesting that hair-growth is wasteful in iodine, which must accordingly be presumed to have been plentiful. The second primary reaction which is held responsible for anthropoid brachiation and for raising

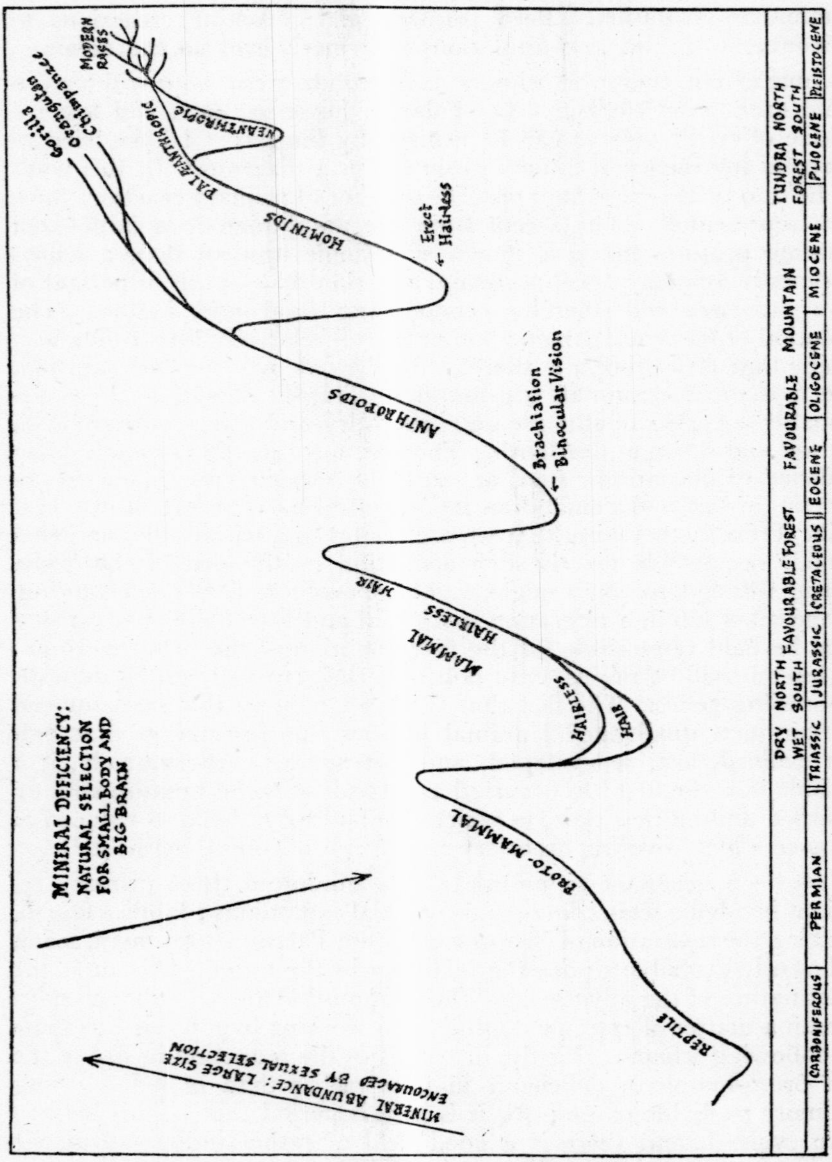

Theory of Mammalian and Human Evolution.

the index of cephalization to the already rather high anthropoid level, is also imputed to lime-deficiency, though in this case there is reason to suspect that both lime- and iodine-deficiencies might have been encountered together. The heavy rainfall held responsible for washing the calcareous deposits out of the land and into the sea during this period would probably have removed much of the humus and with it the iodine, even if the acid lime-deficient soils of the Eocene may thereby have acquired a capacity for absorbing a fresh supply. Indeed, assuming that the ancestral anthropoid was adapted to a low concentration of iodine, as well as of calcium, it might be possible to explain the puzzling delay of human ossification that takes place as a result of iodine-deficiency. One could consider the genes for slow growth and small size to be equally well adapted to either circumstance.

The third and, from the anthropological point of view, the most important primary change is that held to have overtaken a large anthropoid at the time of migration above the tree-line on newly raised mountains. This would involve iodine but not calcium shortage. It must be held responsible for the loss of body-hair, as well as for the shortening and simplification of the anthropoid arm and hand. The evolution of a manipulative dexterity, the erect attitude, and a social behaviour, can thus be considered as secondary adaptations of this primary crippling. Lastly, it is suggested that one branch of the enlarging Hominidæ were at length driven to seek refuge in the Tundra, while another re-invaded the forest. The glaciation of the mountains might have accounted for this, though the Miocene seems somewhat early for any such a happening. At all events, the Neanthropic stem is supposed to have undergone a fourth, though perhaps minor, reaction, which again increased the index of cephalization. Finally, this small-boned and large-brained variant is believed to have become mixed with the coarse-boned and probably smaller-brained stocks evolved on the Tundra. From this cross the known, together with other unknown, fossil Hominidæ are deemed to have sprung. These in their turn were fused into the various modern races.

THE RELATION OF MAN TO THE GREAT APES

It is suggested that the great size distinguishing the large anthropoids, including Dryopithecus, and also that of the Hominidæ, including Modern Man, as compared with that of some small arboreal ancestor common to them all, developed in response to iodine-deficiency. In working out the details of such a speculative hypothesis we are, however, at once faced with the problem why size could have been increased both in the human and in the non-human stocks respectively, while, at the same time, this common enlargement allowed of so great a degree of anatomical differentiation. The Gorilla, the Chimpanzee, and the Orang-utan differ from Man not only in the matter of their intelligence, but also in their skeletal proportions, as well as in the fact that all of them, like most other mammals, are covered with hair. Nevertheless, it is part of this theory that the size of the apes as well as that of Man, and the hairlessness of the latter no less than his increased intelligence, are all directly or indirectly the result of natural selection for iodine-economy.

We are faced, then, with the two alternative ways of explaining the large size of these two, obviously related, groups ; that is, in terms either of convergence or of direct inheritance. Or one may combine these possibilities by imagining a specific differentiation, or primary reaction, to have intervened in the course of a slow selective process promoting the same order of size in the two heads of the divergent stem. On this last view the large size of both the Hominid and Great Anthropoid strains may be regarded as the end-product of a convergent process, which began when their ancestries were common, and continued until the present stage was in each case achieved. The human characters may have developed during a temporary arrest of this process, which in the great apes was more continuous.

Man may either be held to have developed his hairless skin at or after the moment of separation from the anthropoid ; or the latter must be believed to have gone through a human stage of hairlessness. Actually, therefore, if large size and lack of hair are both, in point of fact, good methods of economizing iodine, it is harder to account for the hair of the great apes than it is to explain the bare skin of Man.

Many would doubtless regard this notion that the great apes may be degenerate Hominidæ as too far-fetched to require either consideration or refutation. Nevertheless, if one is to admit the possibility of one sort of atavism, namely, one leading from hair-covering to hairlessness, the reverse process cannot be dismissed as altogether unworthy of consideration. Indeed, at an altogether earlier stage of mammalian evolution I believe this very thing to have occurred. It will be argued later that the genes making for a lack of hair actually inhibit the action of those which try to promote its growth. If so, it must be presumed that they were evolved after the genes that they were selected to hold in check. It must be pointed out, however, that, whereas hairlessness in Man is presumed to have evolved in response to a very unfavourable environment, and would accordingly be expected to arise within a small and in-bred group, a return from hairlessness to hair-covering, unless dictated by severe cold, could in the case of the large anthropoids be attributed only to the favourable condition, iodine abundance. If so, natural selection could not actively encourage the change. Thus, either on an orthodox theory of mutation and selection, or on the much more conjectural hypothesis of selective predominance, it is the unfavourable condition alone that could produce the phylogenetic change. As a faint possibility worth keeping in mind, it is conceivable that first of all iodine-deficiency might have selected a large hairless Hominid with a terrestrial form of foot like that of Man or the Kivu gorilla. Afterwards, intense cold might have necessitated a return of the hair-covered condition. Finally, one branch of the hair-covered species could have returned to the forest, and have been differentiated into the great apes ; while the other could be represented as evolving by way of Sinanthropus into Neanderthal Man. On this theory, Modern Man would be as far removed from Neanderthal Man as he is from the apes. The points of greater resemblance between the two first would be due to convergence.

Fortunately, there is an alternative. Moreover, it fits in better with our distinction between primary and secondary reactions to environment. Hairlessness, as will be argued in a special section, seems to stand for the return of a primitive mammalian character. It still occurs among individual animals, and it occurs suddenly. Using the useful, if somewhat unsafe, analogy between changes of ontogeny and of phylogeny, we might guess, therefore, that the hairlessness of a race must also occur quickly, and among small numbers. Size, on the other hand, seems more likely to increase gradually, even if its reduction might be sudden. Within living races nature sometimes tolerates wide variations of size ; whereas difference of organic specialization, on the other hand, seems always to result in a cleavage into distinct species. To put it in another way, size seems to be controlled by a large number of unit-characters of which the individual influence must be small. A character like hairlessness, on the other hand, is often considered as a single gene mutation. When hereditary, it mendelizes. On the theory of somatic revolutions, the single gene can be thought of as repressing the dominance of many others, while promoting that of their rivals. As applied to the problem of size in Man and the great apes, then, it seems probable that the increase in it was gradual, and that selection for it was encouraged by iodine-deficiency acting on relatively large numbers, and without much in-breeding. Hairlessness, on the other hand, is more easily conceived as having occurred quickly within a small group under conditions where physiological efficiency alone was required, and where inter- or intra-specific rivalry was mild or non-existent.

Accordingly it seems more reasonable to imagine some part of the large size of the Anthropoid and Hominid groups to have developed separately and in each case slowly, that is to say, by convergence. If so, the hairlessness of Man and greater degree of his adaptation in a direction away from all arboreal requirements might be regarded as a further continuation of the action of the same selective agency—but pushed, however, to a much further extreme. Large size may well have been gradually evolved. Hairlessness, however, and also, as will be pointed out later, the upright posture, seem more likely to have appeared suddenly and together among a mere handful of isolated and in-bred individuals. Man, on this view, was in very truth created.

Whatever hypothesis we adopt there is some negative evidence indicating a very long human occupation of the terrestrial habitat. Keith has pointed out how, despite the large number of atavistic monstrosities on record, never once has a human child been born with the foot of an ape.[1]

[1] Keith, A. : *The Human Body*, London.

Now as regards the size of the great apes, it does not seem impossible that iodine-deficiency could have operated as the responsible selective agency. Nevertheless, it must be pointed out that such a hypothesis does throw some strain upon the soil and climate theory. We are driven to an explanation in terms of geology and geography. Trees of any sort imply a comparatively heavy rainfall ; and, except where the whole of the underlying formation was chalk or limestone, one would expect them to achieve a sufficient soil-acidity to absorb iodine from the parent material. In a limestone country, however, where the rock itself would be deficient in iodine, the food-supply might nevertheless reflect the same character. We seem bound, then, to postulate the evolution of the large anthropoids, and incidentally of all other large-sized forest animals, as having occurred within the limits of the limestone formations. The material of the Siwalik fossil beds may have created, as well as merely preserved, its specimens.

Assuming the Himalayan area as the centre of human and simian differentiation and diffusion, the theoretical conditions are complied with. We can believe that the Hominidæ may have become specialized for life above the tree-line, while the remainder of their (then) close relatives remained in the forested lands immediately below. Under these circumstances alone can we conceive how a similarity of physiological requirements—leading to large size—could have made itself felt under different sets of circumstances favouring a mechanical adaptation along two totally different lines.

Nevertheless, this explanation also is not without difficulty. We have got to explain why an arboreal animal suddenly left the shelter of its trees—which we have just postulated as continuing to grow—and proceeded to carve out a new career in an altogether novel and unfamiliar environment. Two, by no means mutually exclusive, possibilities suggest themselves. First of all, there is the example of the Kivu gorilla, which is the largest of the primates and lives above the tree-line among rocks. He would be too heavy to climb trees. Perhaps, then, though I do not regard it as probable, it may have been increasing size, directed by cold and iodine-economy, and possibly accelerated by sexual selection and in-breeding, that demanded a descent to the ground. Without wishing at this point to go into details, I find good reason for supposing a sexual selection for masculine ferocity to have contributed to the habits and appearance of the gorilla, who is polygamous ; and mountains, we may remember, offer much the same facilities for isolation and in-breeding as do islands. Increasing size, then, may have been partially responsible, though it has not helped the gorilla towards the evolution of an erect attitude. Moreover, there are anatomical reasons for supposing that the human foot was developed by a relatively small animal.[1]

Again, it was during the Tertiary period that the Himalayas were

[1] Le Gros Clark, W. E. : " Man's Place among the Primates," *Man*, 1935, 2 ; cf. Morton.

being actually built. We may imagine them rearing their heads above the hitherto unbroken carpet of forest. All of a sudden, therefore, they would offer an escape from the intense competition of the relatively crowded forest. In return, however, they would demand an adaptation to a new way of life. Thus, we may perhaps suppose that our ancestor, either forced by his own increasing weight, or attracted by relatively unoccupied feeding grounds, or perhaps for both reasons at once, would adopt a complete change of habitat.

CONCLUSION

This and the next two chapters deal with an attempt to account for the sudden development of a big brain, an erect posture, and a hairless skin. The " bull-dogging " of the face and the consequent reduction in the jaw and dentition are also touched on. The whole of this primary change is believed to have occurred in response to iodine-deficiency, and to be the result of a renewed predominance of genes selected in earlier stages of mammalian evolution. It was of a sort that would normally be considered pathological. Nevertheless, under the exceptional circumstances offered by the untenanted treeless " Alps " of young limestone mountains, the maintenance of an earlier and now outmoded form of mechanical efficiency could, for a time, be neglected. Iodine-economy would be almost the single criterion of survival.

The " bull-dog " calves studied by Crew seem to afford some parallels to the primary achondroplastic reaction believed to have overtaken Man's last non-human ancestor. The activity of the pituitary would appear to have been greatly reduced. The problem is thus raised whether this alteration of endocrine activity could have been produced by any cause except direct and accidental gene-mutation. I incline towards the belief that iodine-deficiency might exert a direct influence upon a series of related individuals, and that these would in consequence gain in survival-value at the expense of others whose pituitaries failed so to react. The less plastic variants would be the first to die out.

The primary reaction would be bound to bring in its train, not only a host of minor disadvantages, but also a few qualities offering the possibility of secondary adaptation along lines destined to be useful in overcoming the unavoidable drawbacks. In addition to useless qualities, dragged in from a previous stage when they had been of value, there might also be subsequent mutations that had occurred during the recessive phase of the linkage-group to which they belonged. These would suddenly manifest themselves—for the most part disadvantageously—at the moment when the group in question returned to dominance. These degenerate genes would probably serve to reduce size when doubled by in-breeding.

The development of the brain throws light on the primary reaction as subsequently modified by a slower evolutionary process. Tissue hydration, leading to swelling of the brain and skull, affords a chance of developing a more complex system of instinctive reactions. It is believed to have included the potentially useful character of increased crowd-consciousness—a return of an aquatic, and again probably an early mammalian, phase of development, that once more became useful in organizing numbers as an offset to individual inferiority. This inferiority, as judged in relation to the other mammals, would be manifested in the matter of the hairless skin and the reduced dentition. The ability of the mammal to grow small is regarded as an important character predisposing towards the evolution of a relatively large brain. This contention supports the idea that early Man may have been smaller as well as weaker than his closest and most recent simian ancestor. Sudden increments in the index of cephalization of the growing child may reflect reductions of body-size that have occurred during the evolution of the human race. Twinning is regarded as a disadvantageous character brought back into the heredity by the primary reaction, and annulled in the case of Man by social forces. Iodine-deficiency might also be credited with selecting in favour of nervous inhibition as a means of economizing endocrine and muscular activity. Lethargy was, up to a point, of value.

The problem of man's relationship to the great apes is discussed. Were hairlessness and large size achieved together? If so, could the great apes be degenerate Hominidæ? A more probable explanation would make Man the hairless, achondroplastic and smaller mutant of Dryopithecus. If so, he then subsequently regained part, or all, of his lost size by a convergent process similar to that responsible for the evolution of all the living and extinct great apes from a common ancestor that was smaller.

CHAPTER VII

THE HUMAN BODY

Iodine and the Erect Posture : Correlation of Characters making for Physiological Efficiency and Anatomical Defects : Ontogeny and Natural Selection : Individual Reaction, a guide and check to Racial Adaptation : Plasticity versus Specialization : Achondroplasia and Human Evolution : Specialization and the Mountain Habitat : Man's Face and Jaw : Man's loss of Hair.

IODINE AND THE ERECT POSTURE

EVEN GRANTING THE SUDDEN INVASION OF A MOUNTAIN HABITAT by Man, it still remains difficult to explain his upright posture. The gibbon, it is true, can walk erect along a branch, and may occasionally be driven to take a few steps upon the ground. So, too, in the case of the three great anthropoids, a total support of the body on the legs is not impossible ; but the animals habitually support the weight of the shoulders, as well as the forward projection of the head and neck, by means of the long arms and the knuckles.

In view of the form and habits of the gibbon and of his three greatly enlarged relatives, it would be much more reasonable to expect a life above the tree-line to select in favour of a return to a quadrupedal form of locomotion. Indeed, it is necessary to look only as far as the baboon to witness a most successful realization of this possibility. Mechanical explanations seem thus to break down. The upright stance, in itself, confers no more survival-value than did brachiation in the trees. Each trait seems much more probable to represent an ingenious escape from an impending calamity. I suggest, therefore, that, just as a failure of limb development favoured an arboreal specialization of the arms at the expense of the anthropoid legs, so, at a later stage, some similar disadvantageous change of environment tended to wither the arms, and throw upon the Hominid legs the whole responsibility of bodily support.

It must be admitted that the ecological and physiological basis of such a theory is slender. It will be assumed, however, that a lack either of iodine, or of lime and vitamin D, is inclined to increase the tendency towards a failure of normal limb-development. If this be true, the proportion of cripples should show a positive correlation both, on the one hand, with the goitre and deaf-mute figures, indicative of iodine shortage, and with the incidences of rickets and other calcium-deficiency diseases on the other. I have not yet, however, had an opportunity of investigating this point. It may be significant, nevertheless, that, just as particular localities, such as Ireland, are noted for the rearing of giants, so do others—Yorkshire and Norfolk, for instance—seem particularly prone to the production of dwarfs, in many of whom the limbs fail to develop.[1]

CORRELATION OF CHARACTERS MAKING FOR PHYSIOLOGICAL EFFICIENCY AND ANATOMICAL DEFECTS

This shortening of a pair of limbs, resulting in the greater growth and specialization of the other pair, seems to have happened, not only in the evolution of Man, and previously in that of his brachiating ancestor, but also in the case of the kangaroo and of a majority of the extinct dinosaurs.[2] Let me attempt, therefore, to account for this first of all on an orthodox theory of random mutation and selection, and afterwards on the hypothetical, but more accommodating, theory of selective predominance and somatic revolution. In either case it will be assumed that a physiological gain, namely an economy of iodine, has been the main advantage thereby achieved ; and that the remarkable influence upon anatomical structure is but the fruit of a correlated variation resulting in a shift in the incidence of natural selection, owing to the need for secondary and compensatory adjustment.

Let me presuppose, then, that the legs of the vertebrate were short before they were long ; and that the ontogenetic development of the individual recapitulates the anatomical and physiological characters of the ancestry. If so, on a theory of mutation and selection, it would be intelligible if a renewed need for a primitive character resulted in the selection of a mutation whereby further ontogenetic development was arrested.

Applying this theory to explain a sudden shortening of the limbs, we may reflect, firstly, that each successive stage in the evolution of the early land-vertebrate may well have been accompanied by an increase in the available iodine, a supply of which was being slowly absorbed by the soil from the primary rock ; and, secondly, that the sudden onset of desert conditions, or migration to limestone soils, could re-impose the primitive need for an economy of the rare material. Under such circumstances the lizards of the Triassic deserts, or the anthropoids in Central Asia during the Tertiary, would alike be encouraged to delay a full ontogenetic development. The advantage of this would be that less iodine would be required ; while the result would be an arrested development of all the limbs. Here, however, the theory threatens to break down. It is difficult to see how the specialization of a single pair of limbs could be achieved merely as a result of a general and accidental hypotrophy, tending to affect all the limbs at the same time.

[1] Wood, E. J. : *Giants and Dwarfs*, 1868.
[2] Wells, Huxley and Wells : *The Science of Life*, p. 508.

At this point two further sets of facts must be considered; and the first of these can be interpreted in terms of the second theory of somatic revolution. I refer to the fact that disadvantageous changes of the environment are found to hinder the development of the faster-growing parts of the body before they affect those in which the metabolism is damped down.[1] This is explicable if it be assumed that the genes in the fast-growing tissue are more accurately adjusted to their nutritional supply, and that the specificity is due to a later mutational adjustment.

ONTOGENY AND NATURAL SELECTION

To return, then, to the question why the fore-limbs of Man and the dinosaurs were shortened, so as no longer to serve as adequate body supports. This could be answered on the assumption that the fore-limbs were originally the more fully specialized and developed. This is consistent with the view that Man evolved from a brachiating anthropoid. As for the dinosaurs, we may reflect that the front fins of fish are usually stronger than those behind, and that the vertebrate probably first emerged from the water by raising its head by means of the rudiments of the present shoulder-girdle and arms.

It will be realised that this theory of a sudden change of environment affecting the somatic influence of a part of the inheritance is rather at variance with the previous hypothesis whereby a mere survival-value attaching to an arrest of development was held responsible for the selection of a mutation. On this latter assumption it is suggested that, in all or at least in a significant number of cases, whenever the environment falls short of the previous expectation, the animal will automatically react by failing to develop. On the previous theory it must be held that millions of individuals would be wasted until blind chance happened to provide a satisfactory solution of the adaptational problem.

As a further means whereby the individual's reaction to the environment may become a factor in affecting the direction of natural selection, allowance must be made for the ontogenetic influence of use and disuse. In the vertebrate, more than in any other class of animal, the expression of the genes concerned with skeletal development particularly depends on whether the cells encounter their proper and accustomed mechanical forces. Similarly, it is probable that, just as a limb will degenerate if its nerves are severed, so will an abnormal degree of nervous stimulation or exercise extend the growth-process to an extreme not usually found among the average of individuals. It is reported, for instance, that puppies born without front legs develop the limb-proportions of hopping animals.[2] In view of all this, we may expect that a failure of fore-limb development might result, firstly, in a compensating hypertrophy of the hind limbs; and, secondly, supposing the disablement to be sufficiently severe, the hind limbs, by taking over the task

[1] Cf. Huxley and de Beer, loc. cit., p. 344.

[2] Huxley and de Beer, loc. cit., p. 434, cft. Oppel, A., and Roux, W.

of the others, could rob these even of the opportunity to develop to the average degree consistent with their genetic potentialities. There must be a critical degree of abnormality, after which the inferiority of an organ will not only result in a specialization elsewhere, but will liberate it from its old use and offer it for the purpose of further adaptional experiment.

INDIVIDUAL REACTION, A GUIDE AND CHECK TO RACIAL ADAPTATION

Now it is clear that this ontogenetic plasticity, which enables the development of the individual to be to some degree dependent upon the experiencing of needs, must have a profound influence upon the survival of mutations, and so upon the direction of evolution in the group. Such plasticity, it seems fair to assume, is an evolved character achieved, like all others, by mutation and selection. Its functional value, I suggest, is that it enables individuals to explore some distance along the various paths open to the slower, but more permanent, adaptional progress of the race. If the ontogenetic reaction is successful, a few individuals who are able to develop furthest in the desirable direction will reap a reward. There will be a slow selection of modifying factors allowing an easier individual adaptation. At the same time, the alternative reactions, being no longer required, will tend to decay. If an increased length and strength of hind-leg is the requirement of the moment, mutations allowing of a great degree of growth in response to a minimum of mechanical and endocrine stimulation will be encouraged. At the same time the older genes, in which this capacity was less developed, will be themselves mutated, or else the new mutations may act by directly holding them in check.

This conception of ontogeny prospecting ahead of phylogeny is suggested by Fisher's theory of the evolution of genetic dominance.[1] As I understand it, he considers that a favourable primary mutation will be relatively recessive, and will thus exert only a small influence upon the expression of its unmutated partner. As time goes on, however, secondary modifying mutations will be selected, all of which will help the full expression of the first mutation, while tending to repress that of the original and older gene. This theory must assume that the original mutation tends to direct the organism in a favourable direction. It thus seems fair to assume that a latent capacity for an ontogenetic development in a similarly favourable direction would likewise receive a secondary mutational encouragement. We may imagine a slow selection of such mutations allowing of an evolutionary advance in the direction of the greatest ontogenetic modification. At the same time the retreat would tend to be cut off. Natural selection could no longer maintain the efficiency of genes already used in the previous circumstances. Some of these would become mutants in the

[1] Fisher, R. A.: *The Genetical Theory of Natural Selection*, Oxford, 1930, pp. 68–69.

interest of the new change, and others might undergo changes without affecting immediate survival-value.

Having embarked upon this quest for a theory of adaptation by gene-mutations, we had better look also to the possible disadvantages of inheriting such an ontogenetic plasticity.

PLASTICITY VERSUS SPECIALIZATION

In so far as the individual's reaction prevents a change of environment from causing death without issue, the evolutionary process will be arrested. Only individuals who react too little, or in the wrong direction, will be eliminated. Thus a capacity for individual adaptation will result in a greater stability in the size of the group, and this in its turn will prevent periods of severe in-breeding. There will thus be a less rapid elimination of unsatisfactory dominants. The chances of the new recessive undergoing the full test of being doubled will be reduced.

It thus would appear as though a capacity for ontogenetic plasticity must possess both advantages and drawbacks—at all events if the achievement of complete and stable adaptation be taken as the criterion of success. For the land-vertebrate, whose environment is liable to comparatively rapid, though recurring, and regular, change, it seems probable that a relatively high potentiality for individual adjustment has been of value in guiding the destiny of the race. It may have been this very fact, however, that has prevented the evolution of any striking difference of pattern—a vertebrate with six or more legs, for instance. Moreover, a consequent and relative stability in the size of vertebrate groups might be held responsible for the retention of an exclusively bi-sexual form of reproduction. A hermaphrodite species, if reduced in numbers to the extent that individuals had lost touch with each other, would seem to stand its optimum chance of evolving a distinct and superior type ; for self-fertilization is the most intense form of in-breeding. Every mutation would make its mark without fear of being masked by an older allelomorph from a foreign zygote, backed by the vested interests of a host of modifying factors, all chosen to maintain the dominance of each other. The land vertebrate, then, perhaps on account of the greater instability of the environment, would appear to have protected itself from accidental extinction by the evolution of ontogenetic plasticity. This in its turn has resulted in a failure to achieve perfect adaptational stability, and so has led to a prolonging of the evolutionary process right up to our own time.

ACHONDROPLASIA AND HUMAN EVOLUTION

After this digression into a theory of vertebrate adaptation, it is time to return to the original problem, namely, how and why the arms of the anthropoid were shortened, and the legs fully developed and modified to the upright stance. The abnormal growth of the arms and legs in human beings (acromegaly and gigantism) has been noticed to be correlated with an over-development of the anterior-lobe of the pituitary. Similarly, cases in which the limbs fail to develop have also been associated with lesions of the hypophysis.[1] The under- or over-development of the soft tissues, especially those of the hands, is affected in each case—a fact that suggests an evolved adjustment rather than a mere accidental disturbance of the mechanism of bone-growth.

A condition very similar to achondroplasia in Man, but occurring in cattle, and in this connection studied by Crew, is hereditary.[2] This type of case must be of interest to the student of natural selection, since the simplex condition of the genes for achondroplasia result in the short-limbed, but otherwise economical and desirable, Dexter cow.[3] Their duplex condition, however, results in a monster that is unable to live. This fact demonstrates the possibility that even under natural (as opposed to artificial) selection, a mutation might possess survival-value, even if in its duplex condition it was lethal. Perhaps, after a sufficient number of generations, this lethal effect might be mitigated by the selection of modifying factors.

Some of the anatomical characters of these "bull-dog" calves, inheriting short legs and imperfect pituitary and thyroid glands as a result of their duplex inheritance, cannot fail to interest the more speculative anthropologist. These monsters are completely round-headed (C.I. 100), resembling Man also in their very poor development of the nasal and facial bones as also of the jaws. Moreover, their spines are twisted into a caricature of the human lumber-curvature. As for the hindquarters, the whole of this part is particularly swollen, being distended with liquid in a manner suggestive of steatopygia. Indeed, the whole condition is associated with an extreme and pathological degree of tissue-hydration.

Crew attributes this hydration to a lack of capillary constriction, due to an inherited defect influencing the posterior-lobe of the pituitary. The weakness of this gland was proved by the failure of its extracts to expand the melanophores of Fundulus. Now, whatever may cause this failure of the posterior-lobe in the Dexter cow, it may be worth noting that either a complete failure of the whole pituitary might achieve such a result; or, alternatively, an inhibition of the posterior-lobe by a hypersecretion of the anterior-lobe might possibly do the same. The two hormones seem to be antipathetic.[4]

Now, since it is suspected that iodine-deficiency may have caused a direct ontogenetic inhibition of posterior-lobe activity, it becomes a

[1] Hueter, C.: *Virchows Arch.*, 1905, CLXXXII, 219.
[2] Crew, F. A. E., loc. cit.
[3] A similar case of "bull-dogging" with limb shortening and abnormality has been reported in the guinea pig. Sewall Wright: "Polydactylous Guinea Pigs," *J. Hered.*, 25, 9, 359 (1934).
[4] Cf. Hogben, loc. cit.

plausible view that the thyroid and anterior-lobe assist each other. Thus it is possible that iodine-deficiency would encourage a hyper-secretion of some hormone of the anterior-lobe, which, by inhibiting the posterior-lobe, would allow of a general tissue-hydration with brain and skull expansion. The objection to this view is that anterior-lobe activity might be expected to encourage the growth of bone, whereas our theory of the relative expansion of the head demanded an inhibition of bone-growth in general.

Of course, it is always possible that the anterior-lobe may govern bone-growth and thyroid metabolism by two separate hormones, and that a great demand for one substance automatically reduces the supply of the other. This, however, is mere speculation, though it is consistent with the occurrence of " tall " and " fat " types of pituitary dystrophy. In any case, it is proposed to proceed on the assumption that an ontogenetic effect due to iodine-deficiency affected the whole pituitary and thyroid relationships, and resulted in a big anthropoid, which then degenerated into a smaller proto-Hominid with an enlarged head, swollen buttocks, hairless skin, and withered arms.

On the anatomical side a word must be said concerning the failure of normal cartilage-development, which gives achondroplasia its name. I suggest that it is a mild form of this same root-cause which is responsible for the " double-jointed " condition of clowns and many mongoloid idiots ; as it also explains the ease with which these latter, in common with the Orang and the racial Mongol, adopt the " Buddha " position when seated.[1] A looseness of the joints, possibly caused by an excess of sinovial fluid, would further the acquisition of the erect posture. This accidental association of pituitary failure both with limb shortening and with tissue hydration could have been utilized both in the evolution of brachiation by the quadrupedal primate, and later on when Man had come to stand erect. In itself the tendency of tissue hydration to be associated with a looseness of the limbs, and vice versa, may be conceived to have been evolved from the need to utilize a fin or paddle for the purpose of supporting part of the body's weight.

SPECIALIZATION AND THE MOUNTAIN HABITAT

As pointed out in the last chapter, Man is here supposed to have evolved as the result of a migration of a few anthropoid apes to a region above the tree-line. The arms are assumed to have been more developed than the legs, and thus to have become more liable to developmental arrest. One minor point in favour of this theory is that it seems capable of explaining the origin of right-handedness. It is the left side of the body which carries the high point of the asymmetrical growth-gradient, or, in other words, is best developed.[2] It would be the left side, therefore, that would be most susceptible to an adverse environmental

[1] Crookshank, F. G. : *The Mongol in Our Midst*, p. 59.
[2] Huxley and de Beer, loc. cit., p. 362.

change. I suggest, accordingly, that the left arm withered more than the right, and that the latter thus remained more competent to acquire manipulative skill through specialization.

When we look to the legs, it becomes necessary to explain not only the vertical superimposition of the bones, and the shortening of the toes, but also the very great increase in length. It does not seem impossible that the mere influence of gravity might here have contributed something towards this end ; the same argument applying with even greater force to the conditions favouring the selection of large legs and a low centre of gravity in the kangaroo and bipedal dinosaurs. A vertical position of the vertebral column must result in a tendency on the part of lymph and other fluid to concentrate in the lower extremities. This, unless counteracted by mutation, will result in various pathological conditions, such as varicose veins, and the swelling common in horses. These disadvantages will at least serve to direct selection into some way of altering the existing heredity. The requirement will not be of sufficient importance to bring about the annulment of its primary cause, namely, the erect attitude. As a secondary adjustment, then, any mutation making for an increase in the trophic and functional activities of the nerves supplying the walls of the blood vessels will be of value. This might be expected somewhat to increase the size of the limbs, and so, by adding still further to the stature, intensify the demand for still greater anatomical perfection.

As a still more important factor we may consider the probable influence of sexual selection. Either male combativeness, causing an admiration of height and good limb-development, or female coyness, as manifested in flight, would alike encourage an autosomal improvement of the new method of locomotion. Probably the whole of this development would take place during a period of environmental improvement. That is to say, supposing the initial invasion of the iodine-deficient habitat to have been encouraged either by a pre-adaptational achondroplasia, or because of population-pressure in the forest below, time would in either case tend to augment the iodine-supply of the mountain soils ; so that the need for extreme iodine-economy would be slowly removed. This would bring about a more normal type of pituitary activity, with its correlated encouragement of limb-growth in general. At this point, however, all mutations making for a response to the greater pituitary stimulation of the legs would have survival-value. Shortness of the arms, however, would be of little disadvantage.

Indeed, if fleetness of foot had begun to confer success, either in winning a mate or in eluding attack, or even in catching game, it is probable that a great length and weight of arm would become a positive drawback. I suggest, therefore, that, just as a relative elongation of the anthropoid arms was initiated by accident, encouraged by use, and rendered permanent by secondary mutation ; so, when the arms withered through a similar nutritional deficiency following upon a change of environment, this shrinkage also was crystallized by the selection of modifying mutations, which also encouraged the compensatory growth and specialization of the human legs.

MAN'S FACE AND JAW

Next to the erect attitude, perhaps the most characteristic of all the anatomical characters differentiating Man from the large anthropoids, and also from the majority of wild animals, is the remarkable " bulldogging " or shortening of the face. This character, however, is one that we share with some of the smaller monkeys ; though Modern Man when compared either with the great apes, or even with the extinct Hominidæ, is particularly conspicuous in this respect. The ætiology of the disease of acromegaly makes it almost certain that the growth of bone in the whole facial region is governed by the activity of a hormone of the anterior-lobe. The latter, as I have endeavoured to show elsewhere, is certainly controlled by heredity, and hence by the influence of natural selection. Moreover, it would appear extremely unwise to rule out the possibility of a direct ontogenetic influence of environment, whereby abundances of iodine, calcium, or vitamin E, may encourage an activity, while deficiencies repress it. Even without postulating an influence of environment upon the interaction or predominance of the genes, it would appear probable that such ontogenetic influences would slowly become permanent as a result of secondary mutation. This point has already been discussed.

Now at the time when I was first led to contemplate an explanation of Neanthropic evolution in terms of mineral-deficiency, my central hypothesis rested on the idea that the reduced bone-growth of Modern Man was the direct result of a selection for an economy of bone-forming material. It thus became tempting to explain Neanthropic man as a specialized and adapted descendant of a coarse-boned Neanderthal or Neanderthaloid progenitor.

The advantages of such a hypothesis were that certain ape-like characteristics of Neanderthal Man, in particular his great facial development and brow-ridges, could be attributed to a direct descent from a simian ancestor. The objections, which were more numerous and less easy to overcome, were that the extinction of Neanderthal Man in Europe did not coincide with the onset of pluvial conditions. And, worse still, the modern inhabitants of similar tundra habitats display a tendency towards a distinct lack of brow-ridge. Lastly, evidence would appear to be accumulating to show that the so-called Neanthropic stem was just as old as, if not older than, the better authenticated and more easily identified Neanderthal remains.

What, then, are the alternatives to the view that Neanthropic Man is the descendant of Neanderthal Man ? One of them is to reverse the hypothesis. If Neanderthal Man is the descendant of Neanthropic Man, and the latter be sprung from a large and achondroplastic anthropoid, it will follow that the simian characteristics of the Neanderthal stem have been reacquired by some convergent process. If mineral-deficiency made Man out of an ape, mineral-abundance might help to reverse the process. The alternative, of course, is to postulate a common ancestor from whom the Neanthropic and Neanderthal stems could both be derived. This, doubtless, is the safest course to pursue, but in doing so the possibility of a very early approach to the Neanthropic reduction of the facial skeleton should be borne in mind. The peculiar Neanthropic character of the chin, which is so definitely non-simian, must be, and will be, accounted for separately. The vitamin C deficiency following on a change from vegetable to flesh food has been held responsible for this. But the ability to live on flesh, which is deficient in lime, is attributed to a calcium-economy perfected in a rain-forest, but arising as a pre-adaptation from an evolved economy of iodine.

For various reasons iodine-deficiency might be expected to result in a reduced growth of bone. We may observe, for instance, that thyroid cretins are often dwarfs with a small face and weak jaws. After all, the growing child has more need of all structural substances than the adult. Thus it is reasonable to expect all development to be arrested at the point when any deficiency becomes serious.

In the very long run, then, the genes now responsible for the fine bone and comparatively " smooth " skull of Modern Man, may be believed actually to have been selected in an early stage of simian evolution for the sake of lime-economy. The present dominance in the existing race, however, might nevertheless be due to a reaction dictated by a deficiency of iodine. At all events, on this supposition we could conceive the evolution of the erect attitude, the hairless skin, and the regression of the human jaw, as all occurring simultaneously in response to the severe iodine-deficiency likely to be encountered above the tree-line of a young limestone mountain-system. The Neanderthal child, we may reflect, shows no signs of the adult brow-ridges ; and the jaw too, like that of any other human or anthropoid child, is reduced. The primitive and coarse-boned Hominidæ, then, can be believed to have slowly regained and augmented their skeletal proportions in an environment where bone-forming material and also, perhaps, iodine were plentiful. This condition would be provided by the arid margin of an ice-sheet, which in other respects would differ little from the cold of their mountain cradle-land. The coarse bone of the Neanderthaloids argues a diet rich in lime, such as could only be supplied by a large ration of vegetable food. Indeed, we would attribute their extinction to an increase of cold tolerable only to the fine-boned carnivores—including Modern Man—or to the much longer and better specialized herbivores, such as the reindeer and to a lesser degree the mammoth.

Now Modern Man first appears definitely upon the scene after the extinction of the Neanderthal inhabitants of Western Europe. By this time, he is already a mighty hunter, and is indeed at a higher stage of cultural accomplishment than some of the lowest existing ethnic types of to-day. His whole evolutionary history, we may say, is typologically a blank. Moreover, it is a mystery that the spade seems reluctant to disclose. All that one can do at the present time, then, is to indulge in theories—the more the better. Any hypothesis, if pushed far enough, must sooner or later reach a point at which it can be confirmed or contradicted by some system of already organized knowledge.

It is in this spirit of enquiry, then, that I suggest that a sudden reduction of the skeletal proportions in general, and of the jaw and face in particular, took place at the time when Man evolved the erect attitude and also lost his body hair. The whole momentous happening seems best interpreted in terms of a sudden return of dominance to genes specialized for repressing the activity of the pituitary gland, and thus of calling into predominance others able to react to the greatly reduced hormone-concentration following from the primary mutation or "revolution." A good parallel, available for our present-day inspection, seems to be that of the "bull-dog" calves already mentioned.

Such a sudden change, brought about in part by in-breeding, appears unlikely, on the whole, to have been accompanied by an increase of size. Most abnormalities are smaller than the species in which they arise. For, even if they do not fairly represent the composite result of the original genes of a smaller ancestral type, nevertheless the returned predominance of a hitherto inactive linkage-group would be expected to bring with it a number of disadvantageous and even lethal mutants, that had avoided elimination during the long period in which their influences had been suppressed.

It is submitted, then, that the change from ape to Man was sudden; and that it implied an immediate size-reduction, not because of external requirements, which could still tolerate if not encourage large size in any vertebrate, but on account either of the inherent nature of the mammalian heredity, or of the returned dominance of disadvantageous mutations, or of both. The primary reaction, imposed either by iodine-deficiency itself, or by gene-mutation, caused iodine-economy; and this resulted, accidentally, in reduced size and fine bone. The very same iodine-deficient and lime-abundant habitat, however, might then have been expected to set on foot a slower secondary adaptation favouring the return of coarse bone. Indeed, this seems in some cases to have occurred; the process culminating in Neanderthal Man. As an explanation of the fine bone of Modern Man it thus seems easiest to postulate a return to the forest, or at all events to lands where lime or phosphorus were deficient. Indeed, if the action of severe iodine-deficiency had been to recall genes formerly useful for economizing lime, there would be a good reason for a change of habitat. If this view is correct, then, the modern reduction of face and jaw, even if it be as old as hairlessness and the upright stance, must nevertheless be considered as an accidental return of a still older set of characters, such as were evolved, probably, when primates were driven to the tree tops in a search for the meagre mineral supply only accessible to the deep roots of rain-forest trees. As such, it is in truth a character originated in response to lime-shortage. The iodine-shortage served only to recall it.

It was pointed out in the earlier chapter that the evolution of iodine-economy must serve also to economize lime and phosphorus. In this case, then, the general nature of the accidental return of characters already actually used for this very purpose cannot but be doubly significant. My own picture of early Man is of a small, short-limbed and indeed achondroplastic figure : in fact, virtually a pygmy. He would have the choice either of remaining on his mountain top, where the smaller individuals would die of cold, or of re-invading the forest, where the larger individuals would suffer most from lime- and phosphorus-deficiency. In comparison to the larger forest-apes, however the whole "Neanthropic" stem—if thus we may designate so very remote and hypothetical a species—would be at an advantage. They would be able to tolerate a more humid environment than could the much larger Dryopithecus. It would be interesting to know if this still holds good of the gorilla and the Congo Pygmy. The latter is certainly the more numerous of the two ; partly perhaps because his fine bone enables him to be an eater of flesh.

It is not proposed at this point to discuss the origins of the modern races. Let it suffice, therefore, to suggest a fine-boned, if not pygmy, ancestor for both Modern and Neanderthal Man. The stocks leading to the evolution of the latter would start straightway upon their specialization to withstand cold. The forefathers of the modern races, on the other hand, would at some stage return to the forest ; but would later emerge into various more arid regions, each of which would stamp upon them the marks whereby they can now be recognized. All would carry within their heredity the possibility of a return to the pygmy condition.

MAN'S LOSS OF HAIR

Enough has been said already to indicate how an ontogenetic reaction may be believed to give rise to an hereditary character, supposing its full development to be exercised over a sufficiently long period. The explanation has attempted to conform with the established facts concerning the nature of the gene. Only on the uncertain questions concerning the manner of gene-interaction has a liberty to form new hypotheses been demanded. Now it is a definitely established fact that iodine-deficiency can cause a lack of body-hair in domesticated animals. Whether such ontogenetic changes are immediately hereditary, or not, does not seem to have been tested. We shall assume, however, that, in general, they are not ; though, on the other hand, hairlessness can admittedly be inherited as a unit character or linkage group.[1]

[1] Mohr, O. C., and Wriedt, C. : *Jl. Genetics*, XIX, 328.

It seems legitimate, in view of this, to regard the power of losing hair as an evolved character. Proof that such a loss can conserve iodine, or promote physiological efficiency in any other way, is lacking ; but such evidence will not be found until it is sought. As an inference, however, it seems legitimate. Indeed, Fleure has already suggested that hairlessness economizes a thyroid stimulus ; which, he suggests, was withdrawn for the purpose of brain-development.[1] The growth of hair demands a considerable amount of cell-proliferation that need not otherwise have taken place ; and, in addition, the hair tends to drop out, so that structural material is actually lost. Over and above the principle that iodine-deficient diets lead to a failure of hair-growth, the differences in the types of human and animal hair-form may be fitted within the frame of the same hypothesis. The long coarse hair of the Mongoloid peoples and of the Himalayan ox, the Yak, may be regarded as economical in iodine. At all events, this view is tenable, if the iodine be held responsible for the encouragement of cell-proliferation. The larger the cell, the fewer hairs per unit area will be required. The increased length will be incidental to the greater size of the roots. On this theory, the greater protection against cold afforded by long hair is regarded as accidental to the form initially encouraged by the economy of endocrine stimulus that can be affected by its growth. As far as Man is concerned, the hair-differences, like skin-colour, are regarded as correlates of physiological types rather than as prime characters upon which natural selection has recently been focussed. If the one trait was encouraged to economize heat, and the other to achieve protective coloration, this must have been accomplished at a remote stage of mammalian evolution. During the evolution of Man, however, such characters could serve to advertise the physiological inheritance with which they were linked. In this way the phylogenetic agency of sexual selection would serve to hasten a compliance with the environmental demand. This point will be elaborated in the next chapter.

[1] Fleure, H. J. : Pres. Add., Anthr. Sect. Brit. Assn., 1926.

CHAPTER VIII

SEXUAL SELECTION IN HUMAN EVOLUTION

Hair and Sex-display: The Location of the Pædomorphic characters: Head-hair and Femininity: Conclusion (Theoretical and Application of Theory).

THIS CHAPTER IS MEANT AS AN INVESTIGATION INTO THE problem how far sexual selection may have contributed towards the evolution of the first kind of Man. It assumes the process to have been directed mainly by a need to economize iodine, and to adapt an anthropoid body to a life on the treeless alp of a young mountain-system. It will be realized, therefore, that it is necessary to go beyond Darwin's conception of sexual selection as a mere aspect of the mechanism of specific variation whereby novelty is admired for its own sake, and the novel character intensified and perpetuated by an intra-specific struggle between members of the same sex.[1] I am adopting the perhaps novel principle that no system of sexual selection could have been initiated unless it conferred an inter-specific survival-value by accelerating a useful adaptation of the whole group wherein it arose. In particular, an attempt will be made to recognize sets of display organs and instincts that may possibly have served to accelerate a phylogenetic change in the direction of a physiological economy of iodine. This might be secured by an inhibition of racial femininity, and by a slow rate of growth, as well as possibly by fœtalization; dispensing with the need to undergo certain developmental processes to their full extent. In addition, however, the almost contradictory demand for a physiological economy of calcium may, at another time, have been met. In this case the mechanism may be very old, and might have fallen into disuse when not required; though it appears to have been recalled and used both before and after the critical stage of human emergence.

It will be apparent that the discussion of sexual selection raises problems concerning instinct; which may be shortly defined as inherited behaviour. Thus it is proposed to treat instincts as though, like other hereditary characters, they depended upon the actions and interactions of the genes. Moreover, since sexual selection is held to obtain its results by altering the predominance or interaction of the sex-linked

1 Darwin, C.: *The Descent of Man and Selection in Relation to Sex*, London, 1871.

genes in relation to the remaining autosomal factors, it becomes clear that both the two interacting external agents, namely, display and appreciation, must either be correlates of a single gene, or else phenotypic expressions of closely linked characters. At the very least, they must be both sex-linked, or both autosomal. A predominant and strongly expressed sex-linked appreciation could have no influence, were it to fasten upon the display of an autosomal character. If it did, the resultant pairing of extreme but opposite types of individual would produce offspring in whom the sex-to-autosome interaction was merely normal. Only an autosomal admiration of an autosomal kind of display, or a sex-linked appreciation of a sex-linked character, can influence the sexuality of the race as a whole.

Even apart from the question of choice, the same appears to hold good of systems based on mere mechanical interactions. Assuming a fixed degree of coyness, encouraging all females to run from all males, the fleetest of foot would mate with each other, and the offspring would be better runners than the parents. Actually, however, even the instincts to run away and to pursue must be hereditary, and, like the power to run fast, must depend either upon sex-linked or autosomal factors, and so be influenced by the general expression, or repression, of the latter. In this case, which seems quite possibly to have contributed towards the specialization of the human legs, both of these, in some sense contradictory, instincts would need to be linked on to the same side as the anatomical character that they were selected to perfect. Assuming speed and staying power to be a male, and therefore autosomal, character, its predominance could only be increased provided that males possessing the greatest anatomical capacity were also spurred on by the strongest instinct. Moreover, unless the females pursued were also urged on by an autosomal instinct of flight before surrender, the offspring would benefit in no way from the parental exertions ; for a sex-linked encouragement of an instinct towards flight would marry the ultra-feminine females to the ultra-masculine males. The offspring would, in such a case, be unremarkable. In this instance, we may thus imagine the single anatomical character, leg development, and its two linked or correlated instincts, flight and pursuit, to gain in their outward expressions as a result of the selection of modifying mutants also linked with them. Of course other forms of natural selection might, simultaneously or subsequently, stress or inhibit the process. Locomotion, even if encouraged at one period by sexual selection, could at length become perfect enough to allow the catching of game. From that point masculine success as a food-getter would count for more than success in the hymeneal chase, and the whole system of competition based on the latter would tend to decay. In such a case sexual selection would have become merged with the more usual self-stimulating kind of natural selection, in which specialization restricts the other possible types of competition, and thus accelerates its own intensification.

HAIR AND SEX DISPLAY

It will be apparent, then, that in theory, at all events, a character evolved in response to sexual selection may be perfected and altered by natural selection. Some space will now be devoted to an almost exactly opposite type of case, wherein a character apparently evolved for a specific and quite non-sexual purpose is, in Man, believed to have become an emblem of autosomal—that is to say male—virility, while it may also have become a warning to the young. I refer to the pubic hair, the extent of which is limited in the female. This sex-linked inhibition, and the fact that neither sex displays it until maturity, will now be dealt with.

As a starting point, then, it must be pointed out that the pubic and axillary hair cover the very parts which in the normal quadruped require no such protection and are usually hairless. Their development is thus best interpreted as an adaptation resulting from the habit of brachiation, when the anthropoid swings through the trees holding the arms above the head, and exposing the chest, pubes and arm pits to be cut and scratched. Of course, if new hair was needed in these places, it must be assumed that the remainder of the body was already similarly clothed. It remains to be explained, then, why, after the rest of the body-hair is lost, these lately evolved additions should remain.

A satisfactory solution to this puzzle seems also of great assistance in supporting the idea that hairlessness is an atavistic character recalled from the inheritance of an earlier quadrupedal ancestor. We may picture a returned activity of genes that had formerly been useful in inhibiting hair-growth on the back of the quadruped ; so that they would neglect to influence other areas which in their previous stage of predominance they had never been called upon to control.

The action of genes for hairlessness, when expressed in cattle, commonly allows some hair on the muzzle, upper jaws, eye-lids, ears, horn processes, and the top of the head. This seems analogous to the retention of human hair on the face and head. A few hairs are also retained upon the umbilicus and external genitalia, which suggests that no active inhibition of hair-growth in these last regions has ever needed to be evolved in any animal. In the cases of this hypotrichosis studied by Mohr and Wriedt,[1] as also in the bull-dog calves, the recessive mutant is lethal. In each case, however, it is arguable that the main characters have once possessed survival-value, and that the lethal effect is due to a failure of successful interaction with subsequently selected modifiers. Mohr and Wriedt's hairless calves were not achondroplastic, and had hair also on the pasterns. This suggests the evolution of modifiers selected to prevent achondroplasia by lowering the developmental threshold of the legs.

[1] Mohr, O. C., and Wriedt, C. : *J. Genet.*, XIX, pp. 315–329.

Yet, whereas the whole foregoing hypothesis may suffice to explain the location of the human pubic and axillary hair, it is obviously quite insufficient to account for the time at which it makes its appearance. Somehow or other, the requirements of sexual display may be suspected of having complicated the issue. It may be useful, therefore, to attempt to draw a partial parallel, while at the same time taking due note of differences, between the postulated history of the pubic hair in Man and the analogous theory of the evolution of antler in the stag.

Now it was suggested that the development, if not the origin, of antler arose in response to a need for fighting-efficiency ; which later became modified as a means of overawing young males, and possibly of attracting or subjugating females. The inhibition of horn-growth thus became a sex-linked character. In the case of the pubic hair in Man, however, it seems unlikely that any mechanical advantage could ever have laid the foundations of such a process. It seems legitimate, therefore, to look for a physiological superiority that could be visually indicated by a vigorous growth of hair on a limited portion of the body's surface ; though this assumption, it is true, implies from the first some sort of recognition (either active or passive) on the part either of the female or of the adolescent male.

At all events, if iodine-deficiency can now cause an ontogenetic reaction resulting in a loss of hair, it seems possible, *per contra*, that an animal with the most efficient iodine-metabolism, and so the most active endocrine system, would be the one to develop the most luxuriant growths in all spots in the body at which no direct hereditary repression could operate. Thus, an instinct of female choice, if and when it arose, could confer a definite survival-value on the offspring by securing fathers whose endocrine systems were superior. Hair-growth in these special parts would become the advertisement of the valuable physiological character of iodine-retention ; while the limited areas of display could do little towards wasting the supply. Thus would come into being a sexual selection for increased activity of an autosomal character favouring the growth of pubic and axillary hair.

The theory so far, however, has had to postulate female choice, and has not accounted either for the sex-linked inhibition of this character in the female, which certainly exists, or for its total inhibition in both sexes until the time of sexual maturity. Moreover, we have been led to depart from, and indeed practically to reverse, our preliminary parallel with the stag, where the male sex-emblem—the antler—was regarded as primarily useful in overawing the adolescent rivals, and only of secondary and doubtful value in impressing the female.

Now it is easy to see that, if only the process could be given a start, a certain amount of useless rivalry between the full grown and the immature males could be prevented by a delayed exhibition of any sign of sexual maturity. Moreover, following the argument used already in the case of the repression of horn-growth, it would seem to follow that any developmental delay in the male is best governed by means of the simplex sex-linked factors, whose restraining influence can suddenly be flung off at the end of the anabolic growth-period.

The difficulty, though perhaps a minor one, is to imagine how such a sex-linked inhibition began. In this connection, all one can do is to suggest that some sex-linked repression of hair-growth is a character of all mammals; dating, perhaps, to their emergence in the age of reptiles when, according to my theory, the female may have been larger and more economical in iodine and fluid than the male. Many animals are born without hair of any sort, and it is at all events consistent with this general hypothesis to regard the display of many infantile and anabolic characters as encouraged by the predominance of sex-linked genes. We may, in any case, conceive a process whereby the primal fight opened with the showing of adult colours by the hitherto weaker vessel. Thus banishment from the family group at too early an age would tend to end fatally; while a prolonged sex-linked inhibition of all signs of sexual maturity would encourage survival. Hence, under conditions of iodine shortage, there could be built up one half of a mechanism later to be used for purposes of sexual selection. So far at least we can explain the retention and specialization of body hair in the male, and the inhibition of this character in the female and the adolescent.

It will have been noticed, however, that this theory fails to explain the presence of even a limited area of pubic hair in the female. One could have expected the two female sex-chromosomes to have caused as complete a repression as that occurring in the young male. We may reflect, therefore, that if the admiration of hair-growth could assist females to choose virile sires, a similar admiration on the part of the male for a female display of the same character would be even more efficient for promoting a sexual selection in favour of a similar type of endocrine activity. Females who could show a good development of hair would probably be mothers to more active and disease-resistant offspring. The latter, however, would tend to suffer the concomitant disadvantage of early puberty and its resultant banishment. Thus, caught between two selective fires, there would be for them but a single line of retreat, consisting in an ever-increasing delay of maturity, coupled with a final complete overthrow of sex-linked inhibition.

THE LOCATION OF THE PÆDOMORPHIC CHARACTERS

It is still, I think, possible to conceive how most—though by no means all—of the genes making for a delay of puberty may be sex-linked. (In confirmation of this one may note that puberty is somewhat later in girls, who, of course, are homogenetic.) If the danger of the young male encouraged a long-continued repression of the sex-linked factors, the mutual admiration of pubic display between adults would be responsible for an eventual explosion of autosomal catabolism as soon as the delay-action of the sex-linked powder-train had allowed its ignition. If this is the truth, however, the initial theory that regards femininity as a correlate of small size—and to some extent of early maturity—such as would be suitable in a tropical forest, must be considerably revised.

We are faced with the corollary that a two-directional sex-dimorphism seems to have been used for the building up of three conflicting sets of bodily characters. It may be well to remember, therefore, that femininity may once have been correlated with large size, slow growth, and fluid economy; and that only later, on the demand for a female economy of calcium, is a feminine smallness likely to have evolved.[1] It is not impossible, therefore, that there may be early-acting sex-linked factors which slow down, but do not arrest, the growth process, whereas, later, genes in the same sex-chromosome may be stimulated to act as checks. The evolution of these latter primary female sex-characters will be dealt with immediately. Their activity is believed to have been increased by a process of sexual-selection directed by a heterosexual admiration for fine hair and other definitely feminine features. It seems probable, therefore, that a useful distinction can be drawn between an admiration of, with selection for, the adult male or female characters, and one directed towards youthful, and to some extent, therefore, intersexual, characters. The latter may be older, and would appear to have played the more important part in changing the anthropoid into the fœtalized and slow-developing Man. The latter might have contributed more towards the subsequent differentiation of the human races. If any of the former pædomorphic characters were evolved before the adaptation and evolution of the homogenetic female, it might thus follow that some of them have been autosomal since the initial and hypothetic capture of femininity by the genes for large size and fluid economy, when the previous reptilian sex-chromosome is deemed to have become an autosome. Supposing some pædomorphic characters to be autosomal, their activities might similarly have been increased by the selection of suitable autosomal and close-linked modifiers. Whether sex-linked or autosomal, they could still serve to delay puberty and so to stave off the attacks of the adult male. Their activity might, thus, in any case be increased by a simple natural selection.

The speed of this adaptation towards delayed puberty might, however, be increased by sexual selection, provided that a strong antagonism of developmental influence existed between the sex-factors and the autosomes; but it could not act if genes of the same kind were equally distributed on both sides. If slow development is a predominantly feminine character, a sexual selection for a permanently youthful form of figure might increase the sex-linked predominance, and so intensify itself. Similarly, if it were predominantly autosomal, sex-linked interference could be still further reduced. Such processes would not,

[1] Cf. Chapter I.

however, seem to have been important. The sexual selection must in every case occur after puberty ; whereas the character for which survival-value is postulated, namely, slow development, ceases to confer advantage at this time. It must be realized, therefore, that we are merely engaged in the most hasty running survey of this immense and important question concerning the causes of physical—and perhaps mental—infantilization in Man. It is possible that the childish characters of some races might be due chiefly to sex-linked characters, whilst the ontogenetic development of others was delayed mainly by their autosomes.

HEAD-HAIR AND FEMININITY

Now the particular growths of hair so far discussed form only a part of the whole human display. They differ in kind from the head and facial hair ; though this difference of texture is possibly more pronounced in the White and Mongoloid races than in the Blacks. I have later attempted to account for this on the hypothesis that, whereas the Negroid hair may have been evolved for the single purpose of protection from heat, and is thus under the control of autosomal genes selected for this strictly practical end, the long coarse hair of the Mongoloid stock, and the finer hair of the Whites, are the results of a sexual selection for physiological characters secured through an æsthetic appreciation of these race-marks. In the Bushman, a specialization of the peppercorn type of hair is regarded as an extreme and perfected protection from heat. Sexual selection for the feminine character of steatopygia is held to have diverted attention from most other forms of physiological advertisement on the part of the female. The difference between the Bushman's peppercorn hair and the less curled and rounder-sectioned hair of the Negro will be discussed later. I propose also to defer the question of the evolution of the long coarse hair of the Mongoloid peoples. It will be argued that this has served as an advertisement of iodine-economy, though probably at a date much later than that at which Man first developed from the ape. Since it is now suggested that a sexual attention focussed upon the head-hair favoured the specialization of a female form of display, it is not impossible that the Mongoloid hair may represent the most recent variant of all. Here admiration for an autosomal mutant (coarse hair) in the female may have led to a reversal of a previously evolved fineness, so that being autosomal, it was at once strongly projected into the male, in whom it came to be admired at a later stage.[1]

Let us look, then, to the White race, which in the matter of hair evolution appears to stand midway between the Negroid and Mongoloid peoples. Here the head-hair almost certainly plays an important part in stimulating the various sex-instincts. In the male a vigorous growth of the beard is recognized as essentially masculine,

[1] *N.B.* In Chapter XII Tibetan polyandry is suspected of selecting for male characters in the woman.

though the woman's response to this sex-emblem would appear to be delicately balanced between appreciation and repulsion. There is much less, if any, ambivalence in the masculine reaction to long fine hair in a woman. It excites heterosexual appetites in the male and calls forth the narcissistic self-appreciation of its owner. The reactions of other women are less easy to define, and are of less importance. In so far as these exhibit jealousy, they will strengthen the conscions element in the display.

I propose now, therefore, to try and explain why fine long hair grown upon the head should have become an advertisement of ultra-femininity. It will be assumed that it requires more cell-proliferation, and is thus less economical of endocrine activity, than coarse hair. Let it be assumed also that this extra endocrine activity is more wasteful in iodine. This need not, however, be a disadvantage. Supposing a migration from a goitre area to acid- and iodine-abundant lands, the previously evolved economy would be of no advantage, while some correlates of this character, a high calcium requirement, and physical lethargy, perhaps, would be definite drawbacks. Thus, assuming fine head hair to have been admired, one can see that a process of sexual selection based upon this admiration could have contributed towards the accommodation of a mountain Hominid to life in a pluvial habitat. Indeed, I suspect it of having contributed towards the evolution of Neanthropic Man.

In regard to the origin of hair on the head and its sexual appreciation, it seems necessary to use an argument analogous to that employed to explain the pubic and axillary tufts as relics of adaptations made subsequently to the initial stage of hairlessness hypothetically attributed to all mammalian lines of descent. Since the head-hair is longer, is more abundant, and develops earlier than the pubic hair, it would be consistent to attribute it to a pre-brachiating period of anthropoid evolution. This suggests that the brain may have undergone one of its (three ?) critical stages of relative expansion between the times of the first hairlessness and the first brachiation, perhaps during the evolution of the Tarsioids. If the rest of the body was covered with fine hair at this time, the same thing might happen to the enlarged cranium as well. When once it had developed, the returned atavistic predominance of the genes evolved for the first hairless phase would leave this new head-hair untouched, just as they would also be unable to influence the later-evolved pubic and axillary coverings. To complete this theoretical construction, it is next necessary to assume lime-shortage and iodine-abundance as the causes of this early reduction of body-size, with its relative increase of skull vault and fine hair. The coarser pubic and axillary adornment must be attributed to iodine-deficiency ; and this last deficiency is also the more probable cause of the leg-hypotrophy held responsible for brachiation.

We must next explain why, when the sexual rivalry was directed towards the pubic display—thereby resulting in its late development—

it did not similarly concentrate upon the hair of the head. This could be due to the close association of the pubic hair with the genitalia, which arose relatively by chance. If so, as seems probable, the arrest of the axillary display until puberty must be regarded as non-functional, and dependent upon an initial linkage with the now more important feature. In addition, or alternatively, however, the early phylogenetic and ontogenetic development of the head-hair may have rendered it a normal trait in all children before their size or strength could possibly provoke the paternal wrath.

Finally, before disposing of the origin and validity of fine hair in the female, it may be pointed out that monkeys spend much of their time grooming each other, and appear to obtain some form of libidinous satisfaction from this activity. Supposing it were necessary to evolve a form of sexual selection suitable to a small nocturnal animal like Tarsius, it would be possible for a tactile appreciation of fine fur both to bind the mother to her offspring, and to encourage a selection for small size and endocrine activity as a result of a sexual search for femininity among adults. It may be, therefore, that a sexual selection for ultra-femininity occurred during an early phase of primate evolution, and that its recrudescence in the evolution of Modern Man is, in some sense, atavistic.

The hint that the same psychological mechanism that links the mother to the suckling may likewise operate in the adult's search for sexual gratification, leads straight to the problem how far the observations and theories of Freud could be explained or amplified in the light of a satisfactory theory of sexual selection. It does not seem impossible that this whole mechanism of the sexual selection for ultra-femininity may rest upon an unconscious identification of the mate with the mother. This would be strongest in the most fœtalized and least sexually differentiated individuals, but would lead them to select mates in whom the feminine, but not necessarily the fœtalized, characters were most fully developed. The general evolutionary trend would be thus towards both goals simultaneously.

It is rather more difficult to perceive the psychological, as opposed to the genetical, basis of the female's admiration of masculinity. It may depend upon an unconscious identification of the undeveloped self with the fully developed male. An " organ inferiority " in regard to the female's lack of masculine emblems of display would amount to much the same thing ; and the opposite male appreciation of essentially feminine characters might similarly depend upon an unconscious sense of inadequacy, even when " rationalized " in an ambivalent contempt or fear of contagion.

Actually, this theory of an opposition between two main classes of sexual selection raises a host of psychological and sociological problems, some of which are dealt with in later chapters. Enough has here been said to show the vast importance of sexual selection as a formative influence in organic adaptation. Among animals it seems probable that instincts serve mainly to guide a sexual selection dictated by purely material needs. In the higher cultures, however, the instincts themselves may become the subjects of natural selection. In such cases it is no longer necessary to strike a balance between the possibly conflicting claims of anatomy and physiology ; for the third factor consisting in the psychology must also be accommodated, and may, to some extent, inhibit the perfect interaction of the other two.

I have also postponed a discussion of the phylogenetic influences of the various systems of human marriage. Roughly, it will be argued that male competition can function most easily under a system of polygyny, and that monogamy allows the females to exercise choice in favour of males less masculine and virile than those to whom she would otherwise have been forced to submit. Thus the offspring of polygynous marriages will tend to be more masculine than those of monogamous unions. The rather complicated and important case of polyandry can then also be examined. This in its turn seems to be bound up with the question of incest, in-breeding and exogamy. It will be argued that Man has attained to the extreme degree of his adaptation by the aid of in-breeding, but that a horror of incest stepped in to arrest the process and prevent undue specialization. Both the incest-taboo and the prohibition against killing within the home-circle are held to have arisen as correlates of an evolving nervous inhibition, resulting in an ambivalent pivoting of all the more primitive and primary instincts.

This inhibition is initially a character of youth, rather than of femininity, and may be responsible for Freud's " Œdipus complex." It is probably selected from mutants occurring on the sex-chromosome. For the general influence of all the secondary sex-linked characters is held to be discarded at the time of puberty ; this release of catabolic vigour being, of course, more complete in the male than in the homogenetic female. It is regarded as a mechanism primarily useful in defending the young male from the aggressive behaviour of the adult. It would, however, be of almost equal value in protecting the immature female. It is thus initially an outcome of male competition used to motivate a sexual selection for racial masculinity and full autosomal development in the adult. Supposing, however, the race to be later selected for a general increase in the predominance, or expression, of the sex-linked feminine and youthful characters, it then becomes probable that the initial tendency towards an inhibition of aggressive and libidinous behaviour would be still further increased. It is now well recognized that the higher parts of the brain act by inhibiting the lower and more primitive portions. Thus both types of sexual selection may be held responsible for important, though indirect, contributions towards the development of the large cerebral hemispheres of Man.

CONCLUSION: A (THEORETICAL)

A general theory concerning the origin and validity of the process of sexual selection has been presented, and its theoretical outline may be considered apart from the applications used here in support of the particular theory of human evolution already outlined. The processes of sexual selection recognized by Darwin as being probably responsible for the differentiation of the existing human races have been briefly mentioned. Only the evolution of the Palæanthropic and Neanthropic stems from a presumed anthropoid ancestor has, however, been discussed in any detail.

In principle, then, sexual selection is regarded as a type of intraspecific competition, but it is competition carried out according to relatively artificial rules. The complicated rules themselves, however—that is to say, the nature of the display or other effectors, and their relationship to the appreciative or other receptive mechanisms in the opposite sex—are believed to be themselves the products of simpler systems of natural selection. In this manner the artificial intraspecific competition within the sexes has been harnessed to the task of adapting the species to the more intractable aspects of its outer environment; and, in particular, to the mineral balance of its food supply. Not only economy, but the full utilization of an abundance, can be secured through sexual selection.

The success, and widespread adoption, of this method of phylogenetic adaptation are made to rest upon the ease with which a rough, but ready, racial plasticity can be obtained through alterations in the degree of interaction between the sex-linked and autosomal portions of the inheritance. This could occur as a result of random gene-mutation; and almost as certainly—and this time in a probably useful direction—as an effect of racial mixture with a more successful and invading group.[1] Moreover, it seems quite possible that a favourable turn might also result through the direct action of an environmental change causing slight variations in the gene-interactions of the offspring, conveyed by way of the altered nutritional states of the mothers. If we assume this general plasticity in the matter of more, or less, sex-to-autosome interaction, it could " pave the way " for more limited and specific criteria of success. Indeed these specialized sex-characters may be narrowed down, and come so intensely into demand, that breakdowns might possibly part the genes responsible for the selective mechanism from those responsible for the more " practical " physiological or other correlates on whose behalf the former were first pushed into prominence. Starting as a sexual selection for a general greater or less degree of interaction between all the sex-factors and all the autosomes, the process might, in theory, narrow itself down until only the interaction of a single sex-gene with a single autosomal unit character was involved. In practice, one would conceive of natural selection as imposing a mounting resistance towards the more extreme intensities or absences of general interaction. If so, the few particular factors, whose altered interaction was directly encouraged by the sex-limited intraspecific parts of the general struggle for existence, would tend to

[1] This last point is discussed in Chapter XII.

be held back by the interests of the more numerous, and more widely responsible, factors that were still linked with them, and had hitherto followed their lead.

The whole mechanism of bi-sexual reproduction is built up upon two fundamental tendencies of living organisms. One of these is to conjugate with organisms of similar general type and common ancestry. The other is to be attracted by minor differences. It is the first of these tendencies which forms the basis of all systems of sexual selection. The second, which could be responsible for the eventual automatic division of a group of potentially bi-sexual organisms into moieties of fixed sign and sex, is actually of less interest in reference to the particular question of sexual selection. Provided that bi-sexual reproduction can continue, sexual selection will proceed fastest when individuals of opposite sex can in some way exercise choice in the direction of any secondary sex-characters already abnormally displayed by one of themselves. It depends thus upon homosexual tendencies inhibited by the limitations of a heterosexual mechanism of reproduction. All the genes actively involved in a given mechanism of sexual selection must start with locations upon the same side of the sex-autosome divide. It seems probable that the new mutants will cluster even more closely as the process in question advances and focusses itself.

Lastly, considerable stress is laid upon the point that structures and processes evolved for the special requirements of sexual selection may later be re-adapted by minor modification until, first, the sex-limitation, and, finally, the intraspecific limitation of their survival-value, tend to be lost in favour of an inter-specific usefulness. Similarly, as already pointed out, mechanisms first evolved for the purpose of an inter-specific struggle, as measured by reactions to the physical aspects of the environment, may be elaborated into, and accelerated by, emergent processes of sexual selection.

CONCLUSION: B (APPLICATION OF THEORY)

The growth of hair in Man is regarded as having become deeply involved in the systems of sexual selection responsible for much of his striking differentiation from the anthropoid apes. The pubic hair is an autosomal sex-emblem developed out of an evolved protective covering —also required at the armpits—which dates back to the beginning of brachiation, and could not be cast off when the genes specialized for a former hairless condition, as needed in a quadruped, had resumed predominance. The full development of these growths is held to have indicated a catabolic endocrine activity particularly difficult to support at a time when iodine-deficiency was acute. The admiration felt by either sex for it when displayed by the other could thus confer survival-value, by marking out partners in whom the nutritional state was good, and in whom the anabolic growth-phase had come to an end. Thus, its inhibition until puberty is ascribed to the danger of adult jealousy, which might otherwise be aroused towards the young of both sexes ; though it is especially the safety of the immature male that is held to have been thereby secured. The aggressive instincts are held to have become inhibited by the same parts of the inheritance as those restricting the adolescent's pubic display. Thus the progressive strengthening of the latter in the interests of a long growth-period may have likewise fortified the associated, and probably sex-linked, inhibition of combativeness. Later, and especially in Neanthropic Man, the activity of the sex-linked inheritance is held to have been resuscitated, and somewhat diverted, by a sexual selection for a sex-linked and feminine character—fineness of head-hair. This is considered to have proved useful in an environment offering chances for an increased utilization of iodine, and for a return to the calcium-economy evolved by the smaller smooth-coated forest primates.

CHAPTER IX

ENVIRONMENT AND MORPHOLOGY

Animals and Environment: Animals and Domestication: The Bones of Man (*a*) *Environment and Ossification*; (*b*) *The Skeleton as a store:* Skull Form and Physiology.

BEFORE GOING ON TO DISCUSS THE SIGNIFICANCE OF SUCH HOMINID remains as have been discovered, and also the allied subject of the relationship of the living races of Man to their geographical and economic environments, both initial and present, an attempt will here be made to test some of the more general contentions of the mineral hypothesis with the aid of a somewhat mixed assortment of zoological and anthropological observations. First of all, attention is drawn to an apparently causal connection between the cold, dry, and so probably calcium-rich, soils of Pleistocene Europe and a fauna whose skeletal development displayed a very exuberant growth, particularly as regards the development of tusk and horn. Secondly, it will be argued that the domestication of animals has done little to arrest the main drift of natural selection. On the contrary, artificial selection, like sexual selection, has served mainly to accelerate a process of which the main features were already determined by the long-rehearsed reaction of the land-animal to the various common kinds of habitat to which it has been bound to adapt itself. The evolutionary stream may be canalized or diverted, but it can never be dammed or made to run uphill. Actually, it was in attempting to understand the causes responsible for the Jersey breed of dairy cattle that I was led to formulate most of the leading ideas propounded here. As this special case may still serve to illustrate many of the main parts of the theory, it seems entitled to a brief recapitulation in these pages. Lastly, having indicated the lines of enquiry that seem able to throw fresh light upon the relation of the animal to its environment, I shall try to interpret certain facts of human anatomy in terms of a natural selection for an economy of bone-forming material. Certain differences in the form of the pelvis, and in the occasional flattening of the limb bones, all of which have long puzzled anthropologists, will be touched upon. Finally, the still more vexed question of the causes leading to the racial differences in the form of the human head will be discussed. Without some theory—even a wrong one—in regard to this last fundamental puzzle, the whole work of the physical anthropologist must resolve itself into little more than a wearisome cataloguing of meaningless measurements.

ANIMALS AND ENVIRONMENT

Perhaps the clearest connection between the calcium and phosphorus content of the food on the one hand, and the form of the animal on the other, would be provided by a study of antler and horn development. At all events, it suits this theory to regard the soils of the Pleistocene tundra as being even richer in the bone-forming materials than are those of the corresponding class of habitat to-day. The reindeer stands out as the most successful adaptation achieved by the ungulates: the yearly shedding of the antler being taken to indicate a survival-value achieved by this effective, if drastic, means of ejecting an excess of these elements. Even the females develop and discard their smaller head-furnishing; and this fact may show how even the yearly demands of lactation may be insufficient to balance an active intake, evolved, presumably, at an earlier period, and less easily modified than a compensatory demand linked to the antler-growth. The latter, as has been already argued, is probably dependent upon the interaction of the sex-linked and the autosomal parts of the inheritance, and may thus be rapidly altered by sexual selection, as well as by the more ordinary process of natural selection.

Of course, the antler- and horn-growth of such Pleistocene species as Megaceros, Cervalces and Bos Primigenius was in each case greater than that of their modern relatives reindeer, elk and domesticated ox: and even the sabre-toothed carnivore Machairodos greatly excelled the modern lions and tigers in respect of the material expended on the huge canine teeth. All this is at least consistent with the observation that their human contemporary, Neanderthal Man, also displayed a phenomenal growth of bone, especially, be it noted, upon the head. Moreover, he also, like the other cold fauna of the Pleistocene, is now extinct. Mineral-deficiency thus provides one possible explanation for the complete faunal change. It is not contended that the small extra expenditure of material actually used as bone was itself solely responsible for the disappearance of all these species. All this free development is, however, regarded as a sign of extreme anterior-lobe activity; and this last, in its turn, is held responsible for so energetic an excretion of calcium phosphate that only foods rich in this substance could support life and maintain fertility. Possibly the main value of this endocrine character was the active protein-metabolism and the extra production of heat thereby secured. It may thus be no accident that long horns are considered desirable in the hardy Highland cattle, which withstand cold better than any other breed in Scotland.

Obviously, the yearly growth of deciduous antler is more wasteful than the development of the permanent horn-cores of the Bovidæ; while, again, hornless species are probably more economical still. Such changes in anatomical design are held to have been the result of extreme deficiencies temporarily affecting, and so changing, a small and in-breeding group of the more primitive and less economical species. When once these changes had occurred, the selective agencies responsible for them could vanish. Thus the very great size of the hollow-horned Bos Primigenius as compared, say, with the reindeer, may have been due to the greater degree of calcium-economy previously evolved; and, consequently, to the greater amount of secondary modification necessary, if this now disadvantageous or useless character was to be annulled, and the opposite advantage of an active calcium and phosphorus excretion secured in its place. According to this theory, we might conceive each class of habitat to be particularly suitable for some single order or build of animal. Nevertheless, the adjoining belts of country may be expected to support species derived by secondary modification from the primary ancestral type. The degree of this modification would run in the same direction indicated by the native and longer established order, but its degree would be increased. If the antlered ungulates may be supposed to have evolved, and hence are still found to be least modified, upon soils of high calcium-content, so the hollow-horned species are likely to have undergone least secondary modification whenever the climate is more humid and the soils lack lime. Thus, where hollow-horned and antlered species are found side by side in an arid habitat, the former will exceed the latter in size and in all other marks of anterior-lobe activity. On the other hand, when antlered species are specialized in the humid habitats native to the hollow-horned order, the antlers will diminish in size and may even vanish, whereas the hollow horns will be less affected. If, then, the differences in the size of head furnishings can be of any interest to the anthropologist, animals which show extreme brachycephaly, or a lack of hair, should be of even greater interest. In this last class I would signalize the modern elephant as showing many human parallelisms: the broad head, intelligence, and hairless skin being particularly notable, while the slow sequence of tooth-development, and the presence of a chin, are also worthy of mention. In addition, it is probably fair to consider the reduction in the size of the toes as marking a period of general achondroplasia similar to that postulated in the case of man and exemplified by the bulldog calves. In the case of the elephant, however, both pairs of limbs would appear to have undergone a secondary lengthening, whereas in Man the arms have remained short.

Another brachycephalic animal with degenerate (or over-specialized?) limbs is the seal. Of course, it is usual to explain the specialization as due to the mechanical needs imposed by an aquatic life. It is worth considering, however, that an extreme mineral-deficiency would probably cripple the limbs, and render them useless for supporting the body on land; and, secondly, that life in the water would supply an increase of iodine and possibly of phosphorus also. The different species of seal show a certain correlation between the degree of fœtalization in the adult head and the amount of degeneracy inherent in the limb-development. This seems to argue in favour of the view that physiological rather than anatomical requirements are responsible for the selection of the specific differences in question. Thus, the eared seals, or Otariidæ, not only retain the small external ears, but also have hind flippers that are not turned permanently backwards. This latter feature is also distinctive of the walrus, in which the tusks, together with the greater size of the whole body, seem also to indicate a smaller degree of endocrine repression.[1]

Before concluding this brief attempt to explain what is possibly a new point of view, a word must be said concerning the very significant differences between animals specialized to eat flesh and those which make use of plant-food. Despite the general dependence of the animal upon the plant, it is probable that the first land vertebrates were carnivora. If so, the display of horns and other head furnishings, which are so much more characteristic of herbivores than of meat-eaters, may be regarded as secondary developments in the specialized herbivorous ungulates. This evolution, as already pointed out, is held to be correlated with characters evolved in response to foods of a higher calcium-balance than flesh, such as, more particularly, the vegetation growing on lands subject to an arid climate.

Now the primates are built to a plan which in some ways resembles that of the carnivora rather than that of the specialized herbivorous ungulates ; since neither horns nor tusks are developed. I suggest, therefore, that, whereas the ungulates underwent their critical period of differentiation in an arid habitat, the primates remained in a humid and so forested region, and continued to subsist on foods which, whether animal or vegetable, contained relatively small amounts of the soluble soil-salts. Indeed, the climbing of trees may be regarded as an attempt to reach these rare substances, which each plant has struggled to obtain, both by competing in the matter of growing deep roots, and then in the raising of its catch to the highest point, where it can be utilized despite the jealous shading of rivals. I suggest, therefore, that the primates have been selected in response to a comparative dearth of bone-forming material, and that consequently, for them, a change from plant eating to flesh food, or vice versa, will present less difficulty than it would for animals that have been more specialized for life in regions of lower rainfall.

This question of the differences in mineral metabolism—especially in the matter of the economy of the fixed base—is important to a theory of the evolution of Modern Man as a tropical and perhaps carnivorous counterpart of the more coarse-boned, and probably vegetable-feeding, Hominidæ specialized for life on mountains and cold tundra. The specific difference between the chinless Neanderthaloids and Sinanthropus, on the one hand, and the alveolar regression of all modern races, on the other, may be regarded as the result of a sudden change from vegetable to flesh food, and of a consequent deprivation of vitamin C, which is needed for a proper growth in this part of the body. Thus

[1] Kuhnert and Lydekker : *Animal Portraiture*, p. 6, London, 1912.

life as a forest vegetable-feeder would provide a pre-adaptation to withstand the main obstacle—mineral-deficiency—usually encountered by a carnivore. The regression of teeth and jaw would be in the nature of a secondary and minor adjustment. As a fully specialized carnivore Modern Man would then be enabled to invade the territory of his coarse-boned cousins, there to run down and eat the game that had hitherto competed with the former occupiers for the limited vegetable supply. He would even be enabled to live under the worse Steppe conditions, preying on the specialized herbivora of the barren wastes. The cold, and the high protein-content of the flesh-food, would doubtless encourage the selection of types in whom the heat-production, due to anterior-lobe activity, was well developed. This would tend to encourage a general increase of strength and stature, which the exigencies of the chase would mould into the athleticism that we see when comparing the Upper-Palæolithic hunters with the Neanderthals whom they replaced.

ANIMALS AND DOMESTICATION

A study of the evolution of domesticated animals is of both direct and indirect importance for a study of the evolutionary history of Man. In the later stages of human history grazing animals have supplied not only food but also employment of a kind quite different from that to which either the hunter or gatherer had been accustomed. In regard to this special study concerning the influence of mineral-deficiencies upon the evolution of Man, we may summarize these influences by saying that a change from either flesh or vegetable food, as available for the savage, to the milk and blood that form the ordinary fare of the higher pastorals will at once shield the latter from almost any deficiency-disease that may be endemic to the area in which he lives. To find out what were the influences operating upon the earlier and more primitive occupants of grazing-areas, we may look to the anatomy and correlated physiology of the animal populations rather than to those of their masters. Although in many cases the endocrine attributes of the cow and her owner show a striking resemblance, there may also be sharp contrasts. Of the Nilotes one might say "who keeps horned cattle should himself be tall." The raw-boned Norsemen, on the other hand, would appear to have shielded themselves from the deficiencies of the rain-soaked soils of Northern Europe by appropriating or developing a small, short-legged and hornless animal, the ancestor of our Galloways and Redpolls :[1] though in the earlier Bronze-Age rock carvings of Scandinavia we are shown wide-horned working cattle of a breed that would probably do better, and may have been developed, upon the plains.

Let me now, however, quit this subject of the influence of cattle-keeping upon Man, in order to consider the almost equally important question of the effect of artificial selection by Man upon the cattle and

[1] Wilson, J. : *The Evolution of British Cattle*, Vinton, London.

horses that he has introduced into the several types of geographical environment. In many cases the artificial selection proves too weak to stem the tide of a natural selection acting in the opposite direction. This was noticed by Darwin in the case of the Falkland Island horses, which, despite attempts at selective breeding, continued to degenerate in size unless reinforced by fresh blood imported from the mainland.[1] The soil of the Falklands we now know to be notably deficient in calcium, a fact attributable, presumably, to the heavy rainfall. The continuous export of mutton has now also depleted it of phosphorus.[2] Many similar cases of animals decreasing in size could, doubtless, be collected. Hammond describes a deterioration of British breeds when they are imported into Jamaica.[3] Similarly, Kelly reports how heavy pure-bred Herefords defy selective breeding in Queensland, and have diminished in live-weight to the low average of 780 lbs.[4]

My own interest was drawn to this class of phenonena by engaging in the breeding of pedigree Jersey cattle in their native island. Here small size and fine bone are looked upon as desirable characters, and a considerable export trade has grown up owing to the fact that the descendants of island cattle reared in other countries seldom, if ever, conform to the insular standard. In fact, a progressive coarsening of the skeletons occurs, unless counteracted by frequent admixture with the inheritance of animals imported directly from the home of the breed.

It was suggested to me by Dr. Corner that the small size, fine bone, and other desired characters such as the fine hide, wide pelvis and docile appearance were all feminine characters, and that therefore the breed as a whole might be considered ultra-feminine. At much the same time, after the appearance of Dr. Orr's book, *Minerals in Pastures*, I came to the conclusion that, since the land of Jersey was deficient in calcium, and on account of the great prevalence of milk-fever,—then recently shown to be due to lime-shortage—, this influence had probably been important in moulding the breed. I then suggested that a physiological economy of calcium—assisted by a high ratio of fat to structured substances in the milk—had been secured through a natural and artificial selection favouring the more feminine hereditary strains. The probably high iodine-content of the soil—a result of a natural acidity, supplemented by the prolonged use of brown seaweed as manure—was considered as a condition possibly of importance in permitting the ultra-femininity in question. It may also play a part in warding off bovine tuberculosis, foot-and-mouth disease, and contagious abortion, from all of which troubles the islands have been remarkably

[1] Darwin, C.: *Journal of a Voyage round the World in H.M.S. "Beagle,"* London, 1891, pp. 232–235.

[2] Orr: *Min. in Past*, pp. 109, 121.

[3] Hammond, J.: "Report on cattle breeding in Jamaica and Trinidad," *E. M. B. Publ.*, I, A.B., Vol. 2, No. 8.

[4] Kelly, R. B.: *Rept. Council of Sci. and Indst. Resch.*, Melbourne, 1932.

free. The reason for the yellow colour of the milk and body fat is of interest in view of the relationship of carotin to the anti-infective vitamin A. I have wondered whether it could serve to prevent pathological calcification in the face of acidosis ; and whether its normal presence in the bone marrow, periosteum, corpus luteum, and certain blood vessels, may be accounted for by a capacity to maintain calcium in an ionised state.

Now any views one may hold concerning the speed and degree of specific or sub-specific changes of morphology must depend upon a usually imperfect knowledge of the earlier ancestry of the breed in question. It seems probable, however, that there are limits between which a phylogenetic change is easily accomplished, and outside of which it can seldom occur. A height of seventeen hands marks the range for the upward limit of size in the horse, and I would place 700 lb. as about the smallest weight for an adult cow. One way of explaining this is to regard every domesticated breed as a comparatively recent mixture of heredities, and to suppose the degree of racial plasticity to be determined by the degree of difference pre-existing in the composite ancestry. The relatively quick reactions to environment could then be attributed to alterations of genetic predominance resulting in a series of somatic revolutions. This would be quite distinct from the gene-mutations postulated in cases where quite new developments have occurred.

THE BONES OF MAN

(*a*) *Environment and Ossification.*

It might perhaps seem unnecessary to stress the fact that human stature, like the size of domesticated animals, is prone to wide variations as a result of food and climate. On the whole, however, it is probably true to say that, whereas medical men, social workers, and the general public have accepted this with little question, anthropologists have, on the other hand, demanded proofs, which have seldom if ever turned out to be adequate. Moreover, facts, unless backed by explanations, are seldom convincing ; and it is for this reason that I wish to draw special attention to the importance of the mineral elements of the diet as definite and measurable factors influencing the development of the individual and the local group.

At present I know of no irrefutable proof whereby diet can be shown to have affected the skeletal development of the adult man, though I believe it to do so. Even when an increase in the stature of growing children is seen to follow upon additions of milk and butter, it is always possible, though I think improbable, that the improved diet may have served merely to accelerate an advance to a fixed and pre-determined goal.[1] Such purely temporary arrests of growth have

[1] Corry Mann, H. C. : " Diets for Boys during the School Age," *Spec. Rep. Ser. med. Res. Coun.*, Lond., No. 105 (1926).

as a matter of fact resulted from the deprivation of special protein-constituents from the food of laboratory animals; a return to normal food subsequently proving that the arrest had not affected the inherent capacity for growth.[1] This difficulty can, however, be circumvented by arguing that deficiencies of tryptophane, as used by Osborn and Mendel in the experiments referred to, are not regularly encountered in nature, and so have not been allowed for by the evolution of any developmental plasticity on the part of the growing individual. Alternatively, one might assume that such deficiencies have been sufficiently rare, and are so difficult to overcome, that no alternative substances and compensatory physiological processes have been utilized as substitutes.

Now we do know that foods, like the soils from which they are grown, vary considerably in their acid-base equilibrium. It is of great interest, therefore, that Balint and Weiss succeeded in permanently altering the form and structure in the bones of rats by adding acid and alkali to the diet. They found that animals fed on alkaline rations develop a better skeleton and weigh more, and that this extra weight is not due to water.[2] They did not, it is true, attempt subsequently to cure the distortions in the bones of the acid-fed individuals; but it is most improbable that this could have succeeded. In human beings pathological changes cannot be completely annulled (e.g. "cured rickets").

Survival-value can be seen in this arrangement whereby an alkaline diet, providing an abundance of calcium and other fixed base, can promote the growth of bone. It encourages a utilization of supplies, when these are present, and likewise ensures the quick consolidation of a small light skeleton at times when bone-forming material is rare. It is interesting to note, in this connection, that the finger-bones of women ossify more quickly than those of men.[3] This is confirmed by Sawtell, who points out that the ossification of cartilage is more rapid in the female; as also that the superiority of bone-growth that will finally characterize the male is observable even before birth.[4] It seems legitimate, therefore, to assume, firstly, that the speed of ossification and inhibition of cartilage-proliferation is determined both by environment and by the activity of female-determining substances and hereditary characters. Secondly, one may note how this inhibition of bone-growth by the sex-linked factors seems to be a character evolved in the interests of a female economy of material. It might even be fair to suggest that, since a deficiency of fixed base leads to a rapid ossification and to the inhibition of cartilage-proliferation, which are feminine

1 Osborn, T. B., and Mendel, L. B.: "The Suppression of Growth and the Capacity to grow," *J. biol. Chem.*, 18, 95, 103.

2 Balint and Weiss: *Tissue Proliferation and Acid Base Equilibrium*, London, 1932.

3 Dixon, A. F.: *Manual of Human Osteology*, London, 1912.

4 Sawtell, R. O.: *Sex differences in the bone-growth of young.*

characters, the effect produced is in reality an ontogenetic reaction towards femininity.

Despite the foregoing theory, it need not, of course, be thought that the hereditary differences between the male and the female are merely a passive reflection of the difference of physiological demand which each sex is designed to meet. If so, one might expect the blood-calcium of the female to be lower than that of the male ; whereas Frei and Emmerson, working on cattle, have shown that the whole serum-calcium is higher in females than in males, higher at œstrus than at anœstrus, higher in pregnancy than during lactation, and higher after the administration of anterior-lobe extract. Similarly, the serum-calcium of calves was higher than in adults.[1] In each case—except that of lactation—we may say that heredity has learned to meet a demand with a slight over-supply. Possibly the male relies more upon the buffering actions of the other fixed bases ; and perhaps a higher activity of the adrenal-cortex results in a greater concentration of sodium ions. This same theory was made to fit quite different facts when discussing the males' greater tendency towards melanotic pigmentation.[2] According to Brinkman and Dam the calcium ion concentration—which is distinct from the total serum-calcium—depends upon an acidosis brought about by the bicarbonate ions.[3] It is possible, therefore, that the female may be adjusted so as to tolerate a higher CO_2 content of the blood. If so, the ultra-feminine type of physiology would reflect the higher CO_2 content of the air encountered in tropical and forested regions. The air of the Antarctic, and so probably that of the Pleistocene tundra, in which we are more interested, is low in its proportion of CO_2.

The process of ossification is still far from being understood. Robison has shown that a greater alkalinity exists at points where it takes place (pH 8·4—9·4).[4] This need not, however, invalidate the theory that an acidity of the body as a whole may promote the process. The local alkalinity may represent a necessarily lowered threshold, whereby cells selected to become bone are better enabled to mark, and so adjust, differences of acid-base equilibrium occurring in their vicinity ; the acidity being thus seldom allowed to rise above a point when a calcification of the soft and unspecialized tissues could become a danger.

(*b*) *The Skeleton as a Store.*

Before going on to any close inspection of differences of skeletal development among racial types and single fossils, it is necessary not only to understand the nature of the heredity and environmental influences possibly affecting the speed of cartilage proliferation and calcification

[1] Frei, W., and Emmerson, M. A. : *Biochem. Z.*, 226–355 (1930).
[2] Cf. Chapter IV.
[3] Brinkman, R., and Dam, E. : *Proc. roy. Soc. Amsterdam*, Eng. Trans., Vol. XXIII, p. 1263 (1922).
[4] Robison and Soames : *Biochem. J.*, XVIII, 740.

affecting the epiphyses of the long bones and the sutures of the skull; but, in addition, the twin rôles of the skeleton as a support and as a reserve of fixed base should be clearly distinguished. The demands of lactation must withdraw some very high proportion of the calcium-phosphate originally present in the bones of the parturient woman, and it is reasonable to suppose that the female skeleton has been selected to withstand this periodic withdrawal of structural material. In the case of dairy cattle, for instance, although only about one per cent of the body's calcium is contained in the blood (0·01 lb.), the remainder being in the bone, nevertheless the quantity yielded in a gallon of the first milk, or colostrum, is just twice this amount.[1] This shows, not only the importance of a physiological reserve during lactation, but also the speed at which the bone-to-blood exchange must take place. For even a momentary reduction to a half of the normal calcium concentration would probably result in tetany; and milk secretion takes place mainly at the time of withdrawal.

Now it seems probable that different parts of the skeleton vary in the ease with which they part with their calcium supplies. In cases of disease and old age the tabular surfaces may be reduced, and may even vanish, before the cellular structure, or diploe, supporting them is seriously affected. Virchow was the first to notice how bone-atrophy occurs most easily at positions where no muscle is attached.[2] If, then, we assume that the main calcium-reserve is bone-surface unattached to muscle, it becomes clear both how the female may claim a physiological superiority on account of her muscular weakness, and how her reduced bulk must automatically increase the ratio of surface to volume. Besides the flat bones, the ribs have been shown to yield and take up lime-salts.[3] We may conclude, then, that any agency capable of increasing the surface-area of the flat bones in the skull, the shoulder blades, the pelvic basin, the ribs, or other parts, and any condition reducing the area of muscle attachment, will tend to possess survival-value in situations where a shortage of bone-forming material is likely to occur. Similarly, where the form of a bone may be varied, flat or triangular sections will be superior to those which are circular; for in the latter case the area of bone surface will be at a minimum. Neanderthal Man, we may reflect, had limb bones of circular section, ribs of triangular section,[4] and a skull well covered by muscle. In modern races the leg and arm bones are often flattened; the ribs are always of flatter section than in Neanderthal Man; and the area of skull-vault above the lines of the jaw and neck attachments is probably greater. In all these features I recognize the signs of a greater hereditary

[1] Little, W. L., and Wright, N. C.: "The Ætiology of Milk Fever in Cattle," *Brit. J. exp. Path.* (1925), VI, 129.
[2] Virchow: *Wurzb*, Verk IV (1854).
[3] Hunter, D.: "The Metabolism of Calcium and Phosphorus and the Parathyroids in Health and Disease," *Brit. med. J.*
[4] Boule, M.: *Annales de Palæontologie*, VII, 1912.

economy of calcium. Rickets causes a further flattening of the ribs, which may be considered as an evolved ontogenetic reaction.[1]

A good deal of discussion has centred about the question as to the cause of flattening in the bones of the leg (platymeria and platycnemia).[2] Posture has been suggested, but the fact, shown by Buxton and Rice, that there is an inter-racial correlation between flattening in the leg and in the bones of the arm (brachic index) seems to rule out this possibility.[3] Either hereditary or nutritional agencies might still be responsible. I suggest that there may be an hereditary character that is not present in all races but, when present, needs a deficient diet for its somatic expression. The Japanese, who may be believed to suffer from mineral-deficiency, are not platycnemic. I have wondered whether the large size of their skull-vaults may furnish an alternative reserve area. If so, it may have been evolved partly to compensate for the absence of the genes for limb-flattening ; which would not have been originally required, if one assumes the Mongoloid race to be the product of arid or mountain regions.

Some brief mention must now be made of the manner in which mineral-deficiency may possibly influence the form of the flat bones in the shoulder and pelvic girdles. It has been shown that the possession of a convex margo vertebralis of the scapula—leading to a greater area of shoulder-blade—carries with it an increased expectation of life. This feature does not appear to be influenced by disease or by malnutrition, and may consequently be regarded as due to hereditary characters liable to affect one or both sides of the body.[4] I suggest that these characters were evolved at a time when severe calcium-deficiency was being encountered ; and that their morphological aspects are due to a need to retain a full development of the shoulder-blade under conditions when it might otherwise have become absorbed. As such, one might expect these characters to be correlated with an active calcium metabolism and economy, and thus, even under the better modern conditions, to possess survival-value.

In regard to the pelvis, it is worth noting that in some localities osteomalacia, or adult rickets, often results in a distortion of the female pelvis.[5] It may also be remarked that the normally flatter form developed in the latter resembles, in its general direction, the type of change frequently brought about by a loss of rigidity due to inadequate calcification.[6] Nevertheless, these pelvic differences between the sexes

[1] Topinard, P. : *Anthropology*, London, 1878.
[2] Cf. Duckworth, W. L. H. : *Morphology and Anthropology*, Cambridge, 1904.
[3] Buxton, L. H. D., and Rice, D. T. : " Report on the Human Remains found at Kish," *J.R.A.I.*, LXI (1913).
[4] Graves, W. W. : *Eugenics Review*, London, Oct., 1931, also *J. Hered.*, Vol. 23, No. 8, Aug., 1932.
[5] White, Corsen, E. P. : *Archiv. intern. Med.*, 30, 620 (1922).
[6] Duckworth, ibid., p. 302.

are present before birth, and are thus clearly the product of heredity unaffected by mere mechanical and nutritional agencies.[1] I suggest, however, that the hereditary character was evolved in response to a previous set of circumstances, wherein the adult female pelvis underwent a regular distortion due to these agencies ; so that, on the return of improved nutritional conditions, it became simpler to adapt the genes controlling the pelvis than to alter the whole form of the child, which in the meantime had accommodated itself to a passage through the rachitic and distorted girdle. I have been puzzled by the fact that the Negro pelvis is longer, or more male, than that of the White or of the Pecos American Indian, for I had regarded the former as in other ways the most feminine race of the three.[2] This anomaly might be explained, however, were it assumed that the Negress is, or has been, more regularly subjected to calcium-deficiency ; and that consequently, during parturition, a slight rachitic distortion could annul the difference that we find when drawing comparisons between the bones of the dead. Of course the form of the child's head must presumably have influenced the selection of the mutations affecting the form of the mother's pelvis. So, too, the form of the pelvis may well have influenced the head-form of the child and so of the race. It is worth noting, therefore, that any influence, whether hereditary or environmental, that tends to distort and widen the pelvis will probably select in favour of a shorter and broader form of head. We may thus perceive an advantage in any arrangement whereby a mineral-deficiency could shorten the length of the head, even if by so doing the breadth had necessarily to be increased. Mineral-deficiency could act ontogenetically by allowing a mechanical distortion due to the thrust of the vertebral column. In addition, it might initiate a process of natural and sexual selection for racial femininity. This would tend automatically to widen the pelvis, thus following the direction of the existing sex-dimorphism.

SKULL-FORM AND PHYSIOLOGY

I propose now to mention some possible ways in which mineral deficiencies may have played a part in moulding the form of the human head ; and particularly in affecting those two main qualities studied by the anthropologist, the length-to-breadth ratio (cranial and cephalic index), and the projection of the face (facial angle). Looking to the vertebrates as a whole we may say that a long narrow head, composed of many distinct bony plates, is primitive ; whereas in higher animals an increase in the size of the brain is associated with a reduction in the number of bones constituting the skull of the adult. In Man the adult brain-case finally becomes a solid vault, the sutures responsible for its growth vanishing entirely. On the theory of Balint and Weiss the mechanism responsible for the ossification at

[1] Thomson, A. : *J. Anat. Lond.*, Vol. XXXIII, p. 59.

[2] Hooton, E. A. : *Indians of Pecos Pueblo*, Yale, 1930, Appendix II by E. Reynolds, pp. 374–386.

the sutures would depend partly upon the acid-base equilibrium of the blood. If so, one might expect not only that the adult would be more acid than the youth and adolescent, but also that a slow phylogenetic shift towards an increased acidity had also taken place.

It is well known that calcium-deficiency results in acidosis, and I think it probable that iodine-shortage produces the same result. Inorganic iodine, in so far as it can stimulate thyroid and other endocrine activity, would result in the destruction of acid proteins by fanning the " fire of the carbohydrates." The high serum-calcium encountered in cases of myxœdema, like the higher blood-calcium of the female and of the growing animal, may represent incomplete attempts to counteract such an hypothetical acidity. Moreover, in the case of the female we know high serum-calcium to be associated with rapid ossification, and must therefore presume this not to be incompatible with the greater acidity that we have imagined.

As a more general consideration one may note that both calcium and iodine tend to accumulate in animal tissues in which disease has brought about a local acidosis.[1] It is thus reasonable to suppose that, whereas each substance may act as a partial substitute for the other, a deficiency of either or of both will result in an acidity that will be of assistance in attracting and retaining them within the animal and human body.

Besides encouraging acidity and premature synostosis, both iodine- and calcium-deficiency are associated with œdema, or swelling due to the accumulation of fluid. This seems to hold good of the brain, the lower portions of which have been shown to be particularly variable in bulk, and to expand in response to a dilution of the blood with distilled water. Epilepsy is associated with accumulations of fluid upon the brain, and attacks have been staved off by the administration of calcium. Despite the space-compensating function of the cerebro-spinal fluid, I thus suggest that mineral-deficiency serves to increase intra-cranial pressure, and so serves to influence the form of the bones enclosing the brain.

Now the peculiar form of the human head, when compared with that of a more primitive animal, is due to a reduced growth at the basi-sphenoid suture, combined with an increased growth of the sutures, or lines of cartilage, surrounding the flat bones of the vault. I submit, therefore, that mineral-deficiency has served to accelerate synostosis, or the obliteration of all sutures : but, at the same time, that pathological degrees of intra-cranial pressure have selected in favour of an active cell-proliferation along the sutures of the vault. Thus, whereas the phylogenetic reaction of the basi-sphenoid suture has reflected the ontogenetic process whereby it began, in the case of the vault the requirements of the enlarged brain encouraged an active opposition

[1] Orr : *Iod. in Nut.*, cft. Keeser (1923), *Biochem. Z.*, 138, 176.

and reversal of the type of change otherwise liable to occur in the individual.[1]

This process, which I am attempting to explain, is seen at its most pronounced stage in the case of Modern Man. It shows itself, however, in many very different sorts of mammal ; and has been called "bull-dogging," owing to the extreme shortness of the head, and reduction of the jaw and facial skeleton, typical of this breed. It is equally well developed in other kinds of dog—the Pekingese, for instance. Indeed, it may be said to be particularly common among the carnivora, including, as already mentioned, the seals. Reference has already been made to the lethal bull-dogging of the homozygous short-legged Dexter calf. In this case a failure of the posterior-pituitary was considered by Crew as responsible for the water-logged condition of the tissues, and perhaps also for the bursting of the membranes, or hydramnios, responsible for death. All sutures were obliterated and in one case there was marked hydrocephalus. A similar hereditary condition has been reported in the case of some guinea-pigs. In the pathological cases, as well as in a majority of the short-headed species, the limbs show degenerate characters. In the guinea-pig an extra sixth toe was developed in the normal individuals, whereas the pathological homozygotes had "club" or degenerate feet and small, degenerate eyes.[2] Similar club-footed pathological specimens are not infrequent in well-bred studs of Pekingese. Possibly the large eyes of this breed are specialized as an offset against a tendency towards microphthalmia.

This phenomenon of bull-dogging is so widely distributed that it is hard not to regard it as at least one aspect of a character possessing survival-value. Firstly, it could be argued that since a great deal of the efficiency of a primitive animal must depend upon the length and strength of its jaws, any mechanism whereby an abundance of structural material could be allocated to these parts at times of abundance would be valuable. This implies the converse, namely that mineral-deficiency should be enabled to restrict this sort of growth. Thus, using the theory of selective predominance to explain a parallelism between the ontogenetic and phylogenetic processes, we may argue that a predominance of genes making for a reduction of facial development will likewise assist an economy of mineral.

I would put forward what is substantially the same argument to explain the swelling of the brain-case. Not only is a reduced jaw- and limb-development of assistance in economizing mineral, but small size in general is likewise an advantage in that all surface areas are

[1] *N.B.* This retention of an ontogenetic plasticity on the part of the basi-sphenoid suture may be due to a need to shorten the head at such times as mineral-deficiency allows a mechanical distortion of the maternal pelvis.

[2] Sewall Wright: "Polydactylous Guinea Pigs," *J. of Hered.*, Vol. 25, No. 9, p. 359 (1934).

increased in proportion to the bulk of the tissues that they must serve. The bulk of the brain cannot, however, be reduced on a corresponding scale. Thus the mechanism designed to control the size of the body has become adjusted so as to allow for a relative increase in the size of the brain. As a mechanism able to bring this about, I suggest that hormones from the two halves of the pituitary have come to assist each other. Thus, whereas one from the anterior-lobe encourages an expenditure of material for such purposes as the growth of the jaws and limbs, a corresponding activity of the posterior-lobe tends to reduce tissue-hydration, and constricts the bone of the capillaries in the brain and elsewhere, also inhibiting an active secretion of cerebro-spinal fluid. Similarly, a reduced activity of both halves of the pituitary may be expected to inhibit the growth of bone, so permitting, if not directly encouraging, the expansion of the brain and its covering.

The brain of the developing child shows three sudden increments in its rate of expansion relative to the needs of the body it must control. The first takes place between the seventh and eighth months after conception, the second shortly after birth, and the last at about the sixth month. (See diagram, p. 128.) I suggest that the first pre-natal expansion represents an initial reduction in the size of the body responsible for the evolution of the mammal at a time of severe mineral-deficiency. If so, the second may represent an achondroplastic reaction responsible for a limb hypotrophy, and the consequent evolution of brachiation responsible for the hand and eye correlation of the anthropoid. Finally, the last may mark a similar happening, whereby the anthropoid lost the support of his arms, and was encouraged to develop manipulative skill, and so become human. I suggest that the genes whose activity has resulted in these three main steps towards humanity have served likewise to encourage a physiological economy of structural material. So, too, those which gain the upper hand during the intervening periods may be held to promote a faster growth of the body and limbs, but to allow a more wasteful set of processes to bring this about.

Turning now to questions of more immediate ethnological and palæontological interest, we may reasonably suspect that small size in any dimension of the skull must indicate an acid and economical type of physiology. When the cell-proliferation at one suture has been arrested by either an ontogenetic or a phylogenetic change resulting in an arrest of development, we may expect mechanical forces acting in the individual, and also selective agencies affecting the race, to offer compensations. To be more precise, mineral-deficiency may be expected to shorten the basi-nasal length, raise the intracranial pressure, and expand the vault. Similarly, mineral abundance, especially when following an adjustment to a previous deficiency, may elongate the skull-base, while leaving the growth at the vault unchanged, or even still further accelerating it. At the same time, however the intracranial pressure will be reduced, and the sides or top of the skull will cave in, giving the "ill-filled" appearance of the long Eskimo and Neanderthal crania.

Now there seems good evidence in favour of the view that, on the whole, the short- and broad-headed peoples inhabit areas of iodine-deficiency. Of course a survey of soils comparable in detail with the craniological data would be required to prove such a statement. Calcium-deficiency does not, however, appear to have evoked so violent a response. For whereas the Alpine and Mongoloid inhabitants of the mountainous portions of Europe and Asia are almost uniformly broad-headed, the Pygmies of the African rain forests are less markedly round-headed when compared with their taller negroid neighbours. To some extent, therefore, it may be wise to modify this theory. I suggest, accordingly, that, whereas both iodine- and lime-deficiencies may cause some ontogenetic and phylogenetic arrest of ossification at the basi-sphenoid suture, the latter condition produces far greater results. This might be due to the initial brain-development of Man having happened at a time of iodine-shortage and lime-abundance. It may have been positively favoured by the ontogenetic shortening of the base of the skull which then occurred. The individuals whose basi-nasal length was most constricted would be those who would have most need of a frontal and parietal expansion ; and, if a large brain was later to confer survival-value, these latter characters, with their former causal correlate, would be perpetuated, and would achieve still greater somatic expression owing to the selection of modifying factors. I suggest, therefore, that selection for iodine-economy is more liable to cause a shortening of the head than when calcium is the deficiency responsible for change. Calcium-deficiency, although able to reduce the length of the head, may be more apt to bring about a general reduction in size ; though here again an increase in the relative size of the brain, and so a tendency towards an increase in the growth at the sutures of the vault, must be expected. This theory will be applied in an attempt to interpret the observed differences in the anatomy of extinct and living races in terms of the supposed variations in the climates and mineral supplies of their habitats.

The progressive broadening of the human head is almost certainly not a direct result of a natural selection for an increased femininity ; though in many races, but not all, the female head is relatively broader than that of the male. In the diagram, I have examined the relationship between the length of the head and the development of the parietal bones covering the brain ; and it will be seen that, in general, there is a fairly constant slope showing how femininity reduces both head-length and parietal development. It will be observed, firstly, that the Neanderthal individuals fall completely outside the scheme of the Neanthropic races ; and that of these last the Upper Palæolithic or Cromagnon series of crania occupy an extreme position. Following down the direction of the sex-dimorphism in this race we arrive at the

Kalmucks, the Australians and Moriori serving to bridge the gap between the Cromagnon females and the Kalmuck males.

Of course no direct and close relationship between those groups

Study of Inter-Racial and Sexual Differences in the Relation between Head-length and the Development of the Parietal Bone.

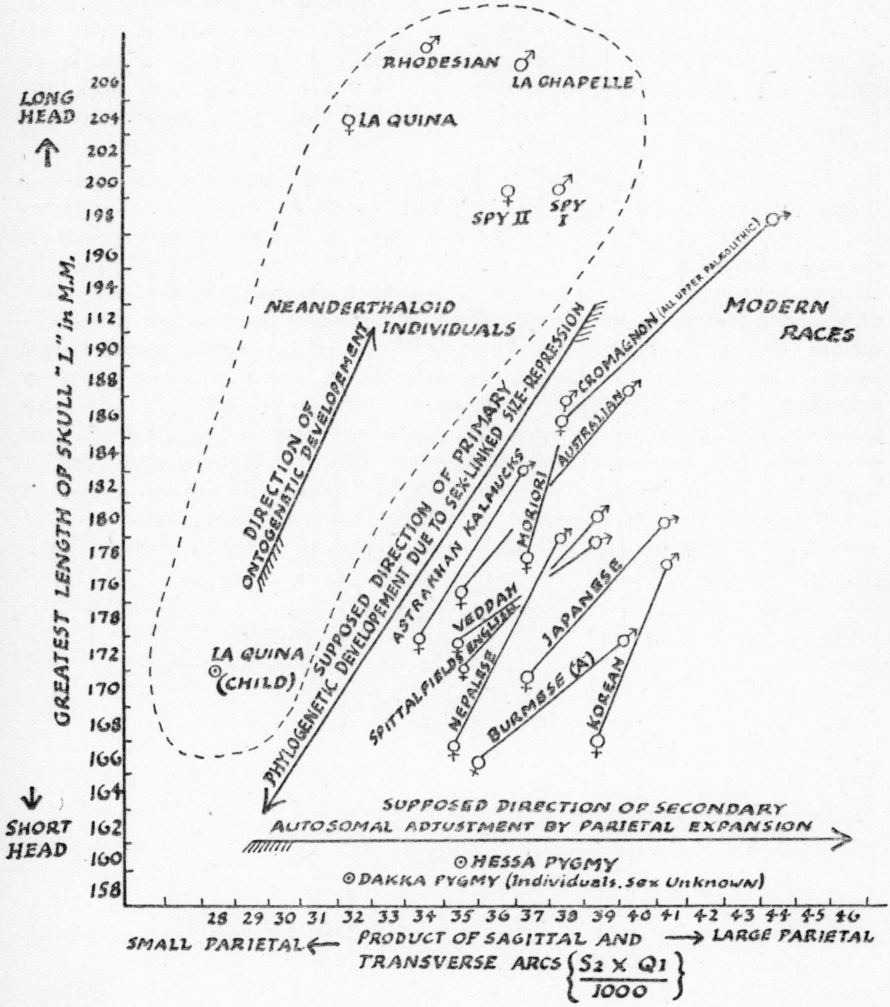

Data from *Biometrika* and *Annals of Eugenics*.

could be claimed on this account alone. It seems justifiable, however, to argue that one way in which they differ is in an increase of sex-linked activity whereby there is reduction in the size, but not in the proportions, of the skull from the Cromagnon standard. The remaining races, and especially the Japanese, Burmese, and Koreans, differ not only in this matter of the reduction in absolute dimensions, which is a sex-dimorphic character, but also in the relative increase of parietal expansion. It is not impossible, therefore, that part of this increase in the growth of the vault may have been developed as a secondary and autosomal adjustment to a preliminary reduction in the length. It must be urged that this diagram is reproduced more for the sake of illustrating a possible theory than by way of an attempt to prove a supposed fact. By this means, however, it would be possible to explain an eventual brachycephalization following from a selection for a calcium-economy achieved by the evolution of a more feminine type of physiology.

Lastly, a word must be said concerning the thickness of the skull at different points. In theory, if the parts unattached to muscle, such as the vault, serve as the reserves of fixed base, the thicker of these portions should reflect the nutritional state of the individual, whereas that of the muscle attachments at the sides and occiput should be more closely dependent upon the heredity. I have examined some measurements of skull thicknesses at the parietal eminence, which is uncovered by muscle, and of the occipital protuberance which, of course, is so attached. In every age-group, except the youngest (12–25), the female parietal-thickness was greater than that of the male. This may indicate a greater power of storing calcium. The standard deviation of the female was less ; and this fact could argue the action of her duplex, sex-linked factors. The thickness of the female occiput was slightly less, except for the same relevant (12–25) group.

CHAPTER X

THE EXTINCT HOMINIDÆ

Racial Mixture of Northern and Southern Stocks: Metabolic Rates and the Dominance of Racial Characters: Nutrition and the Dental Growth Gradient: The Food and Form of Neanderthal Man: The Mandible and Racial Mixture: The Chin and Neanthropic Man: Minerals and Dentition: Vitamins and Dentition: Climate and the Fossil Hominidæ: Java and China.

THIS CHAPTER REPRESENTS, FIRSTLY, AN ATTEMPT TO SUPPORT the mineral-hypothesis by drawing attention to the various anatomical characters of extinct forms of Man. On the whole it will be realized that the more coarse-boned variants have vanished, and that in Modern Man we are thus justified in seeing a type of which the survival-value has rested largely upon a more economical form, and physiology, whereby the requirements of mineral, and especially the bone-forming minerals, has been reduced. Secondly, it has been found necessary to interpret the association of certain anomalous characters in terms of racial mixtures between two hypothetical Northern and Southern sub-species of the original human stem. In conjunction with this, the analogy of Goldschmidt's experimental intersexuality produced by crossing two similar local strains of gypsy moth has been used.[1] Thus it is argued that the Southern strains of the human family may similarly be endowed with a higher metabolic rate, whereby certain of their characters tend to advance ahead, and so mask the features derived from the Northern ancestry. This influence would be greatest in respect to characters of the most recent evolutionary age and ontogenetic development. This high rate of the Southern metabolism is attributed to an initial selection under conditions offering an abundance of such catalytic substances as iodine, iron and manganese, and to the reduced importance of heat-economy under such circumstances.

It is proposed to deal with the origin and probable survival-value of most of the more striking Hominid features in the course of a discussion of Neanderthal Man. After this an attempt will be made to understand the more doubtful climatic conditions, and the curious mixture of wasteful with economical characters observed in the earlier specimens.

[1] Crew, F. A. E.: *Animal Genetics*, pp. 209–217; cft. Goldschmidt, R.: *Biol. Zentralb.*, 43, 446–452 (1923); Goldschmidt, R.: *The Mechanism and Physiology of Sex-Determination*, London, 1923.

I have presumed a reader who is more or less familiar with the general nature of the better-known and more important fossils. References are given to the facts as recorded in Sir Arthur Keith's two fascinating volumes, as these are so much more compact and easier of access than the large bulk of palæontological and other literature from which they have been compiled.[1] These books are full of useful comparisons between one fossil and another, the nearest variety of Modern Man being used as a control. At numerous points their author draws attention to the main fact that it is here hoped to explain, namely, the progressive deterioration of skeletal robustness found in nearly all such cases. The observation that this reduction has happened first at one point and then at another, instead of proceeding uniformly, may be hard to account for in view of our great ignorance concerning the mechanism of organic evolution. It need not, however, invalidate the main contention.

It seems worth while at the outset to consider the general nature of the interpretations to be placed upon fossil evidence. Do the specimens represent stages in a sequential plan, or are they random and unrepeated experiments? Should they be classed as orders, species, races, or treated merely as temporary and local variants of the human family? The mineral hypothesis supports the idea that they represent races in the ordinary meaning of the term. To risk a definition, a race may be considered as the temporarily stable product of a mixed ancestry that, for the time being, is not being subjected to either in-breeding or intense selection. On this view "races" should not be confused with "species." The latter are considered to be the immediate products of in-breeding. This is itself a result of a changed environment, and consequently of an intense, and sharply focussed incidence of natural selection acting in conjunction with the increased variability that it is itself thereby enabled to produce. On this view the "missing link" would be one of the relatively small number of individuals born during the adverse circumstances wherein one branch of the anthropoid apes was driven to become human. If so, the chances of finding a specimen are remote; though the preservative power of limestone, which is believed to have provided the first human cradle-land, affords some hope.

The Hominid remains so far discovered seem more probably to represent fair average samples of what were once relatively numerous and, for a time, successful races. There are two reasons that support such a view. Firstly, the chances of preservation of any single example are so remote that the more numerous types offer the best chance for one or more of their number to escape destruction and so court discovery. Secondly, if mineral abundance—and especially calcium-abundance—is as important a factor in the control of fertility and

[1] Keith, A.: *The Antiquity of Man*, 2nd edn., 2 vols., Lond., 1925; Keith, A.: *New Discoveries Relating to the Antiquity of Man*, London, 1931.

numbers as I suppose it to be, it must follow that arid conditions should provide the opportunity for the increase of numbers, and also the optimum conditions for the preservation of skeletons. The acidity of the soils during a humid epoch would seldom allow bone to be preserved. Even when specimens are preserved in travertine, which is lime washed from the surface, it should follow that the species in question was probably evolved in the earlier period when the surface-calcium was accumulating. The onset of pluvial conditions will scarcely have had time to make great alterations in the physical development.

RACIAL MIXTURE OF NORTHERN AND SOUTHERN STOCKS

There is a further important consideration that arises out of this line of thought. If our fossils represent members of relatively numerous populations, derived in their turn from less numerous and more in-bred stocks, it seems to follow that at these times of group-expansion racial mixtures will occur with relative frequency. Thus the known fossils are probably all the products of unions between more specialized and unknown species or sub-species. In attempting, therefore, to relate them to environmental conditions, it will be necessary not only to consider the climate, soil, and food, appropriate to the fossil race in question ; but at the same time allowance must be made for the conditions to which the contributory hereditary stocks may have been individually adjusted. Hence it is not impossible—indeed I think it probable—that all the fossil Hominidæ may represent racial mixtures. I propose, therefore, to try to interpret these distinct types in terms of a fusion between a Northern and Southern sub-species : the former adapted to arid, lime-abundant lands, and the latter to a habitat in which the rainfall and soil-acidity was greater. The latter strain may be held responsible for most of the genes now predominant in modern man ; and I propose thus to make use of the well-known term " Neanthropic " when referring to it. Before the evolution of the chin, the Southern branch might be called Proto-neanthropic. Conversely the Northern stocks, adapted to arid tundra and mountains, will be called " Palæanthropic " since, in all the known specimens of the primitive Hominidæ, some of the appropriate coarse-boned features have been conspicuously in evidence. As a further claim to the senior title it could be urged that the mountain habitat, in which the first change from anthropoid to Man is deemed to have occurred, probably bore a closer resemblance to the arid tundra than to the tropical forest at its Southern slopes. If so, the Southern migrants would take some long time before changed circumstances forced their departure ; and the great difference of environment would then demand a more extreme form of phylogenetic modification. The stock adapted to cold and aridity would tend to develop a strong anterior-lobe activity such as would cause the development of a massive skeleton ; and the material for this would be abundant. The Southern stock, on the other hand, would tend towards small size of fine bone; and after death the same conditions that had encouraged this character in the living would tend to destroy their remains. This, I suggest, accounts, at least partially, for the fact that so many extinct species, including the Hominidæ, are known to us mainly or solely by forms that are larger and coarser than those of their living relatives. These heavily built specimens may truly represent a large numerical majority of the individual ancestors; nevertheless, I suggest that the numerous gaps between one known race and the next have probably been bridged by smaller and more economical species than those of either the ultimate forbears or the descendants. These last may well have been less anatomically specialized than either of the more different and larger forms available to our examination. If their physiological superiority was purchased at the expense of an arrested ontogenetic development, a return of favourable conditions would allow a re-expansion accompanied by anatomical specialization along some novel line.

Now, when examining the primitive human fossils, our notice is naturally attracted to points in which they resemble and differ from ourselves, as also to points of resemblance with the anthropoid apes. All except Piltdown Man, and to a lesser extent the Galilee Neanderthal specimen, are characterized by a low sloping forehead and fused frontal torus. This last is a feature which is most fully developed in the Gorilla, and least in the Orang-utan and in the immature Taungs fossil from Africa.[1] It does not, therefore, seem legitimate to assume this to be a character that is essentially primitive both from a simian and from a human point of view. It may be a late specialization used in strengthening the jaw of the ancestral gorilla-like ancestor during a period of body expansion; and it may have accompanied somewhat of a reduction in the size of the brain. For the brain-case, if large and domed, provides not only an adequate attachment for the jaw-muscles, but also an arch strong enough to transmit the pressure from this upper attachment to the palate and teeth. I submit, therefore, that the supra-orbital development of Palæanthropic Man almost certainly proves a former remote relationship with a large gorilla-like anthropoid. It does not, however, rule out the possibility that the first human being possessed a smooth and domed "Neanthropic" frontal bone.

If the original man was smaller, and of greater physiological efficiency, than his last anthropoid ancestor, there is no reason why the subsequent enlargement of one line of his descendants should not have redeveloped the heavy and expensive brow-ridges, while that of another, specialized for a different habitat, retained its earlier—if accidentally achieved—economy. There are considerable difficulties in the way of imagining the erect posture as having evolved in any but a rather small and gibbon-like animal.[2] Thus, the whole of this argument supports the

[1] Keith, A.: *New Discoveries*, p. 37.

[2] Le Gros Clark, W. E.: *Man's Place among the Primates*, Man., 1935, 2, cft. Morton, D. J.

idea that a smooth-skulled Proto-neanthropic Man may stand as close or closer to the original point of human creation as any of his coarse-boned and extinct relations. The evolution of Modern Man from a forest-dwelling vegetable-feeding pygmy to a carnivore, and then into two strains of hunter, specialized for hot desert and cold steppe respectively, will be dealt with later. For the present, it remains necessary to remember the possibility of a Proto-neanthropic inheritance having contributed towards the development of all or any of the extinct forms. This will be definitely suggested in the case of the large-brained Piltdown and Neanderthal races; and it cannot be altogether ruled out even in the case of such small-brained specimens as Sinanthropus and Pithecanthropus. The latter may have a pure "Palæanthropic" head, but it was supported on thin, if not exactly Neanthropic, leg-bones. Five femora are now known.[1]

METABOLIC RATES AND THE DOMINANCE OF RACIAL CHARACTERS

It has already been mentioned that the recombination of characters that are assumed to have evolved separately will be explained on the analogy of Goldschmidt's *Lymantria* intersexes. The fact that it happened to be degrees of masculinity and femininity which were found to be alterable by the differences of metabolic rate does not seem vital to the analogy. The point of importance is that the final state of a late-developing character, in that particular case maleness or femininity, was influenced by the geographical origin of the genes responsible for its display. Some of the Japanese genes worked faster and could thus mask the influence of any of their English partners. The mineral-hypothesis attempts to explain this higher metabolic rate in terms of the increased iodine, iron, and manganese supply; and it is not impossible that calcium-deficiency might similarly have a direct contributory influence by promoting a greater membrane permeability. All these were the reasons given for the belief that the Southern races of Man were more feminine. Such femininity should therefore display itself more in the case of late- than of early-evolved and ontogenetically developed characters. As a fact, it is well-known that a relatively minute proportion of Southern or Negroid blood becomes increasingly recognizable as age advances, and that this is particularly true in the case of women.

I have used this plausible, though unfortunately unchecked, hypothesis in order to overcome a number of major anthropological difficulties, both in this chapter, and later when the bodily and mental results of racial mixtures in Modern Man come up for review. For the moment let me draw attention to the anomalous, yet perhaps now explicable, combination of the heavy brow-ridges with the long thin Neanthropic leg-bones found in the case of Pithecanthropus, Rhodesian Man, and

[1] Dubois, E.: *Congrès Internat. des Sci. Anthropol. et Ethnol.*, I, Londres, 1934.

the Australian aborigine—all, be it noted, from tropical habitats. The legs develop later than the head, even if the brow-ridges of the latter are themselves a late development. We must remember, however, that the latter are endocrine characters, and thus depend upon the interaction of a hormone with the tissue cells ; thus probably involving the dominant genes in their cell nuclei. I suggest, therefore, that the slow maturing Northern inheritance of Palæanthropic Man is permitted to become dominant, or rather predominant, in the cells of the frontal bone ; and that, when such ascendancy is once achieved, the potentiality to develop brow-ridges at puberty is thereby secured. Incidentally, this Palæanthropic heredity is probably older and therefore more dominant. In regard to the legs, however, these develop later than the skull, and thus afford the Southern and Neanthropic parts of the inheritance a far better chance of determining the whole of their final form. In their case the influence of the old or " wild type " is outdistanced before it can try to assert itself.

The same theory is of value in attempting to understand the differences of Palæanthropic and Neanthropic dentition. The teeth are essentially late-maturing organs, and as such will be mainly influenced by the fast or Southern portions of the inheritance. There is thus a correspondence between the teeth and limb bones such as may show a failure of any similar inter-racial correlation when compared with the skull or other early developing parts of the body. The two tropical Hominidæ, Rhodesian Man and Pithecanthropus, as well as the living, though Neanderthaloid, Australians, have the cynodont kind of teeth, which are otherwise associated with Neanthropic Man and the great apes. They are thereby sharply contrasted with the partial or complete taurodont expansion of the pulp-cavities, and fusion of the molar roots, seen in the other Northern examples, particularly in Neanderthal Man, and to a lesser extent in the Mauer and Piltdown mandibles. In a later section it will be argued that the mandible itself is a somewhat late evolutionary product, and is thus prone to be influenced by the Southern and faster heredity. In this way a lack of correspondence between the skull and jaw might be explained.

NUTRITION AND THE DENTAL GROWTH GRADIENT

Keith points out the existence of a zero point in the dentition situated between the second premolar and the first molar. This junction of the two-functional areas—the front and back—is stated to be the most stationary or conservative part of the dental series in the group of animals to which Man and the higher apes belong. If the molar teeth in the higher primates undergo a change, it is the last or third of the series which is first affected.[1] It is worth noting, therefore, that in the large gorilla the last molar is bigger than all the others, whereas in the much smaller chimpanzee this tooth is the smallest.[2] This could

[1] Keith, A. : *The Antiquity of Man*, Vol. II, p. 663. [2] Loc. cit., p. 680.

be quoted in support of a contention that the two types arose from a common ancestor of intermediate size, and were afterwards differentiated in accordance with the needs of opposite types of environment. We are reminded by this of the cases in which an arrest of development tends to manifest itself towards the extremities, where the inherent potentiality for fast growth and rapid metabolism is greatest.[1] This principle has already been postulated to account for a supposed shortening of the anthropoid arm.

Keith publishes drawings made from X-ray photographs of various teeth and jaws, and in these it is of interest to note that in the small third molar of the chimpanzee the pulp-cavity appears as bigger than that of the first and second molars. In the gorilla, on the other hand, this third molar, which is the biggest tooth of the three, shows the least degree of pulp-cavity expansion.[2] On the next page he gives similar drawings of a modern jaw as compared with the Piltdown, Krapina, and Heidelberg specimens. In all of these, as in the chimpanzee, the pulp-cavity of the last molar is the biggest. In his later book the same authority shows that alike in the modern child, the chimpanzee, and Sinanthropus, the pulp-cavity is larger in the posterior- than in the anterior-root of the molar.[3] All this, I consider, can be taken as evidence that pulp-cavity enlargement is an aspect of infantilism, or arrested development, of the sort that can be produced by some shortage or shortages in the composition of the diet. As such, it is most liable to influence the later-evolved characters, and to affect organs selected at times of increased metabolic activity.

Much the same argument can be applied to the reduction of the anthropoid canines to the small size met with in Neanderthal Man. In the large anthropoids there is a sex-dimorphism, which is not, however, found in the gibbons.[4] In the latter case it seems possible that a reduction of body-size has threatened to eliminate the female canine, so that some mutational adjustment or translocation has intervened to save it. Alternatively, it is possible that sex-linked repression, or autosomal exaggeration, of this character has not been necessary to the gibbon. If the canine be regarded as an emblem of male sexual display, and likewise as a weapon useful in sexual combats, its great development in the strong polygamous gorilla is explicable. Its curious recurrence in the Piltdown mandible might similarly be ascribed to a sexual selection for masculinity. This will be discussed in a separate context.

THE FOOD AND FORM OF NEANDERTHAL MAN

It is proposed to treat Neanderthal Man as the last and, on the whole, most perfected, if not most specialized, product of the vegetable-eating

[1] Cf. Huxley and de Beer, loc. cit.
[2] Keith, A.: *Antiquity of Man*, p. 683.
[3] Keith, A.: *New Discoveries*, p. 273.
[4] Keith, A.: *Antiquity of Man*, Vol. II, pp. 674–675.

Hominidæ. His extinction will be attributed mainly to a failure of his vegetable food-supply. Extreme cold may likewise, however, have contributed towards his end. This is strongly suggested by the large area of the Neanderthal nasal orifice. For in Modern Man the nasal index shows its closest correlation with summer-, and not with winter-temperature, a fact which has been taken to indicate that the nose is used as a cooling organ, as well as for protecting the lungs against cold.[1] Neanderthal Man thus appears to have been adapted to a climate in which the summers were hot. This in no way prevents us from still regarding him as a Tundra form. It merely supports Simpson's theory, whereby the glacial advances are set down to increments of solar radiation accelerating the atmospheric circulation, and so to consequent increases of precipitation in all climatic belts except the Tundra.

We are not prevented from supposing some large portion of the Neanderthal food to have been obtained from animals. Assuming a heavy rainfall, and a consequent growth of forest in most belts except the Tundra and hot desert, one might expect a concentration of herbivorous animals in the few spots wherein the soil-calcium remained high enough for them to retain their fertility. The Tundra would become crowded, and game abundant. There would also, however, be a lime-rich vegetation, whence the human population, no less than the animals that they hunted, would be able to obtain that balance of mineral which an exclusively carnivorous diet would probably be unable to supply.

Some of the Neanderthal characters are displayed by all of the remaining, though older, fossils here to be discussed ; and it may therefore be worth while to mention them, together with the deductions it is proposed to draw from either their presence or absence. The brow-ridges have already been treated as signs of a pituitary activity re-evolved after the dawn of humanity. It only remains to point out the apparent absence of sex-dimorphism in this character. In the probably female Gibraltar and La Quina Neanderthal skulls, the brow-ridges seem to be almost as well developed as those of the remainder, considered to be males.[2] We are thereby encouraged in the pursuit of verificatory evidence for the inductive theory that the economy of bone-forming material arises through the intensification of a sex-linked character, and vice versa. It is unfortunate that few of the other orders of fossil Hominidæ afford a chance of accurately distinguishing the sexes. In the probably immature, and possibly female, specimen of Sinanthropus the brow-ridges are distinctly reduced, as compared with the adult example.[3] Of course the Gibraltar and La Quina Neanderthal children also show an almost complete absence of brow-

[1] Thomson, A., and Buxton, L. H. D. : *J.R.A.I.*, 1923 ; also Davies, A. : *J.R.A.I.*

[2] Keith, A. : *Antiquity of Man*, p. 177.

[3] Keith, A. : *New Discoveries.*

ridge. All this strongly supports the original contention, namely that in Man the brow-ridge is a secondary development, though the genes responsible may very possibly have been unmasked from an older giant-anthropoid inheritance.

Mention has already been made of the thickness of the skull. It was pointed out that, although the thickness at the muscle-attachments is probably governed mainly by heredity, the vault-thickness also reflects the nutritional state of the body at the time of death. Most of the adult Neanderthal specimens are rather thick as compared with the modern average, though the reports seldom give details whereby one example may be compared with another. In any case it must be remembered that the parietal-thickness of modern dissecting-room material may vary between the extreme limits of 2–10 mm., which includes practically the whole range of the prehistoric series. Skull-thickness affords no reliable indication of the age or sex of a single specimen. Some figures that I have examined suggest that the thickness of the female skull tends to be greater and also more variable than in the case of men.[1] This seems to hold good of all age-groups except the youngest (12–25 years), but more data would be required to prove this.[2]

THE MANDIBLE AND RACIAL MIXTURE

Apart from their common lack of a chin, the Neanderthal mandibles are far less simian than those of either Piltdown or Taubach, the last of which is almost certainly associated with the high-vaulted and moderately brow-ridged Proto-Neanderthal skull of Ehringsdorf. The Piltdown cranium is also high and, considered by itself without the jaw, is less simian than the Neanderthal specimens.

It seems possible that this curious association of two high-vaulted skulls each furnished with an excessively narrow and simian mandible may—like the other anomalies—respond to explanation in terms of a mixture of fast- and slow-acting heredities. The mandible is a relatively late development in vertebrate history. It is very much younger than the skull. It would follow, therefore, that a quick-acting Southern heredity might have taken charge during the formation-period of the mandible after that of the slower-acting Northern ancestor had already decided upon the form of the skull. Of course, any gross maladjustments arising from such a cause would receive secondary mutational modification. I suggest, however, that the evolutionary and ontogenetic juniority of the mandible may have condemned it to a permanent servitude whereby it is destined to follow rather than to lead the earlier palatal evolution. The cranial development, of course, besides being more complex, is influenced for a longer portion of the developmental period. It will thus tend to be more affected by changes of environment; and we may reflect that the ontogenetic

[1] Anderson, R. J.: *Dublin J. med. Sci.*, 1882, Vol. 74, pp. 270–280.
[2] Author's unpublished material.

changes produced in this way are the nursery of the later phylogenetic modifications. Thus the mandible will be less subject to the plasticity of the well-nigh automatic reactions of the heredity to the environment. It will require the impact of more direct environmental pressure through selection to mould it to the palate that it is destined to fit.

Several rather puzzling corollaries seem to follow from this theory. If the Southern and fast-maturing type of heredity is in truth responsible for the development of a simian type of mandible, it seems to follow that this Southern type was itself more simian than the slow-maturing Northern form with which it later became mixed. It could, further, be argued that the high skull-vault and the domed-forehead belong to the slow-maturing Northern inheritance ; and indeed the absence of brow-ridges in the Neanderthal child suggest that the first man was to some extent " Neanthropic " in this respect. Moreover, if he was evolved in an area of severe iodine-deficiency, his metabolic rate would probably have been low, and the influence of his characters would thus easily be overtaken by any faster-maturing heredity that might later have become selected. It seems necessary to assume that somehow the fast Southern heredity is able to counteract the tendency to develop brow-ridges ; though these must be considered of later evolutionary date than the mandible. Nevertheless, as argued already, they are likely to have re-evolved in Man, and indeed to have evolved in the first instance upon the skull of an enlarging ape specialized for calcium-abundance and probably for cold and iodine-deficiency. Now it was already suggested that the brow-ridges of Pithecanthropus, Rhodesian Man and the Australian were allowed to develop because the ontogenetic foundations of the skull were laid before the final plan of the legs was taken in hand. To account for the domed forehead of the Piltdown skull, and for the high skull-vault of the Ehringsdorf specimen, it seems necessary to regard this process as having advanced one stage further. In these cases the development of the skull is not allowed to complete itself before the faster-acting Southern heredity steps in to counteract most of the potentiality for brow-ridge development. Similarly, the Southern heredity takes almost full charge of the mandible development.

To fit in with this theory, it seems necessary to assume that a narrow, anthropoid type of mandible was once characteristic of the Southern heredity. The truly human " horse-shoe " or parabolic arrangement, with its less parallel alignment of the back teeth, must thus be assumed to belong to the Northern slow-developing branch. On the whole this all agrees with the idea that the first man was markedly brachycephalic, and that the articulations of the jaw, together with the muscle-attachments and the back teeth, were forced apart, and later became adjusted to this form by secondary mutations. If this widening of the skull and of the gonial width occurred as part of a complex reaction to iodine-deficiency, it is reasonable to expect something of an atavistic return to the primitive simian condition, following upon any change of habitat which could once more supply iodine in abundance. The iodine-deficiency would damp down the metabolic rate, and might thus cause a relative lack of racial dominance in respect to the later evolved and human characters of the Palæanthropic mandible.

Although this hypothesis is the best that I can advance, it has several grave objections. For instance, one could expect the same simian mandible to appear in Rhodesian Man and Pithecanthropus : for it might have been expected to be correlated with the thin and long Neanthropic form of the limb-bones found in these two tropical forms.[1] We may reflect, too, that there are but few signs of a simian mandible displayed by the living Australians or other tropical races. Only the Talgai youth shows something of the same parallel anthropoid type of palate as is indicated by the mandibles of Piltdown and Taubach.[2] In living races it is probable that the Melanesian negroes come nearest to this form. For in their case the canines tend also to be large, and to mark a right angle between the transverse lines of the incisors and the fore-and-aft lines of the molars and pre-molars.

Now actually there is no suspicion of a simian mandible having fitted the palate of Rhodesian Man. The upper teeth are arranged in a horse-shoe similar to that of the true Neanderthal specimens. In this case the strength of the Northern heredity must be held responsible for this, as also for the huge thickness of the frontal torus. As for Pithecanthropus, it seems probable that the chinned Kedung Brubus mandible must now be associated with this already famous specimen.[3] The chin, also as will later be argued, would appear to have been evolved by the Southern branch, but only after the invention of hunting and the specialization of the long thin leg-bones. If, then, there is a Southern strain in the Piltdown and Taubach-Ehringsdorf races, it is that of an earlier short-legged and chinless proto-Neanthropic stock ; not that of Modern Man as we now know him, or even as he may have been before the formation of the Rhodesian or Java races.

THE CHIN AND NEANTHROPIC MAN

The lack of a chin can only be explained in terms of its evolution in the case of Modern Man. A single primary cause, namely the evolution of hunting, may be seen to produce a variety of physiological strains and to impose deficiencies of minerals and vitamins. The former will be dealt with first.

Chins are of very rare occurrence in the animal kingdom. With the exception of Modern Man, they are found in the case of the elephant, and in that of a rather large gibbon, though in the latter case the degree of mental protuberance is not striking. Clearly, then, it is

[1] Note, however, the new view concerning the femora of Pithecanthropus.
[2] Keith, A. : *New Discoveries*, p. 452.
[3] Loc. cit., pp. 295–297.

impossible to explain the chin merely in terms of a mineral-deficiency affecting the teeth. The normal influence would be to influence the pituitary, and so to reduce all parts according to an evolved and pre-arranged plan. I suggest, then, that the chin arises through a physiological strain, but a strain imposed, not from without, but by the sudden need of the animal to increase its size for mechanical purposes, while making use of a constant, or possibly diminishing, supply of structural substance. The elephant with his long trunk is a much more efficient tree-browser than a primitive Baluchithere, or even a giraffe, whose whole reach must be secured by the use of bone. Mineral-deficiency can again explain the origin and usefulness of the serial development of the elephant's molar teeth. By increasing the length of life they have done away with the need for frequent parturition with all its attendant danger and physiological expense. My suggestion, then, is that in both Man and the elephant the chin arose through a reduction of dentition encouraged by a mechanical demand to increase stature. The elephant required more reach, and the man needed speed to run down game.

There thus seems no need to postulate the chin as being older than the hunting phase. If the ancestors of the Neanthropic stock became specialized for a calcium-deficient diet as vegetable and omnivorous feeders in a pluvial habitat, the normal simian absence of a chin would be retained until they took to running down the larger game; such as would be encountered in drier and more favourable surroundings. It seems necessary to postulate a change of environment of a sort that precluded the possibility of a return to vegetable food. The cold steppe seems best to fulfil this requirement; since man cannot eat grass and thus must hunt or herd the herbivores. Moreover, the cold steppe would exert a second influence towards the encouragement of large size. Besides requiring fleetness of foot, which is helped by long thin legs, it would also encourage large size and pituitary activity as a means of generating and conserving heat. We have thus found two influences which require a large, size with a corresponding expenditure of skeletal material. At the same time, we may reflect that meat, while supplying plenty of protein for purposes of heat-production, will be deficient in bone-forming material. Can we in this way explain the limb-flattening of the tall Cromagnon Man?[1] Despite his stature, can this still be considered a sign of deficient diet?

It remains difficult to explain why the reduction of the teeth has been accompanied by no great reduction in the strength of the jaw. Perhaps the best way to regard the change is to imagine a general increase of stature to have been accompanied by a change of food, such as not merely demanded no improvement of the dentition, but even actively selected in favour of its reduction. The vitamin C deficiency of meat

[1] See Chapter IX for theory that bone flattening assists calcium economy.

seems capable of doing this. It is likewise suspected of having played a very different part in modifying the Neanderthal taurodont molars when Man took to eating seeds and roots, having previously made use of leaves, shoots and fruit such as are available in a warmer habitat. I propose, therefore, to discuss the influence of vitamin-shortages under a separate heading. Before doing so it will be best to dispose of the possible influences of mineral-deficiency upon the evolution and retention of the two types of human teeth, the cynodont, or modern form, found also in the apes, and the taurodont, or more specialized form seen fully evolved in Neanderthal Man.

Before finishing this discussion of influences liable to affect the mandible, reference must be made to the great width of the ascending ramus, noticeable in many primitive jaws, and to the shallow sigmoid notch. These features are most pronounced in the case of the Mauer proto-Neanderthal jaw, and have been used as an argument in support of the authentiticy of the otherwise modern and chinned Moulin Quignon and Galley Hill mandibles claimed to be of early Pleistocene age. The researches of Draper have recently shown that liability to certain forms of disease is correlated with the gonial angle of the jaw.[1] This, in its turn, supports the view that a natural selection for physiological characters could result in important changes of anatomy. A correlation of anthropometrical and biochemical observations, taken on the healthy as well as sick subjects, might throw new light both upon the ætiology of these diseases, and so explain the mechanism responsible for the anatomical variations in question. I suggest that a study of mineral metabolism affords the surest approach to any bridge-work between anthropometry and pathology.

Finally, in regard to the evolution of the chin, it must be pointed out that the two halves of the jaw ossify separately ; and are, later, joined together by the expansion of secondary centres of ossification, which are retained as the mental protuberances. These are more marked in the Negro, whose ancestors are on other grounds regarded as having been subject to severe calcium-deficiency. It is possible, therefore, that some of the chin-development in Modern Man is the result of an imperfect ossification of the two halves of the fœtal mandible, and a consequent selection of mutations whereby an active secondary ossification of the symphysis was thereby encouraged. This, however, could yield no more than a very partial explanation ; and, as a matter of fact, the chins of Negroes are not well-marked.

MINERALS AND DENTITION

It is later to be argued that both the reduced Neanthropic dentition, with its resultant chin, and also the taurodont molars of Neanderthal Man, the Mauer jaw, and the Piltdown mandible, were all partially caused by changes of diet that reduced the intake of vitamin C. In

[1] Draper, G. : *Disease and the Man*, London, 1930.

the first case, however, the deficiency is held to have been associated with calcium-deficiency and iodine-abundance, and in all the rest with just the reverse ratio characteristic of the arid Tundra. Lime-deficiency and iodine-abundance are also probably the conditions to suit which the anthropoids have been evolved. It is thus no wonder if the same conditions have favoured the retention of the ancestral form of tooth. The taurodont tooth, on the other hand, is the specialized product. Indeed one may legitimately wonder whether its evolution began with the very dawn of humanity, and has since been reversed.

It seems probable that the taurodont tooth was more efficient for purposes of grinding down large amounts of vegetable food, and for withstanding the wear that would result from grit adhering to roots. This would be a new danger if there were a change from fruit-eating to root- or seed-collecting. Probably the enlarged pulp cavities of the taurodont teeth would be enabled to secrete more secondary dentine, and so to prolong the lives of their possessors. At the same time, this enlargement of the pulp-cavity, and the associated failure of development on the part of the roots, strongly suggests a primary degeneration which has been seized upon and forged to a new use.

It is one thing to claim usefulness for a character and another to explain its origin. This failure of normal root-development strongly suggests some maladjustment between the separate parts of the heredity, or of the latter to the environment. The enlarged pulp-cavity, too, could be claimed as evidence of a general tendency for cartilage-proliferation to outstrip ossification owing to an alkalinity of the internal environment.[1] In this context it can be considered side by side with the great development of the Neanderthal brow-ridges. All this suggests, though it does not prove, that Neanderthal Man may have arisen through racial mixture, and that these new developments are the result of the interaction of fast- and slow-maturing types of heredity. The enlarged pulp-cavity is known as an infantile tendency in Modern Man, after which it is gradually modified. In Neanderthal Man it appears to have been hurried on so as to pass out of reach of the influence of the genes usually responsible for its subsequent modification. Similarly, the tooth appears to have developed before the roots were allowed time for their division. Perhaps the slower Northern heredity was responsible for this.

On the whole it seems reasonable to believe that some degree of iodine-deficiency was associated with the calcium-abundance that it is necessary to postulate in connection with the enlarged brow-ridges and pulp-cavities. This might have encouraged a compensatory hypersecretion of the anterior-lobe, and might also have influenced the arrested development of the late-developing molar roots. The possibility that vitamin-deficiency may also have contributed towards the expansion of the pulp cavities will be referred to in the next section.

[1] Cf. Balint and Weiss, loc. cit.

So far little has been said concerning the possible influence of vitamin-deficiencies upon animal and human evolution ; for, on the whole, the evidence in favour of a geographical distribution of such deficiencies is negative, with the possible exception, at all events, that a greater supply of vitamin E may characterize the arid habitats. On changes of culture must probably be laid the responsibility for the need to reorganize the vitamin demands and consumption. A change from fruit- or leaf-eating to the consumption of roots or seeds would probably reduce the supply of vitamin C, even if it augmented the amounts of B, and possibly of A and D also. Similarly, a change from vegetable to flesh food would reduce the intake of vitamin C, as well as that of probably all other vitamins except E, the sex vitamin, and the B complex, in both of which flesh tends to be rich. Vitamin D could only be obtained from eating the subcutaneous fat—a fact that incidentally suggests an origin for the practice of chewing skins as a means of making clothes.[1]

Altogether, then, both Neanderthal Man, if presumed to be a seed- and root-eater, and also Neanthropic Man, here regarded as a carnivore, may be expected to have experienced a reduced intake of vitamin C as compared, say, with the diet of a forest-dwelling giant anthropoid. Each stock, I suggest, used the resultant influences on ontogenetic development so as to develop racial and hereditary characters of almost diametrically opposite kinds.

Stated briefly, and in non-technical language, the effect of vitamin C deficiency is to impair the quality of the dentine, to expand the blood vessels, to produce fluid in the pulp-cavities, and to encourage a diseased condition of the gums and of the alveolus in which the teeth are set. These symptoms are most easily produced in guinea-pigs, which are, of course, complete herbivores. Dogs, like other carnivores, possess some mysterious power of manufacturing, or possibly of merely storing, vitamin C. They suffer, however, from very similar tooth-defects when kept short of vitamin D—the lime-vitamin. In the case of dogs starved of vitamin D, Melanby has also noticed a thickening of the jaw-bones, together with an irregularity of the teeth, particularly the lower incisors.

Thus the enlarged pulp-cavity of the taurodont Neanderthal tooth could be ascribed to an initial deprivation of vitamin C, causing a swelling of the pulp cavity in the individual, and thus encouraging a move towards the development of larger teeth, such as the new root or seed diet would encourage and fix through a process of natural selection. Similarly, the change from vegetable- to flesh-eating in the case of Neanthropic Man would also result in the deprivation of vitamin C ; which, on this occasion, would be used to initiate a change towards

[1] Cf. table of Vitamin contents of foods. "Vitamins," *Spec. Rep. Ser. med. Res. Coun.*, Lond., No. 167 (1932).

smaller teeth formed in the original manner. Flesh food would no longer demand big teeth ; and it seems probable that small teeth would be better developed than those governed by an heredity selected to make them grow big. Just as iodine-deficiency was held to encourage fœtalization, so has a vitamin deficiency (E) been shown to cause a cellular degeneration, which proceeds in the reverse order of ontogenetic development.[1] Thus natural selection would encourage an arrest of tooth-development at the childish stage before the demand could rise beyond the concentration of the available supply. In addition to this influence responsible for the reduction in the size of the Neanthropic teeth, one might also suggest a possible encouragement of a phylogenetic expansion in the development of the jaw similar to that produced in Melanby's dogs by the deprivation of vitamin D. Lack of vitamin C may possibly have this same result in a species subject to that deficiency ; and in any case vitamin D might also be lacking in a colder and more northern environment, such as must be compared with a tropical forest, the presumed point of departure. In any case flesh food is not rich in vitamin D.

The difficulty is not so much to find possible causes for the ontogenetic development of a chin, but rather to see why it should have been retained. Possibly it became admired as a male sex-character, indicative of strength and pituitary activity. The change to meat-eating would supply an excess of vitamin E, such as would be useful in accommodating any increased demands on the part of the anterior-lobe. The projecting chin and smaller teeth would be of no disadvantage until Neanthropic Man returned to a vegetable diet. Perhaps, after that, the macrodont, but attractive, smile of the Negro may have played a part in reversing or arresting the process.

As far as the fossil evidence is concerned, it may be noted that the Neanderthal mandibles already show the beginning of a reduced dentition. This character is most marked in the specimen that comes from the region closest to the moist Atlantic, namely the Bañolas mandible.[2] When compared with the much older and stouter Mauer jaw, the ascending and horizontal ramus of the largest Neanderthal specimen—that of Spy—is seen to be smaller ; though the reduction of the latter has not quite kept place with the greater reduction in the dentition.[3] Even here the beginnings of a chin may be said to have shown themselves. Indeed, between the Heidelberg (Mauer) and Spy types of jaw one suspects that there may have been a type intermediate in point of time and evolutionary position which actually exceeded the later and perfected Neanderthal specimen in the question of chin-development. Indeed it could be claimed that the Kedung Brubus fragment represents such a phase.[4] If vitamin C deficiency was acute,

[1] *Vitamins*, p. 107.
[2] Keith, A. : *New Discoveries*, p. 358.
[3] Keith, A. : *Antiquity of Man*, Vol. I, p. 330.
[4] Keith, A. : *New Discoveries*, pp. 295–297.

there would have been a period when the smaller Neanthropic form of teeth would have been encouraged. The taurodont expansion essentially represents an extreme divergence from normal. Such an active utilization of an essentially degenerate character is unlikely to have occurred, unless some extreme disadvantage had already been encountered.

In conclusion, then, we may remember the solid round-sectional limb-bones and the thickening of the Neanderthal ribs, adding to these the signs of calcium-abundance and probably of iodine and vitamin C deficiency exhibited by the development of the teeth and jaw. All these traits, together with the wide nose, bear out a theory that the race in question was evolved for an arid habitat, which was hot in summer, even if it may have been cold in winter. In accordance with such a view, seeds and roots are taken to have been an essential part of the diet. The specialized hunters were the tall Cromagnons evolved for the cold steppe-conditions that followed, and probably caused the Neanderthal extinction ; as also were their relatives, the steatopygous Bushman and his ancestors, evolved for life in the hot, waterless deserts.

CLIMATE AND THE FOSSIL HOMINIDÆ

It now remains to mention the chief anatomical characters of some of the more important fossil Hominidæ. Wherever it may be possible, evidence or theories concerning climate will be used to interpret these characters on the assumption that they have been influenced by nutrition. In the case of Piltdown Man the opportunity will also be taken to outline Simpson's theory concerning the causes of the Quaternary climatic changes. With minor modifications these can then be extended to cover an explanation of the corresponding alternations of temperature and humidity that affected human evolution and caused racial extinction in other parts of the world.

The Piltdown skull-fragments were exceedingly thick, though the external tabular surfaces of the bone were thin. When reconstructed, they showed signs of an upright Neanthropic form of forehead. Keith considers that the cranial capacity was fully human, though Smith Woodward differed from him in allowing less space between the fractured top-edges of the parietal bones. Associated with this was a mandible of very simian affinities ; and a large canine tooth was later found to complete the contrast between forehead and jaw.[1] An implement, and other evidence from a probably contemporary site, suggest that Piltdown Man hunted the largest Pliocene elephant, *E. meridionalis*. Hippopotamus, red deer and horse are also considered to have been contemporary with him. The stegodon and mastodon, also found in association, were probably derived from earlier deposits.

[1] Dawson, C., and Woodward, A. S. : *Quart. J. geol. Soc.*, London, LXIX, 1913, also same authors, same publication, LXXIII, 1917. See also Keith, A. : *The Antiquity of Man*, Vol. II.

This evidence, such as it is, suggests a warm arid climate. At all events, assuming the truth of the mineral hypothesis, *Elephas meridionalis* might well have been rendered extinct either by some subsequent pluvial period responsible for soil-leaching and decalcification, or by cold. It may almost amount to an argument in a circle, but I suggest that the same conditions could have been responsible for the extinction of Piltdown Man, whom I regard as showing signs of an expensive calcium-metabolism. In regard to date, it is worth noting that the teeth of *E. meridionalis* have been dredged from sea-bottom off the Norfolk coast, and that Clement Reid regarded them as derived from the Cromer Forest bed.[1] Simpson dates this deposit between the

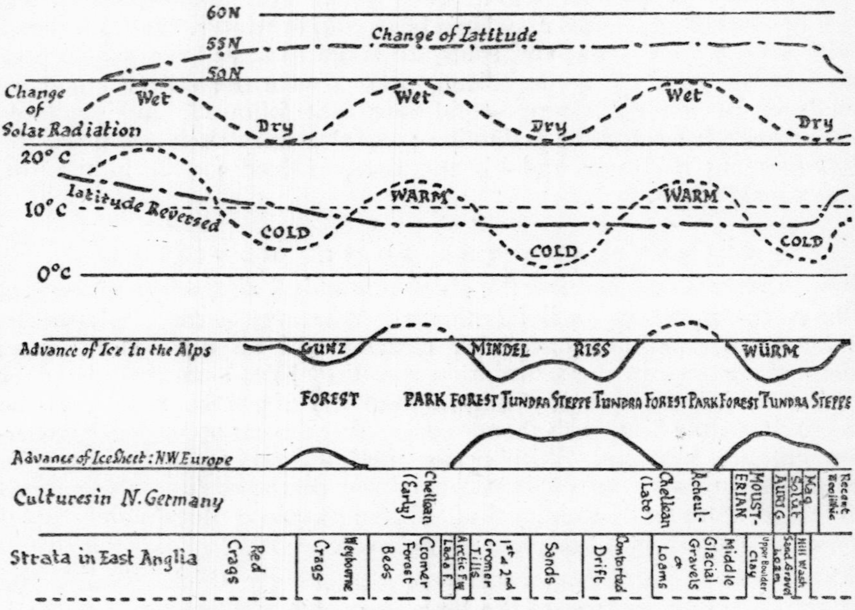

Simpson's Theory of Pleistocene Climate.

Gunz and Mindel glaciations, at a time of the solar warmth, a result of which was to cause the Mindel glaciation through the deposition of ice at the pole. His conclusions, rendered in diagrammatic form, are here reproduced.[2]

As a sequel to the period of solar warmth responsible for the Mindel, it will be seen that the next long period of the Mindel and Riss glaciations appears to have been cold and dry. The Mindel ice-sheet perished through lack of nourishment, and not because any increase of temperature had caused a general thaw. It seems probable that the

[1] Clement Reid : *Submerged Forests*, p. 39, Cambridge, 1913.
[2] Simpson, C. C. : "The Climate during the Pleistocene Period," *Proc. roy. Soc. Edin.*, 1929–30, Vol. V, Part III, No. 21, p. 267.

Mauer jaw should be assigned to some part of this long and, on the whole, arid epoch. M. Rutot places it in the Mindel glaciation which on Simpson's interpretation spread Tundra conditions over north-west Europe.[1] This view suits the physiological theories here being tested. Perhaps the steppe-conditions that intervened between the Mindel and the Riss dealt almost as hardly with the proto-Neanderthals of Heidelberg as did the later Steppe conditions with the true Neanderthals of the Würm glacial advance. Between these two very strong-boned types we find the less typically Neanderthaloid skull and the somewhat simian mandible of the Ehringsdorf-Taubach people.[2] This was imbedded in Travertine, whereas the Mauer jaw was in sands. Travertine strongly suggests a period of increased rainfall. Under such conditions the food would probably lack calcium, which had previously been abundant in the upper soil. This may, in part, account for the special features of the Ehringsdorf race. It might furnish conditions suitable for the northern migration of an earlier hybrid type. I hesitate to claim the thin skull of the Ehringsdorf specimen as a racial character, since a thick piece was also found in the same deposits.

To apply Simpson's system of European climates to the rest of the world, a large number of interacting influences would need to be allowed for. For instance, as Brooks has pointed out, the ice-caps at the Poles have a critical size, above which they tend automatically to expand, or at all events, to remain stable.[3] Moreover, the larger the ice-sheet, the greater will be both the diameter and width of the surrounding ring of arid Tundra, swept by the outflow of dry and cold wind from the Polar anticyclone. This extension of the Tundra serves to contract the belt of tropical rainfall ; so that a greater total precipitation, responsible for the formation of large ice sheets, might thus fall within a narrowing belt of tropics.

Climate might also be influenced by alterations in sea-level with the consequent flooding or draining of land. For chronological purposes, too, it is of the utmost importance to understand the relations of the marine and river terraces to the Alpine and other relics of glaciations.[4] The weight of ice at the Pole, and upon mountains, may have served to depress adjacent coast-lines, and so to affect the outfalls and consequently the terraces of the rivers. As a slight off-set to this influence the locking-up of sea-water in the ice would need also to be considered. Finally, if the Poles are migratory, the shifting weight of the ice-cap might influence sea-level. Of course, it is possible that the theories of polar shift and continental drift may be found to be totally invalid, which I doubt. Or, alternatively, we may suppose either process or

[1] Keith, A. : *Antiquity of Man*, pp. 321 and 323. Cf. t. Rutot, M. : *Bull. Soc. belge. Géol. Pal. Hydr.*, 1920, Vol. XXIX, pp. 31, 151.
[2] Keith, A. : *Antiquity of Man*, pp. 191–194 *New Discoveries*, p. 327.
[3] Brooks, A. : *Climate, Through the Ages*, London, 1926.
[4] Cf. Sollas : *Ancient Hunters*.

both of them to have been gradual, as assumed by Wegener[1]; or to have taken place cataclysmically, owing to the release of the pent-up heat of radio-activity, as suggested by Joly.[2]

The extinction, if not the evolution, of Rhodesian Man affords a good opportunity for attempting to make use of Simpson's climatic hypothesis outside the European theatre for which it was originally designed. Simpson made use of Wegener's theory of Polar Shift; and so, in order to be consistent, we must postulate a corresponding equatorial shift in the case of Africa.[3] The same approach of the Pole held responsible for much of the European glaciation will serve also to move the Equator from the basin of the Congo to that of the Zambezi.

Broken Hill, where Rhodesian Man was discovered, is to the South of the present Equator. I suggest, therefore, that it was a Southern extension of the rain-belt that may have contributed towards a decalcification of the soil resulting in his extinction. In addition, it must be pointed out that an increase of solar warmth would increase precipitation in two ways. Firstly, it would accelerate atmospheric circulation and the evaporation of water from the sea. Secondly, not only would it thereby increase the tropical rainfall, but it would also nourish and expand the ice-caps and their surrounding belts of arid Tundra. This, as Brooks has pointed out, would serve to constrict the size of the remaining climatic belts, and so to emphasize their characters. I consider, therefore, that Rhodesian Man was trapped in the peninsula of South Africa, and rendered extinct through a mineral-deficiency caused by an excess of rainfall. It seems most convenient to attribute all this to the Riss-Würm solar warmth; though the alternative of the Gunz-Mindel cannot be ruled out.

Most of the evidence from the bones of Rhodesian Man point to the same conclusion, namely, that mineral-deficiency caused his end. At first sight it could hardly be claimed that the huge frontal torus supports this contention. If, however, the latter be taken as evidence of an earlier-evolved pituitary-activity, a wasteful type of general physiology must be suspected. This would serve to hasten his end, even if it might also have served to select in favour of its own modification. The thin Neanthropic form of the limb-bones has already been dealt with. They are regarded as signs of racial mixture with a Neanthropic form. Perhaps it was this same mixture that helped to lower the receptivity of the cells in the frontal bone, so that the latter were more willing to react than even those of a pure Neanderthal inheritance.[4]

So much, then, for definite signs of racial maladjustment. Looking to

[1] Wegener, E., loc. cit.

[2] Joly, J.: "The Vicissitudes of a Habitable Globe," essay in *Science To-day*, Eyre and Spottiswoode, London, 1934.

[3] This has been omitted in the nevertheless very interesting paper by General J. C. Smuts: "Climate and Man in Africa," *S. Afr. J. Sci.*, Vol. XXIX, p. 125 (1932).

[4] Keith, A.: *Antiquity of Man*, p. 377 *et seq.*

the actual individual, we see that his third molars are very small and degenerate—as in Civilized Man. It is also to be noted that the skull-vault is thinner than in the northern Neanderthal examples. How far these two effects may be individual or racial is doubtful, but in either case I claim that they tell the same tale.

Lastly, to pass to what is definitely an affair of individual maladjustment, mention must be made of the disease of the bone observable in the region of the ear and knee.[1] The trouble seems to have been started by a wound, but I strongly suspect mineral-deficiency of having contributed towards the final outcome. This conclusion finds support in the further fact that the teeth were in very bad condition as a result of caries and abscesses.[2]

Other Hominid remains bearing the signs of disease are the Galilee frontal bone,[3] and the original femur of Pithecanthropus.[4] All this may be due to pure chance ; but it fits in well with the theory to light upon troubles that would be encouraged by calcium-deficiency in these three extreme forms of the coarse-boned races so far discovered in the tropics.

JAVA AND CHINA

It is less easy to apply Simpson's climatic hypothesis when considering the influence of environment upon the evolution or extinction of those two extremely primitive, and in some ways similar, forms, Pithecanthropus of Java, and Sinanthropus, the Peking Man. Recently, too, notice has been given of the discovery of a second Java specimen, the Solo River Man.[5] It is not impossible that this second, and more strongly built, skull may represent the male, and Pithecanthropus the female, of the same race. If so, the correspondence with the two—the large and small—skulls of Sinanthropus is closer than ever.

The theory of polar shift appears to have much less bearing on the Javanese climatic changes than it does on those of China. The Quaternary shift postulated by Wegener serves to depress the Equator towards the point of the African peninsula and to raise it so as to correspond with the present line of the China coast.[6] Java is thus close to the pivoting point and may consequently have been less affected than other parts of the world. The fact that the remains of Pithecanthropus were found in a rich fossiliferous stratum containing many other extinct species could be taken to indicate favourable conditions for animal and human reproduction, and might thus excuse the wasteful form of anatomy, and probably of physiology, displayed by the large frontal torus. The climate was probably more arid than at

[1] Ibid., p. 417.
[2] Ibid., p. 400.
[3] Keith, A. : *New Discoveries*, p. 185.
[4] Dubois, E. : *Trans. Roy. Dublin Soc. N. S.*, 1896, Vol. VI, p. 1.
[5] For preliminary notice and photographs see *Illustrated London News*.
[6] See diagram, p. 74.

present, since otherwise the bones would seem unlikely to be saved for the initial mineralization responsible for their subsequent preservation.

It may be no chance that the remains of Sinanthropus are similarly found in association with large numbers of animal bones ; and this time under circumstances which lead one strongly to suspect that Man is responsible for the accumulations in question. Do Pithecanthropus and Sinanthropus represent the dawn of the hunting phase ? Need even these early specimens embody a pure species ? May they not represent the first blend of the Southern calcium economy with the Northern pituitary activity and heat economy ?[1] Could not the moderately taurodont dentition of Sinanthropus be but a faint reflection of an earlier and fully taurodont state evolved for vegetable feeding, and then partially annulled by the Southern heredity ? The complete absence of this condition in Pithecanthropus might be due to the more Southern and iodine-abundant habitat. For this might well allow rather more racial dominance to be achieved by the indigenous parts of the inheritance. This could also account for the incipient chin of the Kedung Brubus mandible attributed to Pithecanthropus. On this theory a complete Modern Man, with a chin and thin long legs, and probably with a " smooth " high-vaulted skull, must be presumed to have been already in existence in the early Pliocene or late Pleistocene, to whichever period it is eventually decided to attribute these two remarkable specimens.

In my own opinion, the figures given on the next page somewhat belie the impression made by the seemingly brutish appearance of these primitive skulls. Need a cranial capacity of 1000 c.c. necessarily indicate so great a lack of intelligence that survival-value would thereby be impaired ? This is one of the fundamental questions to which anthropology must try to give a reply. Thus we must avoid too many preliminary guesses if their influence is not to invalidate our conclusions. It must be admitted that there is an unbridged gap between the 1000 c.c. average of the two Sinanthropus specimens as well as of Pithecanthropus on the one hand, and the 1300 which is the lowest average of any living race except the dwarf Bushman. Thus we are faced with the problem how this space was filled. Why did La Chapelle Man develop his huge 1625 c.c. ? I hesitate to believe that this, or the occasional 1900 c.c. realized in modern civilized individuals, is solely the result of a natural selection for greater intelligence. The study of evolution suggests that effects further their own causes. Every step towards the selection of a character seems to increase the chance that some individuals will display it to an even more exag-

[1] In a lecture recently delivered in Oxford Mr. Lee pointed out the curious mixture of Northern and Southern animals in the Sinanthropus deposits. This could support the theory that the Northern and Southern variants of the human race were also in contact during this period.

gerated degree. Thus I suggest that racial mixture, or in-breeding, and probably both, have resulted in the occasional over-development of the human brain from a size already selected as adequate for the life of an unarmed animal such as primitive man, whose sole advantage lay in this same superiority of intelligence in relation to the other animals with which he was in competition or symbiosis.

Of course the main interest of the China and Java finds centres upon the very small cranial capacity. Various estimates have been made, but the following afford a useful basis for comparison :

	Capacity.	Authority.
Sinanthropus { Adult	1100 c.c.	Davidson Black.
Sinanthropus { Immature or Female	1000 c.c.	Cf. Keith : *New Dis.*, p. 203, 287.
Pithecanthropus	900 c.c.	Dubois, E.
Neanderthal Man { La Chapelle .	1625 c.c.	Cf. Keith : *New Dis.*, p. 297.
Neanderthal Man { Gibraltar .	1200 c.c.	Keith, A. : *Antiquity of Man*, p. 659.
Piltdown Man { Keith's Reconstr. .	1400 c.c.	,, ,, ,,
Piltdown Man { Smith Woodward's Reconstruction	1070 c.c.	,, ,, ,,
Rhodesian Man	1300 c.c.	,, ,, ,,
Bushman (average of 5 skulls) .	1250 c.c.	,, ,, ,,
Tasmanian	1350 c.c.	,, ,, ,,
Australian (average 7) . . .	1340 c.c.	Keith : *New Dis.*, p. 283.
European (average of 10 skulls) .	1490 c.c.	Keith, A. : *Antiquity of Man*, p. 659.
Taungs Anthropoid . . .	500 c.c.	
Gorilla { adult male . . .	518 c.c.	Keith, A. : *New Dis.*, p. 104.
Gorilla { of same est. age as Taungs	390 c.c.	Keith, A. : *New Dis.*, p. 104.
Chimpanzee ,, ,,	340 c.c.	
Child at Birth	300 c.c.	Keith, A. : *Antiquity of Man*, p. 659.
Child at 3½ years (European) . .	1050 c.c.	,, ,, ,,

There is more than a suspicion that certain conditions of life may serve positively to reduce the cranial capacity. If an electrolyte deficiency is needed to encourage a swelling of the brain, a mineral-abundance, might well reduce the cranial capacity. In the case of Pithecanthropus the longitudinal section displays a curious projection of the bregma, which thus becomes the high point, or vertex, of the skull. The bregma overlies the bregmatic pool of the cerebro-spinal fluid, which flows upward to this point in the two sub-coronal streams.[1] This suggests that in Pithecanthropus the fluid system has exerted a greater pressure upon the vault than have the surrounding areas of the brain. Thus, if one function of the cerebro-spinal fluid is to compensate for variations in the cerebral expansion, it seems to follow that

[1] Keith, A. : *New Discoveries*, pp. 286, 288, 470.

in this case the brain has tended to maintain its minimum size, and that the cerebro-spinal fluid has been called upon to fill the gap made through a somewhat over-active growth of bone along the sutures of the skull. I suggest, therefore, that the ancestor of Pithecanthropus had a larger, and not a smaller, cranial capacity than its descendant. Indeed, Sinanthropus might be placed close to the stem of the Java ancestral tree.

The same argument can be advanced in the case of Rhodesian Man. His skull also looks remarkably "ill-filled." In this case the vertex is further behind; and the endocranial cast reveals a sinking in of the inner table of bone above the parietal lobes and their parasagittal cisterns.[1] This character is also seen in the brain of the gorilla, which I suspect of having also contracted it during the last evolutionary stages.[2] In these cases an actual diminution in the pressure of the cerebro-spinal fluid itself is suggested. The small cranial capacity of Rhodesian Man (1300) might be attributed to an iodine-abundance and thyroid-activity of which the influence could not quite be overcome by the probably associated calcium-deficiency. We may recollect, too, that the tropics are apt to provide potash as a substitute for sodium, and that the latter element has the strongest affinity for water. Thus migration from North to South may be expected to reduce the cranial capacity.

[1] Keith, A.: *Antiquity of Man*, p. 391; *New Discoveries*, pp. 470–471.
[2] Keith, A.: *Antiquity of Man*, p. 622.

CHAPTER XI

THE DIFFERENTIATION OF MODERN MAN

Skin Colour : Hair Form : The Races of Man : The Pygmies : The Negro and the Bushman : The Hunters of the Cold Steppe : Neanderthal and Australoid : The Mongoloid Peoples : Man in America.

IN THE LAST CHAPTER IT WAS SUGGESTED THAT ALL OR MOST OF the extinct Hominidæ were the products of racial mixture. The same argument will again be utilized in the following attempt to account for some of the more salient features of contemporary races. In the discussion of fossil evidence there was no need to consider the relationship of habitat to the colour of the skin or to the form of the hair. When attempting to classify Modern Man, however, these two characters become at least as important as the skeletal variations that have hitherto provided our criteria.

The theory that a racial dominance of the Southern inheritance would manifest itself in the later-evolved characters has already been put forward. In this chapter a further hypothesis of the same sort will be entertained, namely, that a character will tend to secure racial dominance in the habitat in which it was originally evolved. Taken together the two theories suggest that late developing and evolved characters of Neanthropic Man will be particularly dominant in the South. I shall attribute survival-value to the three skin-colours, white, yellow, and black ; as also to the three forms of hair, the long coarse Mongoloid pigtail, the curly and peppercorn Negroid coverings, and the finer wavy hair. All these six fundamental characters distinguishing the different branches of modern humanity will be taken to be of two-fold utility. Not only do they confer some degree of survival-value in themselves, but they also will tend to be linked with unseen physiological characters. Thus, used as emblems of sexual selection, they have been helpful in assisting primary and secondary specialization for life in the particular habitats in which the characters themselves were first evolved. This original evolution may well ante-date the evolution of Man as such. Similar adaptations are found in other mammals specialized for the same environment.

SKIN COLOUR

At the outset, then, let me state the advantages that each of these six characters is believed to possess.

The white skin perhaps raises the most difficult of these problems. It can, however, be considered as the most fœtal, and therefore probably the most primitive, stage of skin-development. Thus, if Man is a fœtalized ape produced by severe iodine-deficiency, it is probable that the first man was white. As pointed out previously, in the chapter on sodium-metabolism, the synthesis of melanin appears to be encouraged by heat, alkalinity, and a high metabolic rate. None of these conditions would exist in the case of a hypothyroid species, probably suffering from other mineral- and vitamin-deficiencies as well, and attempting to support life at a high altitude.

I consider it probable that the white skin was retained as a palæanthropic character, and that pigmentation was re-evolved by the first emigrants who made their habitat in the South. Life in the hotter and more humid regions would call for an accelerated synthesis of vitamin D by the skin, as an offset to the greatly reduced calcium-supply of the soil and food. The pigment would serve to absorb the more intense visual radiations, and would thus prevent them from interfering with the action of the short ultra-violet radiations.[1] The greater iodine-content of the humid and hotter Southern habitat would probably help to reverse the initial change towards partial or complete albinism ; indeed, if this depended upon mutations selected under conditions of iodine-shortage, their predominance might easily be overthrown.

Now the white skin has become indigenous to the cold, moist Atlantic region. Under the less intense solar radiation encountered in this new type of mammalian environment it seems probable that the pigmentation needed as an optical sensitiser in the South would here do more harm than good.[2] Moreover, any of its other purely protective functions would likewise be unnecessary. At the same time, an efficient auto-synthesis of vitamin D would be more necessary than ever ; for the moderately heavy rainfall, even if less intense than in the tropical rain belt, would still favour an efficient calcium-metabolism. Indeed, this would be specially required on account of the greater bodily size, and the consequent increase in the skeletal proportions, needed to withstand the increased cold. I suggest, therefore, that the European obtained his white skin from the coarse-boned Neanderthaloids, or from their unknown and remote Palæanthropic ancestors, and that the brow-ridges of the Caucasians were handed on at the same time. This assumes that white skin is an advantage in the North-west, just as pigmentation may confer survival-value towards the Equator. Conversely, then, the Palæanthropic inheritance found in the South may be expected to have become fused with the pigmentation evolved by Neanthropic Man. Thus the colour of the Australians may well have been obtained at the same time as their non-Neanderthal lower limbs.

[1] Cf. Bayliss, p. 572.

[2] Cf. Chapter I in which it is argued that the mammal evolved in response to alternations between cold dry and hot wet epochs. Cold wet and hot dry habitats thus require special and later adaptations.

We must now look to the probable functions of the two contrasted forms of pigmented skin, the dry yellow covering of the Mongoloid peoples and the Bushman, and the chocolate skin of the Negro with its profusion of sweat-glands. The relationships of the two types of physiology, held to be associated with each, was discussed previously. It seems probable that, in the case of the yellow skin, the protective functions will outweigh the positive advantages in the matter of vitamin auto-synthesis. For a desert habitat tends to be rich in lime, so that any great physiological activity of the skin will be unnecessary. The less humid atmosphere will allow the passage of a greater proportion of the short-wave radiation, and the lighter colour of the skin will thus probably be of more value in dealing with this reduced ratio of the more penetrating red. Of course, in addition to the question of this physiological protection, the problem of protective coloration must be noticed. This must have been of as much use to Man as to any other desert animal, though we may note that the hair has not taken on any similarly useful tone. If, therefore, there is much advantage to be derived from protective coloration, it can be held to have exerted its main selective influence in a pre-human, and perhaps in a pre-anthropoid, stage of mammalian evolution.

I thus consider that the primary function of the yellow skin has been protective, and that later it may have served as an emblem of sexual selection for fluid-economy. In the main it seems to be a very old character belonging to all desert animals, and in Man its presence may be considered as largely due to the accident of its continued linkage with the characters evolved for the long associated requirements of fluid and iodine-economy. In the Bushman I believe it to have supervened as a result of a sexual selection directed mainly towards fluid-economy as advertized by the steatopygia. In the Mongoloid peoples a similar selection for long coarse hair, indicative of iodine-economy, might have called in the same secondary effect. In addition, however, the latter are believed to have evolved from a cross between a Bushman ancestor and a coarse-haired Palæanthropic stock.

The survival-value claimed for the chocolate-coloured skin has already been mentioned. It is considered valuable as an optical sensitizer, whereby the longer wave radiation is absorbed, and prevented from hindering the action of the ultra-violet after the latter has penetrated through to the ergosterol of the sub-cutaneous fat. There can be little doubt that a black skin is admired, and has, therefore, almost certainly been encouraged by sexual selection. Since it is probably an autosomal character its appreciation by either sex in the other would serve to annul racial femininity. The stove-black of the Nilote is probably a product of racial mixture between negroes and other—some of them possibly white—stocks of greater pituitary activity. The sexual selections for stature and for dark coloration would probably assist each other. Both would annul femininity.[1]

[1] Cf. Chapter IV.

HAIR FORM

The peppercorn hair of the Bushman does not seem to serve as a decorative asset. Probably the whole powerful phylogenetic influence of sexual selection was focussed upon the steatopygia, or other signs of capillary dilation, indicative of a large fluid reserve. The hair may thus be suspected of retaining the practical value for which it was selected. I regard it solely as a protection from the sun. The curvature of the follicle, and the consequently flat cross-section of the bent tube and its contained hair, may be regarded as a means for securing an external curvature useful in weaving one hair with the next. A maximum protection is provided by these islets or "peppercorns," and we may note that a very small expenditure of material has been used to secure this end. The peppercorn hair is so very different from any anthropoid character that one is tempted to imagine the first man as having been rendered almost, if not completely, bald at the same time as the body hair was lost, so that only the pubic and axillary tufts remained. I regard the short curly hair as the original Neanthropic form. The longer, coarser hair of the Mongoloid and Caucasian peoples is nearer to the simian pattern. It could have been re-evolved by the Palæanthropic branch at the same time as they were increasing in size and re-developing that other anthropoid character, the frontal torus.

Dealing next, then, with the long, straight, coarse, and accordingly round-sectioned, hair of the Mongoloid peoples, this may be conceived as a product of a cold iodine-deficient environment. Under like circumstances the same sort of hair was developed by the musk ox, the mammoth, and the yak. I regard it as a character linked with the physiological advantages of iodine- and of heat-economy.[1] Thus its appreciation as a sexual emblem would be of value in accelerating a change in favour of these far more useful features. I suspect that Neanderthal Man and the Palæanthropic components of his ancestry all had this long coarse hair. Probably they were protected from the extreme cold of their winter habitat by the re-evolution of a simian body-covering as well. Iodine and heat-economy have been held to be characters favoured by racial masculinity. Thus the long coarse hair seems to be encouraged by autosomal characters, and consequently to be inhibited by racial femininity.

An increase in the activity of the sex-linked genes could in this way account for the finer hair of the European. It was suggested that the White race arose through a mixture between white-skinned Neanderthaloids and a finer-boned, and presumably pigmented, Neanthropic strain from a more Southerly habitat. The useful characters of these two, the Palæanthropic white skin and the Neanthropic calcium economy, were considered to be a strong combination in face of the low solar radiation and the humid lime-poor soils of the Atlantic sea-

[1] Cf. Chapter VIII.

board. This environment would require an increase in femininity, and would, in the main, provide any additional iodine necessary in order that the new type of racial physiology might be maintained. Thus a sexual selection for fine hair, or any other feminine character, would be of use in accelerating racial adaptation in a useful direction. There is a good deal of evidence to show that pigmentation in many animals is more developed in males than in females, while also tending to be intensified as age increases. It is at once a masculine and gerontomorphic character. Part of this sexual selection among the cross-bred stock in the North-west might therefore usefully concentrate on an admiration of white skin, blue eyes, and fine fair hair. The possessors of these characters would tend to be physiologically superior in an environment offering a reduced supply of calcium. Possibly fair hair may also be encouraged by iodine-shortage. At the probable centre of Nordic dispersal, the Baltic, iodine-deficiency is common. Also, fair hair crops up with suspicious frequency in mountain regions, and here also iodine is usually scarce.[1] The possibility that the synthesis of melanin may be inhibited by any circumstances tending to damp down metabolism and increase acidity has already been mentioned.

THE RACES OF MAN

Having reviewed these relatively simple theories concerning the survival-value of the main traits which are found in the various human groups, I propose to try to outline a scheme whereby the various combinations of skeletal development, colour, and hair-form may be accounted for in terms of further racial mixtures. Each mixture will be deemed to have been tested by natural selection, and thereby further adapted to the habitat in which it now prevails. I have already suggested that a Palæanthropic inheritance may have contributed towards the building of the Caucasian and Australoid races. I propose, therefore, to begin by a consideration of the purer strains of Neanthropic Man such as are to be looked for in the tropics. These are the Negroes, the Bushmen, and the Pygmies. Like the Negroes, the latter are divided into an African and Asiatic branch.[2] Owing to the possibility of their constituting the purest form of the Neanthropic inheritance, they will be mentioned first. Finally, mention will be made of the Mongoloid peoples, who are often regarded as the most recently evolved branch of mankind.

THE PYGMIES

The great problem in regard to the dwarf forms of humanity is to decide whether they are very primitive or very specialized. Are the

[1] Semple, E. C.: *Influences of Geographic Environment*, London, 1911, p. 39; also Waitz, T: *Anthropology*, London, 1863, pp. 44–45.
[2] Indeed Griffith Taylor divides all the races into pairs of Eastern and Western twins. *Ecology*, Vol. XV, No. 3, July, 1934.

African and Oceanic Negroes enlarged from a common Pygmy ancestor whose pure descendants still survive in the tropical forests? Or are these forest folk diminished Negroes, dwarfed by mineral-deficiency and in-breeding? I prefer a blend of both explanations, having failed to see my way through either without some assistance from the other.

As an argument in favour of the very great evolutionary age of a Pygmy stock it may be remembered that extreme anatomical difficulties seem to stand in the way of the evolution of bi-pedal progression in any but a rather small kind of anthropoid. Thus we have all the time worked on the assumption that the first man was small, and regained the somewhat gorilla-like proportions of Neanderthal Man only after a very long period of evolution in a cold and lime-abundant habitat. If, then, there was a comparatively early occupation of the tropical rain-belt, the first Southern migrants would have been small; and their reduced size would have been an advantage in meeting the calcium-deficiency of their new soil and food. It is under these circumstances, I suggest, that the brown skin was evolved; while at the same time the calcium-economy of use later in eating meat—and later still in eating grain—could have been developed.

Against this theory must be set the fact that Asia contains two sorts of Pygmy, as, for example, the Semang of Negroid affinities and the Sakai of a more Caucasian appearance. This suggests that any group of human beings might become dwarfed if subjected to the extreme hardships imposed by the conditions of life in a tropical forest. We may reflect, however, that the adaptation would be vastly accelerated supposing that the forest in question already contained even a few members of an original Pygmy stock. The small size of these former inhabitants would possess great survival-value and might be expected to dominate the cross, whatever other improved characters the inheritance of the newcomers might contribute.

I propose then to regard both the Bushman and the Negro as derived from a primitive Pygmy ancestor. Thus the fact that the Negroid race seems prone towards a return to the Pygmy condition can be set down either to an unmasking of the old characters by the restoration of the former conditions, or to racial mixture with some of the old stock, or to both processes working together. Similarly the Sakai can be considered as a racial mixture between some original or new Pygmy stock and an incoming strain of larger size and of a different origin. I hesitate to recognize the almost Pygmy inhabitants of the Andamans as possibly the purest form of Neanthropic Man. They may already have been formerly expanded to Negroid proportions, and then again reduced through isolation and in-breeding.

THE NEGRO AND THE BUSHMAN

I suggest that both the Negro and the Bushman are closely related to an ancestral Pygmy who may, or may not, have directly contributed towards the dwarf forms living at the present time. The problem is to decide whether the Negro evolved by way of the Bushman, or whether the latter is best viewed as a secondarily reduced Negro specialized for desert conditions. Doubtless neither of those extreme statements could be entirely correct. On the whole, however, the Bushman is the more specialized type of the two. The Negro can thus be regarded as an enlarged Pygmy adapted to the much better conditions of the tropical park-lands. Here game is more abundant than in the forest, and the vegetable food will reflect the greater mineral-content of the soil. Probably the greatest danger would come from carnivores. Nevertheless, if we are to assume Man to have deserted the initial mountain cradle-land, it must be admitted that life in the park-lands would offer almost every kind of advantage over that provided by the rain-forest. A sexual selection for masculine size and strength would be encouraged. At the same time a black skin, which I consider indicative of an abundant physiological reserve of sodium,[1] would be admired, and would thus become intensified as a racial character. The sodium-shortage of the same region would at a later date encourage cannibalism. This would probably be delayed until the size of the human population and the organization of food-gathering, if not of agriculture, had reduced the available quantity of flesh fare. This matter has been dealt with apart.[2]

An important point, which must be duly noted, is the lack of sex-dimorphism in the Negro. The women are strong and vigorous, whereas the men display a number of characters that in other races would be classed as exclusively female. For instance, the male Negro often shows a bombé forehead ; and, again, the post-coronal depression is of equal frequency in either sex, whereas this too is a feminine character in Europeans.[3] Once more, the male mammæ are very fully developed. The lack of body hair in the male, and the absence of marked steatopygia, or any other special feminine character, in the female are likewise remarkable. The hair of males and females is not very different, and is not particularly emphasized as an object of sexual adornment. All this is in sharp contrast to the marked steatopygia, and extension of the labia minora, seen in the Bushwoman.

It will hardly do to attribute those characters of the Negro to a sexual selection for autosomal activity only ; even if a sexual selection for certain special aspects of femininity can account for the peculiarities of the Bushman. A move towards masculinity could not account for the feminine features in the skull of the male Negro. These could, however, be explained by a rather more complex hypothesis. We could suppose an ancestor of the Negro—the original Pygmy—to have been greatly

[1] Cf. Chapter IV.

[2] Cf. Chapter XIII.

[3] Crewdson Benington, R., and Pearson, K. : " A study of the Negro Skull with special reference to the Congo and Gaboon Crania," *Biometrika*, VIII, 1911–12, p. 326.

reduced in size by a process of natural or sexual selection for ultra-femininity. This would eventually increase the degree of sex-dimorphism beyond a desirable amount, and would thus produce a demand for the translocation of sex-linked characters to the autosomes as a means of assisting the survival of the males. The autosomes would from that moment onwards carry genes for which one could still claim the name of feminine. Suppose now that this translocated feminine strain were subsequently selected for an increase of masculinity, there would seem to be no need for the original sex-dimorphism to be regained. Conditions for reproduction will be improved. Women will secure the survival of their inheritance by giving birth to sons who can succeed in warfare and the capture of wives. A predominance of the original masculine parts of the autosomes will be in demand, and the fact that some few signs of the original, but now translocated, femininity are still allowed to show through will not matter. In this way, we might expect a returned dominance of the autosomes actually to favour the display of hitherto feminine characters by the male.

Who, then, are the Bushmen? If the original Pygmy ancestor is assumed to have already become so feminine and infantile that translocation was needed, it is clearly impossible to view the Bushman as a still further feminized extension of the same process. Either we must regard him as an ancestor of the Negro, and then create a hypothetical translocated go-between for the gap; or, alternatively, we may consider the translocation to have taken place during the evolution of the ancestral Pygmy. The latter develops into the stalwart Negro, who again becomes more feminine, and thus gives rise to the dwarf inhabitant of the hot desert. I propose to work on this last assumption. It permits a scheme whereby the various races evolve in the same order as their climatic belts. Neanthropic Man climbs from the forest to the Tundra making use of some Palæanthropic admixture whenever size needs to be increased. This theory would account for the extreme peppercorn hair as a specialization of the Negroid hair, which in its turn tends to be somewhat more curly than that of the Pygmies.

In regard to the obvious sex-linkage of the genes for steatopygia, which is so much more pronounced in the Bushwoman, it must be pointed out that this peculiar capacity to economize water must be of special value to the lactating female living under desert conditions. Another factor which would be of use would be the capacity to drink saline water and dispose of the excess salt. Now the adrenal-cortex has been recently shown to encourage the retention of sodium. Hence its activity would need to be abnormally great in the case of the salt-starved Negro; whereas, in the Bushman, a considerable reduction in the concentration of its secretion would probably be of value. But an over-activity of the adrenal-cortex has been shown to increase masculinity. It follows, therefore, that a phylogenetic shift towards femininity will thus become doubly desirable.[1] I suggest, then, that the Bushman is essentially an ultra-feminine Negro. Pithecanthropus, Rhodesian Man, and the Galilee Neanderthal, are all there to point to the possibility of a Palæanthropic strain having contributed towards the suddenly increased stature and strength of the Negro. Perhaps this occurred after, or at the time of, his separation from the Bushman. All this, however, is pure speculation. We may take note of the long arms and relatively weak and short Negroid legs in connection with the theory that the legs are of late development, and are thus most affected by the Southern inheritance. The iodine-abundance of the tropics would tend to assist the dominance of all the Neanthropic genes, and especially of those which acted latest in the development of the individual. Altogether, then, even if such racial mixtures did occur, the absence of any marked Palæanthropic features at the present time can be explained. Of all the primitive Hominidæ the stock that seems to bear most resemblance to the Negro is the Piltdown race. The relative absence of brow-ridges, the high thick skull vault, and even the pointed canines, might be hailed as proto-Negroid. In Africa, it is even now common to find the canines filed to a point. Is this a relic from the days when an appreciation of canine display was being used to increase size and strength by way of those advertisements of masculinity? Of course the great differences in the form of the Piltdown mandible would need separate explanation. The Modern form, however, is assumed to have arisen among the hunters of the cold steppe, whose evolution may well be later than that of the earliest Bushman or his presumed Negroid ancestor.

THE HUNTERS OF THE COLD STEPPE

If the Bushman be considered the specialized product of the hot desert, we must remember that towards the centre of the Continent the desert tends to merge into the cold steppe. The latter, even if nearly as hot in summer, becomes extremely cold in winter. On the whole, however, it must often have offered more game to a hunter than either the hot desert or even the park-land; but the herds of horse and bison would be hard to stalk down and kill. I propose, then, to regard the hunters who entered Europe in the Upper-Palæolithic as men specialized for steppe and desert conditions. The extreme types would be the small steatopygous Bushman, just mentioned, and at the opposite end the tall Cromagnon. Probably, in the latter case, the need for more pituitary-activity and heat-economy would have been supplied by some early cross with the Palæanthropic proto-Neanderthal strain. The latter, if considered as inhabitants of the Tundra, would often be cut off from the cold steppe by a belt of wet and inhospitable Taiga. Nevertheless, the two types would be in occasional contact with each other, and cross breeding would be almost sure to occur. The small size, smooth skull, and pronounced steatopygia of the Bushman would all tend to be annulled.

[1] Cf. Chapter IV.

Such Southern features would give way before the Palæanthropic characters dependent upon greater pituitary activity. Doubtless the admiration for female steatopygia would take a long time to die out, even after its direct survival-value had vanished. An almost identical condition occasionally crops up at the present time, and a case has occurred in both mother and daughter. The state is known as lipodystrophia. Fat, or rather tissue hydration, characterizes the thighs and buttocks, whereas the face becomes drawn and haggard.[1] I consider these rare occurrences of what practically constitutes steatopygia in European women to prove the possibility of occasional atavism, and also to indicate an hereditary connection between Europeans and those hunters of Upper Palæolithic whose figurines and drawings still tell us something of the conformation of their soft tissues. Life on the cold steppe would in no way diminish, and might increase, a need for speed in running ; so that, on the whole, the limbs would tend to be elongated without being allowed to grow thick and heavy. All this was discussed in the previous chapter.[2] The final result would be a tall, strong-chinned and athletic Modern Man, with none of the Neanderthaloid clumsiness of build.

Assuming a mixture of desert and Tundra man to have constituted the larger Northern hunters, we must consider the cross to have involved a mixture of yellow- and white-skin inheritance. It is this mixture which I suggest as having separated out to yield the white of the Causasian. For, just as the pituitary activity of the Palæanthropic vegetable-feeders would be useful in assisting the Northern hunters to withstand cold, so would the fine bone of the latter be valuable in equipping the Tundra type of vegetable-eaters for a migration into the more humid Western region. So long as the hunters remained upon the steppe, there would seem no reason for them to adopt the white skin that we have attributed to the Neanderthaloids. My view, therefore, is that the Caucasian and the Cromagnon represent almost the same blend of ancestral heredities, selected, however, for somewhat different habitats and modes of life. All this is supposed to have happened at an extremely early date. I infer that it was the vegetable-feeders who evolved the Chellean and Acheulean bouchers, or hand-axes ; and that a later development was the Neolithic pick and the polished celt. To the hunters is attributed the invention of the flake-industries ; which they handed on to Neanderthal Man, when the latter took to hunting prior to his extinction.

Briefly, then, in this first half of the chapter we have postulated a double exodus from the initial human cradle-land : a Palæanthropic move to the Tundras of the North, and a Neanthropic migration into the tropical forests of the South. The latter produce a translocated feminine Pygmy, who later develops into a full-sized Negro. He is thus considered to be a vegetable-feeding type specialized for the

[1] Curshman, *Endocrine Disorders*, Oxford, gives a striking illustration.
[2] Cf. Chapter X, *The Chin and Neanthropic Man*, p. 203.

park-lands at the verge—probably the northern boundary—of the tropical forest. The Negro's increase of size may quite possibly have received some assistance from the Palæanthropic heredity. The Bushman, in any case, seems to have become secondarily reduced in

Theory of Neanthropic Differentiation (as Hitherto Outlined).

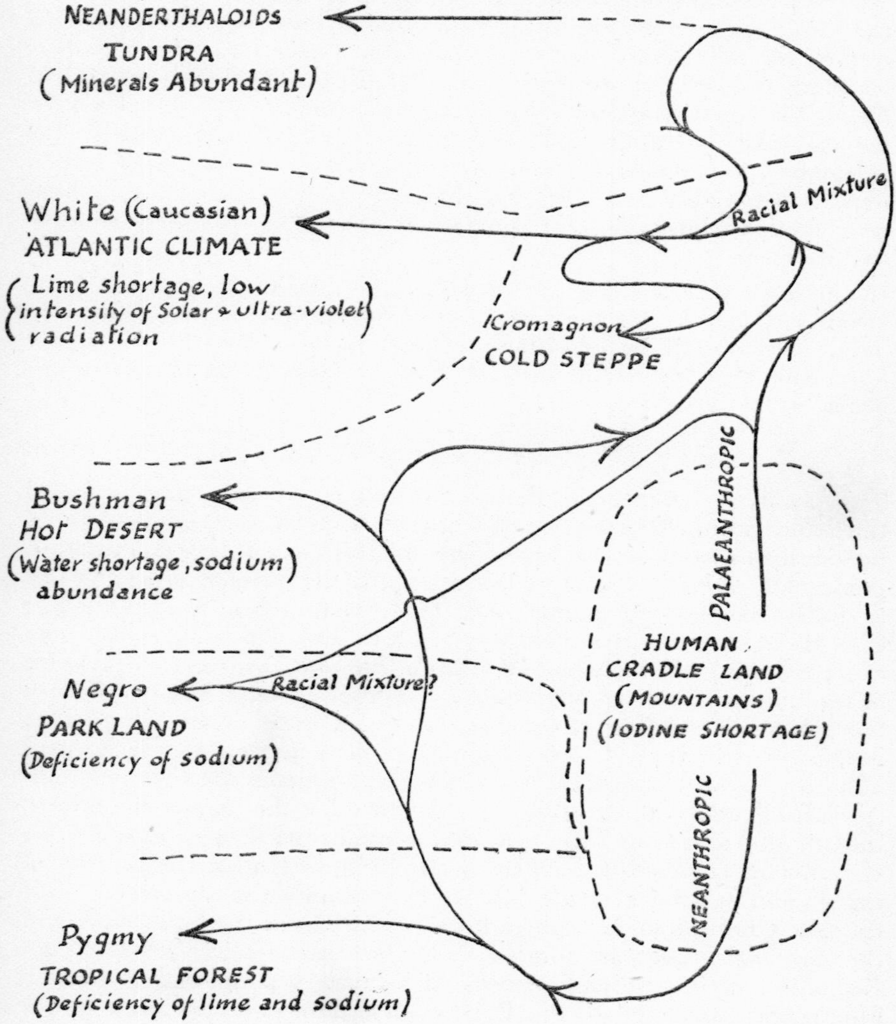

size from an initially larger type, and he cannot thus be considered merely as a modified Pygmy. Later still this small size and extreme sex-dimorphism of the Bushman again gets annulled; this time in order to provide sufficient size and heat economy to support life in the cold steppe. This second increase of size probably again receives a stimulus through Palæanthropic admixture. The resultant cross not only provides the Northern hunters, but could also produce a type of anatomy and physiology capable of supporting life in the humid Atlantic region. This last would be white.

Of course many secondary mixtures will have followed this division into five fundamental types, the Pygmy, the Negro, the Bushman, the Cromagnon, and the European. One of these last two is possibly responsible for the tall stature of the Nilotes and some of the Bantu-speaking peoples. Moreover, it has already been pointed out that a Negro-Bushman cross might itself increase stature, or rather increase the variation in stature, and thus offer a chance for the selection of extreme types. Perhaps, then, the moderately tall people of Africa may be considered as a Negro-Bushman cross, and the Nilotic giants as a further European or Cromagnon cross with the taller issue of the first process.

In the last resort the final results seem due rather to culture and environment than to the mere mechanical interactions of racial mixtures only. Almost all racial mixtures must have occurred. Thus the opportunity to develop almost any form of Man has been granted to nearly every type of habitat.

NEANDERTHAL AND AUSTRALOID

The possibility that a Neanderthaloid admixture may have affected the evolution of the more coarse-featured of the modern races leads us inevitably to a consideration of the inhabitants of the Australasian peninsula. For it is probably fair to regard the passage of early Man to have taken place mainly over lands that are now submerged ; even though one must certainly credit him with the marine transport of himself and his dog across Wallace's line into the previous preserve of the monotremes and marsupials. Another passage which it is very hard, if not impossible, to imagine as having been crossed dry-footed is Bass Strait. Indeed, when the anatomical as well as the cultural affinities of the Tasmanians are considered, degeneration, rather than specialized adaptation, would appear to offer the best explanation, though the absence of the dog in Tasmania tends to contradict this view. The lack of flint makes a fair judgment upon the quality of the stone-industries difficult, but we may remark the absence of both the true Chellean or Acheulean boucher ; whereas the latter occurs in the Zambezi gravels in South Africa, and in the lower levels of the Kamasian, or first pluvial deposits, of Kenya. One may reflect that a Quaternary approach of the Pole towards Europe and Africa would tilt the Equator away from the North of Australia. This would give the South of Australia a colder and wetter climate than is found there at present, though somewhat similar conditions may have occurred previously in the Pliocene. Australia is now, on the whole, too dry ; like many parts of Asia, which nevertheless, are known to have carried big civilized populations in about 4000 B.C. The cause may have been a general increase of precipitation due to an intensification of solar heat affecting both hemispheres of the world. If so, Australia may have enjoyed an epoch of increased rainfall suitable for occasioning a pressure of population and a stimulus towards emigration. This would have happened at a time corresponding to that of the Mesolithic culture-phase of Western Europe.

This may or may not explain the last move of the peoples of this low race to the extreme end of what Griffith Taylor terms the Australasian peninsula. They must, however, be deemed to have evolved somewhere, and I suggest that they are a degenerated group isolated from the better-proportioned inhabitants of the larger continent whose environment now, and always, must have been superior. We have a parallel in the sharp contrast between the degenerate Fuegians of the wet and cold extremity of South America and their nearest neighbours, the giant Patagonians of the Southern desert zone. Here also differences of heredity may also have existed, but they have been intensified by extreme differences of environment.[1]

The physical aspects of the Tasmanians all permit, if they do not positively encourage, a degeneration-theory. The very short face suggests an extreme reduction of anterior-lobe activity, which is also reflected in the weak jaw now overburdened with large, because more slowly alterable, teeth. The rather short stature may tell the same tale. The brow-ridges are retained, but not to the extreme degree seen in the skulls of the taller Australians. The nose remains wide despite the temperate climate. Does this indicate an absence of the genes for narrow nose, perhaps slowly evolved by the Neanthropic hunters of the cold steppe? A wide nose is a Neanderthaloid, and probably Palæanthropic, character as well as being Negroid. The hair, however, is woolly, which suggests that part, at least, of the inheritance has come from a place in the sun. The wavy hair of the Australians seems to mark a greater share, or at all events a predominance, of genes for straight hair. It is usually regarded as the sign of an admixture with a White race, but we do not know the hair form of the primitive Hominidæ. Keith boldly suggests an hereditary connection between Pithecanthropus, with which he associates the chinned Kedung Brubus fragment of mandible, and the Cohuna and Talgai skulls. The latter, of course, are fully human and may represent coarse-boned ancestors of the now smaller Australian, and even of the Tasmanian, aborigines. This big jump from the 900 to 1000 c.c. capacity of Pithecanthropus to the huge 1650 c.c. of the Wajak II male,[2] which is thereby comparable with 1625 c.c. of the La Chapelle Neanderthal,[3] might possibly be a result of racial mixture between Pithecanthropus and some smooth-skulled and relatively large-brained tropical Pygmy. It has already been suggested that the Palæanthropic

[1] Griffith Taylor: *Environment and Race*, Oxford, 1927.
[2] Keith, A.: *Antiquity of Man*, p. 441.
[3] Ibid., p. 297.

skull and long thin femur of Pithecanthropus probably indicate a previous racial mixture. If so, the initial type itself may have been unstable, and in a state of extreme phenotypic variability such as might quickly evolve a new type, supposing the large brain to confer survival-value. Lastly, it must be pointed out how the dangers of life in a volcanic peninsula may have served to intensify evolution through the occurrence of cataclysms resulting in in-breeding. All these are possibilities, though none can carry conviction. This threshold-value of the human cranial capacity, which seems fixed at about 1000 c.c. and is rapidly attained by the young child, certainly suggests a common bond between all the living and extinct races of men. Perhaps all the higher values have been produced in some other way. I suggest that a cranial capacity of 1000 c.c. is a specific and generic character evolved and fixed by in-breeding and intense selection at the dawn of humanity. The remainder of the increase—which in some cases bids fair to double this figure—may be the more fortuitous product of racial mixture between large and small-bodied types of similar cranial capacity.

THE MONGOLOID PEOPLES

Having dealt summarily with every main branch of the human race except one, let us now consider some possible applications of the mineral-hypothesis to the problem of Mongoloid evolution. The Mongoloid peoples are often taken to include the Chinese, Manchus, Tibetans, Japanese, American Indians, Eskimo and the Mongols proper—the horse-culture folk of Mongolia—together with the Neo-Siberian reindeer-nomads. In addition Mongolian elements have been recognized in India and the Pacific, while Western Europe has undergone periodic invasion by Mongoloid hordes. A yellow skin and long straight hair of round and thick cross-section are the hall-marks of the Mongoloid peoples. The skulls are usually markedly brachycephalic ; but this criterion breaks down in the case of the Eskimo, and in that of the Mongols themselves. We may remember, too, that the Cromagnon hunters possessed broad faces hafted to long, and perhaps recently elongated, brain-cavities. It seems almost true to say that Mongoloid peoples are brachycephalic unless they happen to be hunters or herdsmen.

Another partial, but not quite satisfactory, mark of differentiation is an absence of brow-ridges. These, however, occur on the long-headed Mongol skulls, and were present in the case of the broad-faced Upper Palæolithic hunters of Western Europe. They also characterized the round-headed skulls of the early English Bronze Age. Nevertheless, it is probable that there is a strong tendency for the brow-ridges to be reduced or absent, except when the head is elongated, or mixture with a coarse-boned type has been recent. Even in the Neanderthal brachycephals of Krapina the brow-ridges are far from normal either in size or form. Some mention must also be made of the " mongoloid " ape, the Orang-utan, which similarly is devoid of the frontal torus developed in the Gorilla and Chimpanzee, and is also more brachycephalic and with a tendency towards a yellow skin, and red rather than black hair. Reference must also be made to the pathological mongolism which crops up among members of the White races, the Nordic, Alpine and Mediterranean ; the latter being included by Crookshank on account of the frequency of pathological mongolism around Toulon. He states, however, that it is unknown among Arabs and pure Jews, and also that Negroes are never affected.[1] It seems almost to be a question of colour. Whites may be pathological mongols, but the dark-coloured races can not. This brings us to the problem of how far mongolism is a state imposed by environmental agencies, and how far it must be considered as a hereditary reversion to a previously evolved and pure ancestral type. If we accept Crookshank's theory as to the identity of the hereditary characters causing pathological and racial mongolism, it is difficult to reconcile this with the common view of ethnologists that the yellow race is of more recent origin than the white or the black.[2]

One possible way to avoid a number of difficulties is to assume what practically amounts to two similar evolutionary processes, producing much the same results in the same cradle-land, but at different times. I have already put forward my theory of how Man may have evolved in response to the needs of iodine-economy imposed by the deficiency of the Central Asiatic limestone mountain-system. This may have been as long ago as the Miocene, and before the mountains had reached their present height. It is doubtful whether this same region, which seems to be the area of dispersal of the modern Mongoloid peoples, has been continuously habitable during the whole intervening period. It was probably fully glaciated during parts of the Pleistocene.

It is possible, therefore, that the first Hominid was of Mongolian type. That is to say, he may have been "unfinished," or fœtalized, to a maximum degree compatible with an ability to survive. The Palæanthropic and Neanthropic stems may then have been elaborated ; the former regaining the brow-ridges of an ancestral great anthropoid, and the latter also securing a more active thyroid metabolism, but in this case retaining the fœtal and economic type of skeleton.

On this theory the puzzling presence of the yellow skin and epicanthic fold in the Bushman must be regarded not as a sign of Mongoloid admixture, but as a primary character evolved in the desert cradle-land of this race. The yellow skin of the Mongoloid peoples, on the other hand, can then be assumed to have been derived from a Bushman-like ancestor. If the peppercorn hair of the modern Bushman be considered as an adaptation to withstand heat, it need not follow that its evolution was complete in all the steppe-hunters. It would be useless to the rather larger, though similarly, Steatopygous, hunters of the cold steppe, whose decendants are assumed to have been the upper-

[1] Crookshank, F. C. : *The Mongol in our Midst*, p. 26, London, 1924.
[2] Hooton, E. A. : *Up from the Ape*, p. 578, New York, 1931.

Palæolithic hunters. I suggest, therefore, that the modern Mongoloid peoples have re-developed and perhaps over-developed, a very primitive set of fœtal characters responsible for their brachycephaly. The Mongoloid form of hair is viewed as an emblem used in a sexual selection for iodine-economy, such as has thus overlaid all previous hair-characters. The pigtail evolved the Chinaman, rather than vice-versa. The yellow skin and Mongoloid eye-fold are characters obtained from the original stocks that re-invaded the human cradle-land. Long-headedness and brow-ridges, when they occur, are probably the result of mixture with white proto-Nordic stocks. Similarly, when the latter are lightly pigmented, as are the Ainu, this can be put down to Mongolian admixture. The long headed and coarse-boned features are derived originally from a Palæanthropic stock allied to Sinanthropus, in which certain anthropoid features have been allowed to re-appear.

According to this very provisional hypothesis the pathological mongolism in the White need not be taken as a proof of any close relationship with the yellow third of humanity. It may equally well be based upon genes of a common ancestor, whose colour seems more likely to have been white than yellow. This theory, incidentally, allows us to regard the Alpine type of European as a convergent, rather than as a descendant, of the yellow race. We may remember how simple goitre differs from exophthalmic goitre, the former leading to dullness and the latter to irritability. The former types would be least likely to emigrate, and would remain within the area of deficiency to mingle their inheritance with others of similar type. Probably there is a mechanism for adapting the whole physiology and anatomy to meet iodine-deficiency when it occurs. Moreover, the degree of this reaction probably varies in different racial stocks. Mild degrees of pathological mongolism may be regarded as signs of an ontogenetic plasticity of a kind valuable for preserving life in the event of sudden deprivations of iodine. This emergency-reaction could occasionally be thrown into gear by mistake. The thyroid secretion of the mother might fail from too many pregnancies, or even as a result of a former hyperthyroidism here held to follow from a deprivation of calcium or of vitamin D. Whatever may be the causes, Crookshank should be thanked for bringing his facts to the notice of anthropologists.

A word must be said as well concerning the long, narrow, and roof-shaped head of the Eskimo. To attribute the form of the head to the pull of the jaw-muscles savours too much of a crude Lamarckism. It seems worth while to try and explain the change of morphology in terms of an altered diet; for, even if racial mixture may have contributed towards the result, I hold to the principle that characters do not survive except in an environment to which they are suited. The long Eskimo skull argues an active proliferation at the basi-sphenoid suture. This I have already attributed to an abundance of iodine. The same cause may also he held responsible for the collapsed or "ill-filled" appearance ; as also for the flat sides and small extent of the upper dome. This could be due to a reduction of tissue hydration, and to a low intra-cranial pressure, due not only to the iodine-abundance, but to a general high concentration of electrolytes. An abundance of salt might contribute towards this result. Finally, the apparently early closure, or slow speed of cell-proliferation, at the sagittal suture may represent a reaction to an acidity such as even an abundance of iodine is unable to counteract. Alternatively, it is possible that the sutures have been evolved so that they proliferate in response to low electrolyte concentrations, and thus keep step with the expansion of the brain. The food of the Eskimo is mostly obtained from the sea, and is thus probably rich in iodine. Moreover, it contains enormous quantities of fat. These conditions might be expected to produce the combination of iodine-abundance and acidity here postulated. Whatever the exact causes, the polar bear has also reacted to them. He is one of the most long-headed of all the carnivores.

MAN IN AMERICA

Differences of opinion exist as to whether all the American aboriginals should be counted as Mongoloid. Any fresh approach to this problem must bear in mind the probable relationship between racial and pathological mongolism upon the one hand, and iodine-deficiency upon the other. The goitre map of America reveals deficiencies over very wide areas, and due, apparently, to a plurality of causes, among which geological conditions, climatic aridity, flooding, and the removal of humus by ice, have all been suggested.

Boas has led the way by trying to show how the American environment imposes an immediate influence upon the physical character of European immigrants.[1] Similarly, Clark Wissler has mapped almost as great variations in head-form and stature as are to be found among the different races of the Old World.[2]

Finally, Dixon, using his own method of classifying anthropometrical data, has found groups suggestive of all the principal races of mankind.[3] Even neglecting the possibility that the Punin skull may be a genuine Australoid of Pleistocene date[4]—which, if genuine, would imply that the human race after entering America again became extinct like the associated horse and mastodon—there still remains a big problem concerning the nature of the later peoples who crossed the Behring Straits and Aleutian bridge of islands. With Dixon we may adopt the provisional hypothesis that races remain unchanged by their environment ; or we may temper the severity of this assumption by regarding head-form as a strongly inherited character with no survival-value—to my mind almost a contradiction in terms. Nevertheless, it is the

[1] Boas, loc. cit.
[2] Wissler, C. : *The American Indian.* New York, 1922.
[3] Dixon, R. B. : *The Racial History of Man.* New York, 1923.
[4] Cf. Keith, A. : *New Discoveries*, p. 312.

assumption on which most anthropological arguments would seem to be unconsciously based; and it leads, as Dixon has shown, to the postulation of a multiplicity of ancestral American types, from which even the Negro is not excluded.

Personally, I do not believe that a hereditary character, established in a gene or linkage group, will survive long in an environment in which it is inferior to other characters possessed by members of the same race. This assumption, namely, that characters having no special value can be diffused, has been used in the attempts to explain the hereditary blood-groupings, and has proved disappointing. Survival-values may exist without being obvious. Indeed, I do not know how such questions can be settled without a huge amount of statistical comparison involving ecological and physiological data such as have not yet begun to be collected.

As an alternative to the approach previously outlined, one might swing to the other extreme and assume the entry of a single externally-homogeneous population arriving all at a single time. Given two new continents providing nearly all the environmental conditions of the Old World, one might then set down all the observed differences to the selective influence of habitat. The absence of characters such as the white or black skin, or the curly hair of the Negro, would need to be put down to a lack of necessary genes within the racial raw-material; or else to the lack of time, and the difficulties of securing isolation for in-breeding, both necessary conditions if the over-lying modifiers were to be removed.

Actually, we know that both the proto-Nordic Palæo-Siberians and the Mongoloid Neo-Siberians now live quite near the Behring bridge. It is possible that both of these stocks reached America by this route, and I suggest that a small number of proto-Nordics were followed by a larger and longer continued migration of Mongoloid peoples.

This is not entirely a guess based on the predominantly Mongoloid facies of the modern Amerind. On Wegener's hypothesis the Pole is supposed to have migrated from the Pacific through Alaska, Baffin Land, and Greenland, before assuming its present position. This shift would not only have rendered all the Behring area uninhabitable, but would have glaciated a large portion of North-east Asia as well. Now the proto-Nordics are probably somewhat better equipped to stand cold, and less fitted to deal with mineral-shortages, than are the Mongoloid peoples. It seems probable, therefore, that they would be thrust forward towards the arid edge of the moving ice-cap. They would thus be the first to reach America. The long heads and brow-ridges may represent an anterior-lobe activity likely to be of use in providing and economizing heat. If, however, we assume the retreat of the ice to have been accomplished by an increase of heat, and to have resulted in thaws and heavy rain, the soils would be decalcified. Under such conditions it seems probable that the Mongoloid followers would retain their fertility better than the proto-Nordic van. If there is a Negroid or Australoid component in the ancestry of the American Indian, I find it easier to believe in the landing of a few canoes full of Oceanic Negroes than to postulate the presence of an essentially tropical race in an area that can never have been warm during either the Pliocene or Quaternary. Here, as elsewhere in arguments of this type, the last word must be said by the palæo-climatologist.

To conclude, then, it seems probable that America can provide sufficient material to confirm or refute the whole general hypothesis here outlined. It should be possible to discover the mineral balance of the soils and food used by the main sub-races as distinguished by their physical type. The probability that the observed changes have taken place within a geologically short time, and the second probability that the initial genetical material was more uniform than that constituting the populations of other continents, should give the results of such an investigation an exceptional interest and importance. So far I have only worked out one correlation between the cephalic indices of Amerinds as mapped by Wissler and the total goitre-statistics of white males for the regions in question—the latter being used as a measure of iodine-deficiency. The result is not significant ($R = \cdot 19 \pm \cdot 1$). It is noticeable, however, that, whereas all the dolichocephalic groups are drawn from areas where the goitre incidence is low, these areas may also contain brachycephalic groups. This fact may argue that, whereas iodine-deficiency encourages brachycephaly, iodine-abundance or sufficiency does little or nothing to annul such an effect. It thus supports the view that the brachycephal is physiologically, and perhaps in other ways, superior.

CHAPTER XII

SEX AND SOCIETY

Polyandry and Selection through the Woman: Polygyny and Male Selection: Civilization and Racial Femininity: Marriage Systems and the Sex-Ratio: Exogamy and In-breeding: The Evolution of the Œdipus Complex: Ambivalence, Incest, and Primal Religion: Libido, Coyness, and Taboo: Polyandry, Incest, and the First Families: Female Jealousy and Group Solidarity: Conclusion.

WE AGAIN REACH A POINT IN THE ARGUMENT WHEN PSYCHOlogical and social forces must be included within any scheme designed to comprehend the evolutionary history of Man. In a previous chapter (VIII) an attempt was made to identify the distinctive marks of two opposing types of sexual selection believed to have acted at different and alternative periods of early human history. This chapter takes up the argument where it was then broken off. For we have seen, in the meantime, how different systems of sexual selection have probably assisted the specialization of two or more pure races; and in several important instances the results of racial mixture may later have been reduced to uniformity by the same means. The alternative method of phylogenetic adaptation is by in-breeding. This has the grave disadvantage that it seems to entail a reduction of population to an extent hardly compatible with a successful transference of the cultural, as opposed to the organic, inheritance. Thus Man, as a social animal, may be expected to have relied upon numerous and often mutually opposing systems of sexual selection as an alternative method of accelerating adaptation.

Now sexual selection for masculine virility and aggressiveness in the adult was held to have encouraged a delayed maturity, otherwise and independently desirable as a means of economizing minerals. Again, later, a sexual selection for femininity was assumed to have assisted the permanent retention of feminine and infantile characters throughout life. Possibly it was a process of this second kind that accompanied the so-called "primary reaction" involving hairlessness, or at least served to render the ontogenetic reaction permanent and irreversible. This reaction to hairlessness, and the permanence of a childish condition, were considered responsible both for the introduction and for the subsequent encouragement of gregarious as opposed to individualistic behaviour. It may thus be of interest to enquire how far the converse interaction of group-life may have modified, or have been modified by, the mechanisms of sexual selection. This brings us to a consideration of the various systems of human marriage. The argument that polygyny encourages male competition, and that monogamy allows the exercise of female choice, will be borne in mind. In addition, genetical considerations concerned with the need to inhibit in-breeding, as also economic factors bearing upon the efficiency of various forms of the family group, and psychological forces tending to aggregate or disrupt it, must all be mentioned. I shall make out a case for the belief that the whole social mechanism tends to assist a self-accelerating process of sexual selection, and that two opposing principles of masculinity and femininity meet in an ever-increasing instability of equilibrium. Masculinity seems always to be encouraged by an abundance of minerals, and femininity by a deficiency of calcium. The influence of iodine-deficiency is probably more complicated. Meanwhile, in the Himalayas it is associated with polyandry ; and it is proposed to discuss this form of marriage first.

POLYANDRY AND SELECTION THROUGH THE WOMAN

Westermarck, whose sociological enquiries are always related to a biological background, has collected an immense body of facts relating to polyandry in primitive societies ; and reading through his two chapters on the subject one can conclude that polyandry prevails in places where the birth rate is phenomenally low.[1] Indeed, after a careful examination and rejection of the theory of female infanticide as a general cause, he is driven to the conclusion that a better explanation lies in a real and unavoidable shortage among women of marriageable age ; and suggests that this is due to natural and not merely to social causes.

Polyandry is found not only all over the Himalayan and Central Asiatic area, but also in Southern India, South America, in the Pacific and elsewhere. In the Himalayas it is, of course, associated with iodine-shortage, but despite the mountain habitat of the pastoral Todas—the best-known polyandrists of Southern India—it would be quite unjustifiable, and probably incorrect, to claim for all polyandry that it is caused by iodine shortage. It seems that any condition throwing an unusual physiological strain upon the human race will be reflected in a lengthened casualty-list among the ranks of the women. A disproportionate number of deaths and early disablements will result in many of the surviving women having to be shared by two or more men, unless the latter are prepared for a struggle with lethal or economic weapons.

The exact nature of the physiological breakdown most prevalent in the societies practising polyandry does not seem to have been ascertained, and would repay statistical investigation. Where lime- or phosphorus-deficiency was responsible, one might expect retention of the placenta

[1] Westermarck, E. : *The History of Human Marriage*, Vol. III, pp. 107–222, London, 1921.

to cause subsequent sterility and death due to inflammatory conditions. Iodine-deficiency, on the other hand, would probably bring on early ovarian hypotrophy, with almost all other forms of endocrine disorder. When nutritional conditions are bad, female sterility is racially more advantageous than the production of additional offspring doomed to starvation. Thus, nature seems to have imposed the nutritional test at the earliest possible moment, so guarding herself from being burdened with a mass of candidates who must later, in any case, be rejected.

It seems fairly safe to conclude, then, that polyandry reduces the chances of sexual selection by male competition. Yet in regions like Tibet, it is true, some natural selection for male virility might operate ; since the libido seems often to be weakened in both sexes, though especially among the males, vast numbers of whom choose a life of asceticism in monasteries.

On the whole, however, we might have expected a natural selection between the women to outweigh this other factor, given, that is, a true opposition between the two sets of characters encouraged by each process. Actually, however, no such conflict would appear to exist ; not in Tibet, at all events. For if iodine-deficiency is severe, and if ultra-femininity encourages a waste of iodine, there is no *prima facie* reason why a selection for a valuable lack of racial femininity should not actually work through the women. If so, it might reinforce the selection for virility achieved through the men. In this connection it is perhaps worthy of note that from Gilgit in the Himalayas comes the single case wherein the female goitre-incidence is actually less than the male.[1] Usually it is about double. Is this solely the result of natural selection, or does a plurality of husbands assist iodine absorbtion in some other way ? Can the female obtain vitamin E or iodine from the male ?

It may be worth noting, too, that the Himalayan woman is reported as being very masterful—habitually choosing or dismissing her husbands of her own free will. This also suggests that she has been selected for a minimum of sex-linked inhibition of autosomal mental characters. It is not enough to say that the marriage-system itself engenders this attitude. Among the Todas, for instance, girls seem to exercise no unusual degree of choice. Their marriages are arranged between their parents and the senior bridegroom.

By way of further evidence that it is in truth lack of iodine that restricts fertility in Tibet—which, as already stated, is a well-known goitre-area—we may point to the remarks of Candler, who accompanied the expeditionary force into that country.[2] He draws special attention to the huge stores of grain held by the inhabitants, which they were glad of an opportunity to sell. Obviously, there is no lack of carbohydrates,

[1] Stocks, P. : " Some further Notes on Cancer and Goitre distribution," *Biometrika*, XCVII, 1925.

[2] Candler, E. : *The Unveiling of Lhasa*, London, 1905.

at all events ; and this at least strongly suggests a deficiency of some specific element or substance as the agency responsible for the restriction of population.

Baber's remarks, quoted by Westermarck, are also of great interest.[1] He noticed that, whereas polyandry was the rule of the Tibetan hills, polygyny often occurred in the valleys. The valley-soils would be more acid, and would retain any iodine they could collect.

On the whole, then, polyandry may be believed to be merely a social effect of any severe natural selection for a physiological character needed to promote female fertility. Its chief interest to the human ecologist must lie, thus, in its ability to indicate areas and peoples from whom the physical environment still demands much more efficiency than organic or technical adaptation has been able to provide. As such, it may serve to indicate regions and conditions which in the past, as well as recently, have contributed towards the moulding of the human stock. I believe, therefore, that the limestone mountain system of Central Asia is causally associated not only with the iodine-deficiency and with the goitre, which is endemic, but with the polyandry as well. If so, the fierce selection among females, which is responsible for the latter, furnishes a powerful argument for regarding this same region as the cradle-land of Man.

We started with the somewhat naïve assumption that polyandry stood at the opposite pole to polygyny. In the Himalayas, however, it seems probable that a mere intensification of the same conditions normally making for male rivalry and polygyny may have caused the evolution of polyandry, as an escape from the wholesale internecine slaughter required if an active selection were to operate among the males. The change would not, however, involve a radical alteration in the type of sexual selection and phylogenetic influence involved. Thus, from some points of view, the two polygamous systems may be held to result in masculinity, with monogamy as the path leading in the opposite direction.

POLYGYNY AND MALE SELECTION

Under this heading we shall once more utilize some of Westermarck's more general conclusions. He considers that it is only among the pastorals and higher agriculturists, and particularly in Africa, that men seem frequently to evince a desire for more than one wife. Even so, however, it is only a few who can realize this ambition ; for seldom, if ever, do the women so greatly outnumber the men that all can be satisfied. Indeed, it is safe to say that, wherever polygyny is an approved social custom, it leads to weaker or less intelligent men being forced either to die childless or else to resort to wife-sharing. This last generalization can apply not only to the conditions holding within a single organized society, but also to whole areas where

[1] Baber, E. C. : Roy. Geo. Soc. Suppty. Papers, Vol. I, London, 1886.

women from one group are captured or purchased by another. We conclude, therefore, that polygyny favours the survival of the more active and successful male types. For among herdsmen, at all events, who are the chief polygynists, there seems small chance of feminine characters contributing to male success. In this case we can thus imagine no converse to the selection for masculinity such as probably occurs through the women in Tibet.

CIVILIZATION AND RACIAL FEMININITY

Westermarck classes the higher agriculturists with the pastorals as being the peoples chiefly addicted to a plurality of wives. It is worth noting, however, that he refers chiefly to Africa, where women do a great deal of the heavy work. Under these circumstances, the same masculinity that proves useful to the male in fighting would help the woman in wielding her hoe.

Conditions in the agricultural civilizations may well, however, be different. Here the men no less than the women must toil in the fields. Moreover, specialization on the production of grain-crops impairs the balance, while increasing the quantity, of the food-supply. Thus, under conditions where men must labour from dawn to dusk, in return for food of an inferior quality, it does not seem impossible that a selection for mineral-economy might operate through the males of the subject classes thus tied to the land. This would result in the evolution of an ultra-femininity making for greater docility through a sex-linked inhibition of combativeness. The community as a whole might thus acquire a certain survival-value due to the willingness with which the more feminine masses would place themselves under the discipline of more masculine, and initially pastoral, aristocrats.

Genetically, disruption would come, not so much through the uprising of the proletariat, as from the degeneracy of those at the top. Only a strict retention of pastoral habits of feeding, combined with endogamy, could preserve the physical type necessary to afford a psychological ascendancy. The domestication of the agricultural man provides only the same kind of food as that eaten by the serf himself.

As far as the Modern age is concerned, it seems quite possible that the tide still sets in the same direction. For instance, there is reason to believe that, although scholastically-gifted girls are psychologically more masculine than the average, among boys a bias towards feminine interests—probably correlated with a feminine physiology—is associated with success at school.[1] Of course, this does not show either that success at school is correlated with success in later life, though it seems probable, or that success in "life," measured by financial standards, confers survival-value. Indeed, it is very possible that the reverse may be true.

1 "The Promise of Youth," Stanford Press, 1930, Review, *Jl. of Heredity*, Vol. 24, No. 11.

Now Westermarck also adduces a good deal of evidence to show not only that an adequate food-supply results in an approximately equal sex-ratio ; but also that racial crossing, in the case of both Man and certain farm animals (cattle) brings about an abnormal preponderance of females. As a troublesome exception to this rule, however, he notes an exactly reverse phenomenon in the case of pigeons. Also, as Haldane points out, in the case of the fowl-pheasant hybrid only cocks hatch out ; these males being sterile.[1]

Subject to a very necessary confirmation by experiment, we may generalize these findings, in the light of modern knowledge, by saying that, in the case of a racial cross, offspring of the homogametic sex may be expected to be the more numerous. Moreover, this could hardly be put down to the influence of sex-linked lethals operating in the hetero-gametic sex ; for their number would be equal regardless of parental relationship. The explanation might lie, however, in a lack of evolved dominance on the part of the sex-linked modifiers of one parent, when applied to the subjugation of the autosomal characters of the other. Indeed, a partial escape from such an evolved restriction might explain one aspect of the phenomenon of hybrid vigour.

In any case, whatever may be the explanation, but always supposing the facts to be correct, we have here an important principle governing the incidence of natural selection under conditions of plenty and food-shortage respectively. Conditions favourable to the increase of one race can cause it to overflow its geographical borders so as to mix with others perhaps similarly affected. If so, racial mixture will occur, and this will lead to a surplus of females in the population : firstly, on account of racial crossing, as just described, and secondly, because a decreased number of female casualties will follow from an increase of iodine, lime, or phosphorus, in the diet. The result of all this will be polygyny, and the result of polygyny will be a phylogenetic reaction in favour of male strength. Moreover, hybrid vigour, which also may possibly be identical with racial masculinity, could in any case be expected to initiate a new stage of competition. Thus, just as a sexual selection for male strength among animals was expected to characterize times of plenty, so polygyny in Man must assist towards the same end. Indeed, the recognition of polygyny as an approved social institution may be attributed to the survival-value inherent in the phylogenetic change that it is thus able to accelerate or maintain.

In the case of the African agriculturists, it seems possible that polygyny should be regarded rather as a means of withstanding an otherwise inevitable relapse into a disadvantageous degree of femininity. The pure pastorals may set a standard that the rest are, to some extent, bound to follow.

[1] Haldane, J. B. S. : *The Causes of Evolution*, p. 64.

EXOGAMY AND IN-BREEDING

The question of exogamy, which is basic to the whole subject of social anthropology, must here be touched on, albeit with the greatest hesitation. It may be pointed out, that under favourable conditions there will be a tendency for groups to expand, and there will be no great need for the racial type to change. Now specific change, like the smaller varietal changes made in the form and function of domesticated animals, is believed to have been the result of in-breeding coupled with a fierce selection. Exogamy would tend to inhibit such an effect. If, therefore, the social organization is evolved in response to the demands of genetics, one would expect exogamy to be strongest at times of racial expansion and among thick populations. Moreover, it is under these circumstances that polygyny, with its attendant disfranchisement of the younger and weaker males, is believed to hold sway. This supports, and is therefore supported by, the theory that exogamy arises in a capture of women from another group, which later develops into a more organized barter culminating in the dual organization. On this theory incest should mark the misery-spots. Even though exogamy is so general as to cover the polyandrous no less than the polygynous and monogamous marriage-systems, it seems possible that the very strength of the incest-taboo may indicate a prior stage when incest and in-breeding were the order of the day. If, as has been argued, Man is the product of a very small and isolated group of in-bred anthropoids, exogamy may be believed to have arisen as a reaction to the earlier state. It may be held responsible for preventing further specific change, the lesser differences between one race and another being rather the results of selection acting on relatively large groups whose individual variations would be small. The more or less fortuitous changes in the mental orientation used for building up the incest-taboo must be dealt with in the next section.

THE EVOLUTION OF THE ŒDIPUS COMPLEX

Now, while we are still dwelling in the realms of almost pure imagination, it may be instructive to push this general theory of sexual selection in Man to its conclusion. One may say, at the outset, that the old idea of the promiscuous horde need make no more appeal to the evolutionary geneticist than it does to most modern sociologists. The biological requirement is for any theory able to explain the high speed at which human evolution has proceeded. For the basis of the evolutionary mechanism—random mutation and selection—seems at first sight far too clumsy and slow. Thus, any hypothesis of sexual selection that can contribute an increment of adaptational speed should be treated kindly. In a promiscuous horde there can be no sexual selection of the sort previously postulated. Either males must be enabled to protect females from the attentions of weaker (or less sagacious ?) rivals, if masculinity is the goal ; or, alternatively, groups of females must succeed in enjoying the embraces of less virile males—

anyway, limiting the opportunity of the strongest—if the racial reaction is to move towards femininity.

The first of these requirements is afforded by polygyny and the latter by monogamy. Polyandry, as we have seen, can result in a selection for masculinity by way of the female, and so complicates the problem. It is here suggested, however, that polyandry may be sufficiently ancient to have influenced the evolution of Man. At all events, polyandry seems able, theoretically, to pave a way from the rule of the dominant male to a family life in which the female is the central figure.

One must admit the inconclusive nature of the evidence favouring the view that an unbridled male-jealousy held sway at any time during the strictly human stage of history. Evidence to the contrary, however, is even more completely lacking, if mere *ex-cathedra* statements, such as that " Man is instinctively monogamous," are neglected. As a working hypothesis it seems to me far more profitable to assume that male combat has at some time possessed survival-value ; and that, where it is inhibited, special circumstances of an environmental nature have been responsible for the selection of counteracting forces, these usually strengthening, and strengthened by, a social convention. In the realms of psychology Freud's evidence for the Œdipus complex, if accepted, encourages a belief that at some time or other the adolescent was forced to give way before the greater strength of the adult male. Moreover, if it be admitted that the tendency towards a repressed hate is inherited, it must be also assumed that those who failed to inhibit their adolescent combativeness failed also to survive. Indeed, it can even be argued that an early recognition of the father's sex-characters might usefully become involved in the sex-linked psycho-neural mechanism inhibiting combativeness in the child and its mother.

Emphasis may be laid on the argument that the repression or inhibition of the hate may be no less inherited than the combative instinct itself. For, even if hate is an emotion and not an instinct, it may be pointed out that emotions seem to arise through the inhibition of instincts, and that inhibition may be of genetical and internal origin as well as being imposed from without. Indeed, I suggest that, when a repression is rationalized, or abreacted, in psycho-analysis, the débris of an ancient and evolved psychological character is thereby removed merely in order that more efficient, and more consciously controlled, forms of censorship, or forgetting, may be stimulated to hold it again in check.

It seems possible that this raising of the threshold of censorship may allow substitutional escapes of a higher and more rational order of thought and behaviour, such as may truly be deserving of the term sublimation. It thus could well be that a pathological Œdipus complex might result from maladjustments either of heredity or of environment. A strong autosomal combativeness inherited in combination with a weak sex-linked repression might give trouble. Ontogenetically the failure of ovarian function at the menopause could weaken the evolved repression, and thus precipitate paranoic and other neuroses due to this unleashing of a hitherto repressed and so unharnessed super ego. Environmental changes involving a discarding of racial femininity or fœtalization, due to an improvement of diet, might be expected to precipitate neurosis and create a demand for sublimational activity.[1] Natural or sexual selection for femininity or fœtalization might serve thus to increase the happiness of life.

On this view, the Œdipus complex is regarded as evidence of an hereditary repression of male or autosomal combativeness evolved primarily to protect the immature male. Later, however, it could perhaps be of value in checking undue hatred between group-mates, particularly between the co-husbands of the polyandrous family. We may remember that Man is essentially child-like in the build of his body. It is probable, therefore, that as compared, say, with a gorilla, he will possess throughout his life that inherited inhibition of the fighting instinct which the latter casts off at maturity. This theory that an inhibition of actions dictated by hatred is hereditary and instinctive, as well as merely rational, deserves some consideration when the attempt is made to draw the line between the normal and the pathological in psychology.[2]

As far as the present evolutionary hypothesis is concerned its importance rests on the possibility that, whereas an externally imposed fœtalization of the body may have affected the state of mind, the latter could have reinforced the physical conditions responsible for itself. Mental childishness could pave the way for a selective process wherein the inhibition of intra-group aggression involved great survival-value for the individual and race. Thus a fœtalization far beyond the strict requirements of a mere iodine-shortage would result.

AMBIVALENCE, INCEST, AND PRIMAL RELIGION

If it be admitted that the human body, and so probably the mind, has become fœtalized—or permanently arrested at a stage usually passed through by the young of other animals—some light can be thrown upon the inhibition of intra-group sexuality, as well as upon the prevention of fraternal combat responsible for the formation of the groups themselves. Children are narcissistic rather than heterosexual, and this inversion of the libido upon the self is, I suggest, due to the same evolved inhibition as that also responsible for the repression of combativeness and the resultant formation of the superego. On this view, the love of self is a late biological development, and one particularly well developed in Man. Possibly, however, it is also a revival of a very old hermaphrodite phase, the new and later-

[1] See Chapter XV.
[2] Cf. Roheim, G., trans. Money Kyrle, R.: *The Riddle of the Sphinx*, London, 1934, last chapter.

evolved inhibition having served to re-activate the older and long disused tendencies.

Even as a temporary state, associated with all immaturity throughout the animal kingdom, this introversion of libido into a substituted self-regard could be of great survival-value. Directed towards self-excitation through contact, it could serve to ward off the attacks of parasites. More important still, it could develop into fear of injury—especially of castration in the mammal—and thus motivate the behaviour responsible for self-preservation.

At a higher level of specific and individual evolution the same introversion would lead to self-consciousness, which in gregarious animals might otherwise have been absent. By this means we arrive at the paradox that an intensification of an evolved self-effacement, needed for the protection of the young, can become permanent and can thereby contribute towards the development of individuality and personality in the adult.

Freud's discoveries demand that we attempt to class all types of behaviour, whether called instinct or not, in some phylogenetic order. Even if such a family-tree be completed, the name finally to be adopted for the root-stock will not easily find favour with all.

Freud states frankly that nothing is known about the origin of ambivalence. "It may be assumed to be a fundamental phenomenon of our emotional life." He goes on, however, to suggest: "that ambivalence, originally foreign to our emotional life, was acquired by mankind from the father-complex."[1] This, I think, might be accepted, if by "father-complex" we are prepared to understand all the evolved inhibition of libido and aggression derived from processes of natural selection acting on the young throughout a large part of vertebrate history; and if we then regard the strength of the evolved tendency as having itself assisted towards its own intensification by precipitating the evolution of Man as a specialized social animal.

Using mechanical and physiological word-symbols in place of the, perhaps safer, anthropomorphic terminology of psycho-analysis, it seems possible to represent ambivalence in terms of the reciprocal innervation of skeletal muscle. Variations in the strength, or nature, of a stimulus travelling along its common path may result in either contraction or relaxation being conveyed through the same set of nerve-endings. Moreover, drugs, like strychnine, when acting at certain points—probably special synapses—can convert inhibition into motor activity or vice versa. It seems possible, therefore, that an evolved ambivalence, or a liability towards a sex-linked or other hereditary inhibition of a primary or secondary instinct, might similarly arise through mutations affecting sensitivity at the threshold dividing the motor from the inhibitory reactions of a higher set of instinct tracks, when stimulated by the less varying and more primitive

[1] Freud, S.: *Totem and Taboo*, London, 1919, pp. 260–261.

activity of a lower set of centres. Thus a tendency towards the ambivalence of emotions may be correlated with an evolved physiological character implicating a special tendency towards the frequent inhibition of cerebral activity at special levels of the brain. I would venture a step further by suggesting that ambivalence may increase or decrease in response to variations in the electrolyte concentrations of the internal environment.[1]

It still remains to enquire how a greater tendency towards the ambivalent inhibition of primary instincts could become institutionalized as the incest-taboo ; more especially since exogamy would inhibit in-breeding, encouraging a sexual selection for masculine virility, and an arrest of the phylogenetic change previously moving in the direction of an increase of fœtalization and femininity. This last process must, I think, be presumed to have reached a degree altogether in excess of the requirements imposed by the physical aspects of the environment. By the time that such a stage could be attained, however, complete dependence upon group-behaviour would preclude the possibility of a return to uncontrolled male combat. Under such circumstances survival-value could be realized through an outward canalization of the aggressive instincts, which, within the group, would require to be held in check by the fear of some real, or imagined and idealized, male parent ; and for this purpose the imagined father would possess the great advantage of being immortal, even if subjected to sacramental slaying or other form of ritual attack. It seems possible that this promotion of the child's real father (or paternal uncle) to be the " All-Father " of the initiated and adult man may have served thus to inhibit the direct combativeness and associated conscious sexuality within the group. The prospect of initiation is frightening, and the subsequent rite must be painful in order to abreact or rationalize part of this fear, which the child previously associated with the idea of all adults, and especially those of the male sex. This serves to remove part of the unconscious inhibition against all hetero-sexual and direct libidinous behaviour. At the same time, the evolved and instinctive need of some remaining prohibition is met by education in regard to the details of the exogamic rules, while the freed component satisfies itself in marriage. Even when thus partially released, the remaining incest-taboo could still serve, not only to strengthen the unconscious desires, but also to insist upon their sublimation into a more diffuse libido ; such as would be still valuable for the purpose of maintaining the solidarity of a larger group, and no longer dangerous as a path leading towards further in-breeding and undue specialization.

LIBIDO, COYNESS, AND TABOO

In connection with a search for organic and psychological correlates that may possibly have affected the evolution of the human body and behaviour, some mention should be made of the unique character of

[1] Cf. Chapter VI.

the human sexual mechanism. There are two features that may both have arisen during the course of a process of organic fœtalization ; such as, when once developed, could have contributed towards the permanence of the gregarious instinct and the strength of the group-organization. I refer first of all to the fact that in Man the sexual rhythm does not limit conjugation or conception to any short season or seasons of the year. This would help group-activity, if we assume, with Freud, that the gregarious instinct is of libidinous origin. In support of his view we may reflect that even solitary animals must come together in numbers, if any sexual selection is to occur at the mating season. In Man, then, the potential mating season has been either re-spread, or was never constricted, so that it extends from one year's end to the next. This, besides binding the groups together, might serve to provide chances for the evolution of specialized and subtle forms of sexual selection, including selection for psychological characters as displayed mainly in matters of behaviour.

Coupled with this persistence of erotic behaviour, we may consider that anatomical peculiarity of the human female, the hymen, and certain widely ramifying, and probably correlated, instincts. The latter, starting as the young female's evolved fear of the adult male, may be believed to have become permanent, and to have spread their influence throughout most parts of the mind. It may be responsible for the many taboo-reactions, and especially those gathering round first-fruits ; or, again, *rites de passage*. It would appear important for the social anthropologist to remember that a duplicate half of the genes responsible for the organic development of the female nervous system acts similarly upon the male. Thus Crawley's sexual taboo,[1] and indeed a tendency to accept taboos in general, may have been strengthened by the evolution of a raised threshold of coyness found necessary to withstand a removal of seasonal control from the libido of the male. Here again we appear to encounter a self-stimulating process of sexual selection. Greater female coyness demands increased male gallantry and display. The genes for all these seem likely to have developed upon the sex-chromosome.

Now I am aware that this diffusion of the erotic impulse is not limited to Man alone among the primates. It is possible, therefore, that the evolution of the sex instincts and organs may have been gradual ; indeed, so slow, or so often delayed, that Man has, in this respect, merely lagged behind his cousins, all of whom must in their turn be regarded as outstripped by the carnivores and the ungulates, for whom mating seasons are conveniently restricted. The alternative possibility is to view the human, and possibly some of the primate, sex mechanisms as being atavistic returns to the primitive arrangement. In the uniform environment of a tropical forest there is no need for a seasonal control. If the nutritional state of the mother can inhibit œstrus until lactation is complete, all necessary conditions are fulfilled.

[1] Crawley, E. : *The Mystic Rose*, London, 1902.

Female competition will resolve itself into a food-quest, the outcome to be judged by the number and quality of offspring produced in a lifetime. In the cold, arid habitats things will be different. There will be seasons with both of dearth and of plenty ; and we may remember the probable stimulation of the anterior-lobe liable to follow from the inhalation of vitamin E in the pollen discharged in Spring. I suggest, therefore, that Man may be descended from a large anthropoid with a seasonally controlled sex-mechanism ; and that, just as fœtalization may be held responsible for a return of primitive characters in the hand, so the sex-mechanism also returned to its earlier stage of evolution and ontogenetic development. Some such sudden arrest of development could have given rise to the anatomical defects thus probably correlated with coyness in the female and with unrestrained eroticism in the male. Given a start of this sort, the two, probably sex-linked, characters could have interacted to their mutual over-development.

The raw material of this feminine instinct of coyness is probably that same fœtal tendency towards an ambivalent inhibition of libido and aggression that has been already discussed. It may be imagined, however, as conveyed through specially evolved channels subject to their own special ambivalent sensitivity. It seems probable that both the male and female instincts towards congress are closely allied to, and of a common origin with, the aggressive instinct ; and that both sexes are subjected to different degrees of inhibition. On this theory, the so-called masochistic sentiments of the female may be regarded merely as pleasure anticipated from the eventual release of a pent-up and narrowly canalized aggressiveness, such as requires for its release an intense degree of an almost equally specialized type of behaviour on the part of the male. Female aggression is inhibited throughout most of its range of intensity. It can vent itself in diffuse and faint displays of provocative behaviour as a prelude to courtship, and then undergoes a progressive repression until it can finally burst through in the sexual act itself.

POLYANDRY, INCEST, AND THE FIRST FAMILIES

Now, according to the theory of human bodily evolution previously put forward, it was argued that a more or less continuous period of size-expansion from small anthropoid to Man was interrupted by a temporary and accidental retroversion of this beneficial increase of size ; during which short but important period the arms were shortened, much of the hair was lost, and the relative size of the brain increased. To fit in with this scheme it does not seem impossible that in the first part of this period, the expansion from a small to a large anthropoid may have been accompanied and assisted by a sexual selection for male strength, and so by a system of polygyny. Something of the same sort seems, even now, to be taking place among the gorillas. We may reflect, too, that an accidental decrease of size, if occurring suddenly within the small group destined to become human, would intensify the need for a renewal of all the forces able to restore the body to its previous and more satisfactory size. Thus sexual selection for male strength may have occurred after, as well as before, the emergence of Man. If this is correct, most of the adolescent's repressed hatred towards the adult male—still discoverable by psycho-analysis—may have been evolved before the dawn of humanity.

Possibly, indeed probably, we have been wasting time over the discussion of a rather unreal issue. It seems credible that the young and the females of most land-animals, and all mammals, may inherit some repression of the aggressive tendency. Indeed, species such as those composing the carnivores, in which adult aggression is extreme, may owe this valuable character to an intense sex-linked repression correlated with such anatomical characters as their brachycephaly and inhibition of limb-development, to which attention has already been drawn. Repression, whether hereditary or externally imposed, may intensify the strength of the inhibited instincts. Carnivores when young are easily made into pets. Thus the dog, like Man, may be regarded as arrested in his anatomical and psychological development. Even the smell of blood fails to release such full fury as is liable to burst forth from a tamed lion or tiger. I suggest, then, that the tendency to an Œdipus complex is a hereditary and evolved character present to a greater or less degree in all mammalian species. By imposing an ambivalent restraint of the aggressive tendencies it could have facilitated education by permitting play between the young. In this matter, too, Man has retained a perpetual youth.

Let us once more, then, try to envisage the conditions affecting a group of gorilla-like anthropoids led to colonize a treeless limestone tableland. It seems fair to assume that many of the colonists would have been those who had been thrust out of the more suitable and familiar forest-environment owing to the superior strength of rivals. A majority would be males of the weaker and less combative sort. It is necessary, however, for us to postulate their possession of a few females as well.

Under these supposed conditions several powerful encouragements of polyandry would come into play. Firstly, until adaptation was complete, it is fair to postulate that the proportion of marriageable females to males would remain very small. The disadvantages of the new soil and food would kill off more females than males. Besides, fresh male competitors, the subsequent offscourings of the forest-system of polygyny, would arrive to threaten the property of the pioneers. Under these circumstances no single male could hope to keep a female entirely to himself. He would be worn out in warding off constant attacks. If two or more could combine, however, they might each succeed in siring a proportion of the offspring. Probably there is a critical ratio of males to females after which a willingness to turn away wrath and gain an ally by wife-sharing will confer greater survival-value than the more ancient and respectable method of offering battle to all and sundry. Genetically, moreover, fraternal polyandry—now common in some Himalayan regions—comes to much the same thing as marriage with a single male. Brothers of greater combined strength and sagacity, possessed of the new character of willingness to co-operate, would still be enabled to perpetuate their heredity to the exclusion of weaker or worse-organized competitors.

The question of how far incest and in-breeding was practised by these first Hominid groups must, of course, remain a matter of almost pure speculation. It is worth noting, however, that polyandry would appear to provide a better background for in-breeding than either monogamy or polygyny. The longer young males could be encouraged to remain within the group, the stronger they would become. Numbers would be an offset to an anatomical inferiority of the individual, and any physiological advantages correlated with the defect in question would be a clear gain. It is consistent, therefore, to suggest that polyandry and in-breeding may have helped to accelerate the temporary size-reduction believed to have accompanied the crucial change from ape to Man. At the next stage, however, if size was to be once more increased, the practice of exogamy might be suspected to have re-asserted itself. This step is hard to imagine except as the accompaniment of an increased female fertility and a change to monogamy or polygyny. Thus the fact that modern polyandrous societies also practise exogamy suggests that they are atavistic reversions to, rather than direct descendants of, the initial stage of human evolution.

Supposing polyandry thus to have marked the very dawn of the human era, there is no reason why the size-increase still encouraged by iodine-deficiency should not have been resumed. Natural selection would, however, be directed—then as now—upon the females, so that physiological characters alone would be encouraged.

Even if the latter process was achieved in the same manner as the earlier encouragement of combativeness and strength—namely by the annulment of most of the repressive interaction of the sex-inheritance upon the autosomes—there would be other modifications as well. There would be no longer a need for the characters making for combativeness to remain linked to those encouraging iodine-economy, and the latter would be free to develop without any corresponding growth on the part of its former partner. If so, polyandry would assist the chances of a successful group-life, and hence, incidentally, must tend to prolong the period of its own influence. For male jealousy would be always apt to threaten the disruption of such an association, especially if a phylogenetic change towards masculinity was thereby being attained.

The theory of bodily evolution went on to postulate that a branch of the tableland inhabitants returned to the forest after the evolution of hairlessness and the erect posture. At this stage a certain degree of group-solidarity would have been developed. In particular, males would no longer possess the single instinct to fight, but would likewise have begun to recognize the difference between friend and foe. Groups of co-operating males—frequently brothers—would thus tend to gather about each marriageable female and her children. It seems improbable that the initial move back into the forest would immediately convert the polyandry into monogamy, or even back into polygyny. Most, if not all, environmental change tends to be disadvantageous ; and it seems improbable that early Man, when once adapted to life above the treeline, would again re-invade the forest, unless driven to do so by some force beyond his control. Either mere expansion of numbers or a climatic change—possibly involving glaciation—could have been responsible. In any case, the number of available women would be unlikely to increase until after adaptation was complete, when some minor change of environment or habitat could improve the balance of the diet.

In short, then, it is suggested that the matrilocal and matripotestal family grew out of wife-sharing, but that its monogamous character developed later as a result of an increase in the number of available women. It seems improbable that an intermediate stage, in which groups of males possessed more than one wife between them, would be stable. Female as well as male jealousy would break up any such partnership ; which, in any case, would not seem to possess any greater economic or genetical survival-value than monogamy.

On this theory, then, polygyny in one group results in a polyandry at its borders, and the latter, in due course, blossoms into monogamy and a matrilineal organization. Thus, male competition is eliminated, and the race will henceforth be selected through the females. Assuming a forest existence, natural selection will now favour an increase of racial femininity, and this will be free to develop unhampered by the rival claims of masculine efficiency. For the first time the instinctive preferences of the woman will be allowed to exert their full phylogenetic influence. They will act, I suggest, through the more feminine women choosing, and being chosen by, the less masculine men ; the offspring of such unions being blessed with greater survival-value.

FEMALE JEALOUSY AND GROUP SOLIDARITY

As previously pointed out, the assumption of an instinct making for a special preference of ultra-sexual (or feminine) individuals of opposite sex for each other will in no way preclude the independent working of another tendency making for a general admiration of opposites. The phylogenetic effect of the latter inclination, will, however, be small. Meanwhile, to round off this question of the sex-instincts and their relationship to the types of marriage, it must be pointed out that under polygyny jealousy between women who are co-wives will always exert a disruptive force ; whereas under polyandry and monogamy the same instinct would be of value in consolidating the family group.

Now there is some reason to suspect that in an ultra-male stock, which might be expected to owe this racial character to the practice of polygyny, the combative and other masculine instincts of the female, no less than those of the male, will be somewhat imperfectly repressed.[1] They will require a greater degree of male display before they become quiescent, and this assistance we may expect to be supplied. In regard, however, to the combative instinct as directed towards other women, it seems possible that jealousy may represent an escape by substitution, if not exactly by sublimation, from an autosomal rivalry, held frontally in check by sex-linked factors inhibiting combativeness towards the male. If so, one might expect the women of the more feminine races to require a minimum of male domination to stimulate their adoption of the feminine rôle. It would be these ultra-feminine women, however, who might be expected to display the greatest jealousy towards each other. How far the facts fit this theory I leave others to judge, not to say to measure. If the truth lies this way, one can imagine a critical point beyond which female jealousy would offer a stubborn opposition to any polygamous marriage-system; and the resultant monogamy would still further accelerate the change towards racial femininity. Indeed the only theoretical escape from such a one-way process would appear to be a reversion to polyandry, followed by a selection for male characters through the women. In practice, ultra-male and polygynous invaders may usually be relied upon to impose the necessary check. In the polygynous groups female jealousy will be weak by reason of a racial masculinity and a corresponding weakness of sex-linked inhibition. More of the female-combativeness can find discharge towards its true target, the male. Thus masculine sexual selection by polygyny is also self-exciting; and, the further it can proceed, the weaker will grow the internal force of disruptive jealousy.

Even rivalry between the two sexes, such as is presumed to be strongest in the ultra-masculine races given over to polygyny, may have its survival-value. It may be this mood that insists upon a division of economic tasks. If it is female jealousy that tends to exclude them from gathering or gardening activities, the men will engage in war, and the group will benefit from the capture of alien women. Thus will the polygyny and sexual selection for male combativeness be still further assisted. By way of contrast to this state of affairs we may contemplate the life of the less masculine race that struggles in a misery spot, or in an environment where numbers rather than individual strength are favoured. In such conditions the less masculine males will show no undue distaste for work of so unexciting a character as gathering or tilling the land.

CONCLUSION

A connection between the opposing systems of sexual selection and the alternative forms of the family has been dealt with in this chapter. Polyandry is taken first, since it is so common in Central Asia, the limestone cradleland of mankind, and seems to indicate severe food-

[1] Cf. Roheim, loc. cit.

deficiency affecting the number of marriageable women. Sexual selection would not, however, appear to be important in polyandrous systems, though a natural selection for an increase of either masculinity or femininity could operate through the women. The opportunities for incest, in-breeding, and a consequently rapid phylogenetic adaptation seem to be provided, though all modern polyandrists practise exogamy. Polygyny provides the best chance of an increase in racial masculinity ; and monogamy allows women to exercise choice in favour of less masculine husbands. Both the food-supply and the nature of the adjoining groups can influence the form of the family. Good food encourages male competition, polygyny, and racial masculinity ; while lime-shortage promotes femininity through monogamy. Favourable epochs might swell the size of all endogamous groups until contacts occurred ; and the resultant mixture might possibly produce a surplus of female births, and so, still further assist polygyny and its consequences. Polygyny in a favoured spot results in polyandry at its borders, and this in its turn may become stabilized into monogamy.

Since sexual selection is assumed to be one of the agencies leading to the fœtalization of the human body, it is, to some extent, held responsible for the fœtalization, or sex-linked repression, of the mind, and so for the ambivalence, or emotional pivoting, recognized by Freud and other writers. This tendency towards the ambivalence of emotions is regarded as a character of all higher animals, being especially useful during youth. In Man it has become reinforced and permanent ; and not only serves to restrain intra-group aggression, but has been used also to inhibit incest, and so to prevent undue specialization through in-breeding, such as would otherwise seem inevitable in the case of any social animal.

CHAPTER XIII

RACE AND CULTURE

The Steppe and the Sown : Reaping and Rooting : Environment and Animal Domestication : Mediterranean Man : The Polished Axe : The Diffusion of Mixed Farming.

THIS AND THE TWO FOLLOWING CHAPTERS MUST BE REGARDED merely as a rough draught of the manner in which the foregoing theory of human evolution might be applied to problems of ethnology, history, psychology, and politics when efforts are being made to understand the organization of different racial, national, and tribal groups, their constituent elements, and their interactions upon one another. An attempt will be made to trace the course of the eternal conflict between the two main anatomical, physiological, and psychological tendencies : the strong, wasteful, and masculine heredity *versus* the weaker, but more economical and sex-repressed, strain. Each is wont to be most dominant and possess its greatest survival value in the type of environment most closely resembling that in which it was evolved. We may bear in mind the theory that, following upon the evolution of the first human group, specialization in two opposite kinds of environment probably produced two greatly divergent sub-species : the Palæanthropic, adapted to a cold arid environment, and the Neanthropic composed of forest dwellers. The former, although more specialized to mineral-deficiency than a majority of animals, were nevertheless inferior in this respect to the Neanthropic stocks. Thus the latter may be considered to have continued most faithfully in a course of adaptation probably first embarked upon by the ancestral mammal, and seldom departed from without ultimate disaster.

It was suggested that most, if not all, of the primitive Hominidæ known to us by fossils, and also the more basic divisions of modern humanity, are the result of single, or repeated, racial mixtures between these two primary constituents. Further, it was noted that, on the whole, the fine-boned, and presumably economical, types appear not only to have survived, but also to be superior in numbers, if not always in culture, as compared with the few existing remnants of the coarse-boned strain. It remains, therefore, to enquire how much benefit and survival-value has been derived by each system from the other. It will be argued that each mixing of types has resulted in at least one, and often two, emergents which, by the test of survival, must be counted superior to the stocks from which they were sprung. Whether each is then necessarily bound in hostile, but inevitable, symbiosis to the other is another matter. It seems probable that, wherever there is a fission into two practically endogamous groups, each must still act upon the other as a competitive, but perhaps useful, stimulus to further adaptation ; and that this rivalry must continue until, as in a blood-feud, the enemy is extinguished, or differences are again swamped by intermarriage.

It is proposed, then, to try to trace the influences of these two types of mammalian and human inheritance, in the first place as they have influenced the sub-division of the primary continental colour-groups into plainsmen and agriculturists. Then, later, after the fusion of these two elements within the modern nations, the same tendency will be seen in the interactions of country and town, and in the rise and fall of the participants in the economic rivalry of the present mechanical civilization.

THE STEPPE AND THE SOWN

Under this sub-heading, which is borrowed from one of the excellent small volumes of Peake and Fleure, I propose to do little beyond drawing attention to the very common, if not universal, phenomenon of the plainsman's entry into the territory of the agriculturist.[1] Genetical and cultural fusion is the result, and it is probably true to say that the synthetic product, especially after secondary specialization, possesses a greater plasticity and survival-value than either of its ancestral components. These racial and cultural clashes have occurred in all the continents, thereby involving the refusion of sub-types of the same colour-branches of humanity. In addition, members of one colour-type have invaded the territory of others.

To continue with generalizations, it is probably true to say that the invasions from the plains into the cultivated lands have been far more frequent than any reversals of such a process.[2] It must be remembered, however, that historical records are apt to perish with the civilizations that compiled them ; so that, even if some members of an agricultural community should survive the destruction or reduction of their larger group, it is unlikely that we should possess direct records of such a fact. The story of the Israelites' flight from Egypt is thus doubly remarkable. Even here, however, it may have been the zealous preservation of a pastoral tradition that permitted the Exodus, even if climatic change, involving plagues and famine, supplied the stimulus. If the Jews entered Egypt as pure pastorals, it seems probable that they abandoned there the cow-boy's contempt of intensive cultivation. They would

[1] Peake, H., and Fleure, H. J. : *Corridors of Time*, V, Oxford, 1928.

[2] The arid environment encourages fertility even if adaptation to the humid areas increases fecundity. Moreover, the former environment is less stable.

emerge with a vastly improved capacity to adapt themselves to any country or climate.

In the Old World the domestication of animals is of such long standing that we seem almost forced to regard the plainsman as a pastoral or horse-nomad, and the cultivator as a grower of grain. It is thereupon easy to look back to the occupation of the more primitive peoples, which may be described as "hunting and gathering," and then to assume that specialized hunting produced the pastoral life, whereas concentration on gathering led up to agriculture. Let me try, however, to show that there are several obstacles in the way when we attempt to apply the mineral-hypothesis to any such simple scheme.

In the first place, the history of the aboriginal American cultures shows us that the domestication of Steppe animals is not an inevitable prelude to the mastering of the settled cultivators. It is true that the incursions of the plains type of tall bison-hunters into the maize-growing Pueblo regions bore some analogy to an incursion of pastorals. In Mexico, however, the stratification of the Archaic, Toltec, and Aztec cultures, probably reveals two successive conquests of settled agriculturists by other less specialized and less sedentary tribes, all of whom were nevertheless cultivators rather than hunters; the cultivation, however, being on the shifting system involving the frequent burning off of fresh country. All this is explicable if it be assumed that catch-crops grown on the burnt hill-sides must contain more mineral salts than those grown more continuously in the moister soils of the valley. Ash is a complete mineral-fertilizer.

Then, again, there is the question of seed. It is almost certain that maize was developed by man in America; and I suggest that the improved strains of the grain would find their way to the centres of civilization, even if, by a reverse process, a diffusion also occurred. Now maize contains a greater proportion of starch to structural substances than any other type of grain. Compared with wheat, for instance, its nutrient ratio is as 11 to 7. The calcium- and phosphorus-contents of maize are ·01 and ·63 per cent as compared with ·06 and ·93 for wheat. These figures, however, refer to the modern highly specialized grain, selection having focussed itself upon total yield, while mineral- and protein-contents are disregarded. I suggest, therefore, that a semi-savage tribe of cultivators, like the ancestral Aztec, probably supplied themselves with food of better balance than that available in the valleys. The fact that the supply of this better-quality food would be more variable would, of course, encourage attacks upon the folk of the lower country. For these the effect of drought would be less severe, and their higher civilization would have encouraged the storage of adequate reserves. There is reason, thus, to suppose that the nature of the soil can react directly upon the man; the cultural buffering being to some extent secondary.

So much, then, for the influence of domesticated animals; the worth of which will be revealed when we come to discuss the invasion of the humid Atlantic region of Europe. First of all, however, it may be well to point out the difficulty in the way of accepting the other over-simple theory, namely, that the hunter becomes the specialized pastoral. Dietetically there is probably a greater difference between the foods, say, of the Eskimo and the Masai, than could be found when comparing either with that of cultivators or of hunters and gatherers. Flesh-food, as has already been pointed out, is so rich in proteins that the elimination of excess-nitrogen must tax the reserves of fixed base. Since the Eskimo is unable to eat bones, he tries to burn up the acid proteins by consuming as much fat as possible. This, however, must place further strains upon the digestion, since ketosis also results in acidity.

In contrast with this dietary, it is remarkable that pastoral peoples seldom kill their cattle for food. In Africa, in addition to drinking the milk, it is common to drink blood drawn from the living beast. Beef is reserved for ceremonial occasions. Such a milk and blood diet, which the women supplement with some vegetable fare, must be extremely rich in all the minerals and vitamins. This fact is almost certainly connected in some way with the tall stature of the pastoral peoples of Africa and other parts of the world. Nay, I would go further, and associate it with their fighting efficiency as well. These points, however, must wait. I wish merely to point out that, if we are to assume an immediate change from hunting to herding within the same environment, we imply a radical change of diet such as would entirely destroy the survival-value of the small, economical, carnivorous type of anatomy and physiology, and would encourage a natural and sexual selection in favour of an enlarged and much less economical kind of man. I suggest, then, that, since the form and physiology of the primitive agriculturist stands nearer to the half-way point of these two extremes, the physical heredity of the hunters, no less than their culture, must at least have become fused with that of the agriculturist before the tall stature and habits of the pastoral could be developed. Alternatively, it is possible that the idea of domesticating animals arose directly from the idea of domesticating plants, and that it owes little if anything to the hunter. Before continuing with this theme it becomes necessary, however, to say something concerning the different sorts of cultivator.

REAPING AND ROOTING

A fundamental distinction can, probably, be drawn between gardeners and growers of grain ; and it is not impossible that these two forms of agricultural activity may have developed by quite separate paths. In each case it seems likely that harvesting took an evolutionary precedence over planting. In the garden, however, the digging-stick, first used to obtain roots, came also to be used to replace a portion of them so that it might grow again. If this guess is right, it forces us to regard gardening as mainly an affair of the tropics ; for few edible

R

roots can withstand frost. This may account for the fact that, on the whole, it is the fully Negroid peoples of Africa and Oceania who are gardeners. Their primitive outliers, the Bushman and the Australian aborigine, are at the root-grubbing stage; though the former may be suspected of having borrowed the idea of the perforated stone-weight for the digging-stick. As compared with an exclusively carnivorous diet, this garden produce probably supplies much more calcium, though sodium will be deficient. The extra amount of lime will support a stronger skeleton; while the adaptation to withstand sodium-deficiency has already been discussed. It is not impossible, then, that the hunters of the hot steppe may have certain cultural and somatic affinities with the cultivators of the lands merging with the tropical forest. Neither the Bushman nor the Negro can, however, be held responsible for the domestication of animals. Our attention must thus be turned to the cultivators of the North.

How then, did the practice of reaping and sowing begin? We must again rely on imagination, but there are several suggestive facts to guide it. I suggest that the collection and eating of grass-seeds became a primary activity as the result of a scarcity of game, following upon the change from the cold steppe conditions of the Upper Palæolithic. Of course, since the causes of the glacial period are very uncertain, we must remain in doubt concerning the conditions that prevailed at its end. If the snow and ice were removed by a general increase of temperature, the latter would cause a heavier rainfall, with a resultant decalcification of the soil. This would encourage the growth of forest, and would likewise adversely affect the fertility, as well as the feeding grounds, of steppe animals. Alternatively, it is possible that the retreat of the ice-sheet may have been due to a lack of precipitation, caused in its turn by a diminution of solar warmth. After a reduction of the ice-sheet to less than Brooks' critical diameter, contraction would be accelerated, so that the polar anticyclone would soon be powerless to withstand the inflow of moisture-laden winds.[1] This explanation, then, might also explain the reduction in the extent of the game-rich and formerly arid Tundra. In either case the result would be an increase of rainfall in the North, followed by a decalcification of the soil, a growth of trees, and a scarcity of game.

Now the Palæolithic hunting-cultures of Europe were succeeded by those of the Azilian and Tardenoisian. The latter was characterized by Pygmy flints of an accurate geometrical design. Similar small flints are used by contemporary peoples for the manufacture of all sorts of tools and weapons, so that it is not possible to argue directly to their initial or main use in the so-called Mesolithic period. There is one theory, however, that could explain both their invention and sudden utilization—one, too, that can be accommodated to the somatological evidence. For a small round-headed strain appears in Europe at the end of the Reindeer Age. Or, at all events, a number of

[1] Brooks, loc. cit.

Epipalæolithic skeletons show these traits ; which, as has already been argued, may be held to confer mineral economy, and so to possess survival-value at a time of heavy rainfall.

I suggest, then, that the Pygmy flints were used to form the edges of sickles used for reaping some primitive form of grain. Indeed, what were thought to be wheat-husks, together with stones of cherry and plum, were found in the Mas d'Azil cave,[1] though at this site the flints approximated to a Late Magdalenian pattern, the Tardenoisian Pygmies being absent. It is probable, however, that the use of Pygmy flints was a refinement which followed the domestication of the gramineæ. The still earlier reaping-hook was the jaw-bone. Supposing the latter to be in constant use, it is not a big step to gum in chips of flint in place of the teeth, which tend to drop out ; and this idea, in its turn, would lead up to the substitution of the bone and its convenient alveolus for wood cut with a groove, in which small flints could be set either as teeth or, better, in a single cutting-edge. On this hypothesis, then, we can explain how a change of climate favoured the diffusion, if not the development, of a new kind of Man, a new kind of food, and a new type of tool. We must assume that each originated at a centre ; and may conjecture that probably they arose together and diffused side by side.

The exact mechanism of cultural evolution and diffusion is almost or quite as complex as that resulting in somatic change ; and it is legitimate to use any knowledge concerning the one as an inductive hypothesis that may have value in explaining the other. Further, we may suspect that the very same changes of environment are likely to initiate and select special variants ; and that the adaptation will fail unless the somatological and cultural changes are each adjusted not only to the external environment but also to each other. Indeed this last requirement, no less than the other two, may be similarly secured by the initial ontogenetic or individual reaction leading the way towards specialization through modification. In the case we have been considering the somatic adaptation towards a reduced size and brachycephaly—whether produced by racial mixture or otherwise—probably adjusted the body to life under humid conditions, involving food of poor quality and low mineral balance. Similarly, the development of a harvesting technique was probably encouraged by a scarcity of game at the time when the reindeer was giving way to the red deer. Thirdly, however, we may reflect that the somatological modification was of a kind liable to inhibit the aggressive tendencies useful to the hunter, and to favour the greater industry needed in agriculture. In place of the excitement of the chase, men would be offered a dull kind of work requiring little strength but much patience. Such a task would satisfy only the feminine, and probably sex-linked,

[1] Keith : *Antiquity of Man*, p. 79. Cft. Piette, E. : *L'Anthropologie*, 1895, Vol. VI, 276.

instincts and emotions concerning food.[1] For to store food, or to obtain it for others, requires an inhibition of the personal appetites, which must, presumably, be sublimated into the very different channels of behaviour resulting in the joy of giving to others. Without some such spontaneous change of racial psychology it seems improbable that any descendants of the Cromagnon reindeer- and bison-hunters could have taken to the cultivation of grain. There has been ample opportunity to observe how primitive peoples are sometimes content to die out rather than alter their way of life.

Actually, there is fairly good evidence for a racial mixture between the long-headed Upper-Palæolithic hunters and the Central Asiatic round-heads. In the Azilian stratum of the cave at Ofnet, Dr. Schmidt was able to classify eight specimens as round, five as long, and another eight as medium.[2] Similarly, at Aveline's Hole two brachycephalic and two dolichocephalic skulls were obtained from the Azilo-Tardenoisian strata.[3] Other brachycephalic skulls of similar date have been found at Mugem in Portugal. Nevertheless, there is evidence suggesting that round-headedness advanced somewhat ahead of the Epipalæolithic cultures. We must mention in this context the two men and the woman from the Aurignacian stratum of Solutré. The cranial indices of the two males were 79 and that of the woman 77. The woman was unusually small as compared with the men, and the limb-bones were robust, no case showing the flattening associated with the Cromagnon skeleton. Keith also suspects a tendency towards brachycephaly in the Chancelade skull, which is of Magdalenian date.[4] The Furfooz cave in Belgium has also yielded brachycephalic skulls from a Magdalenian horizon.[5] This class of evidence, such as it is, tends on the whole to undermine one's confidence in any close association between cultural and somatic traits, and again raises the suspicion that the form of the head may sometimes vary in response to environment.

It is not impossible that brachycephaly may be racially dominant in some environments, such as France and Central Europe, and, we may add, Central Asia and the Centre and West of North America. Nevertheless other countries—England, for instance—do seem to possess the capacity of reducing extreme values of roundness or length to a medium value. Egypt, too, has absorbed many sorts of invaders without any permanent modification of the short stature and long-headed physical type of the inhabitants. Keith draws attention to the similarity between the facial features of the Magdalenian Obercassel Man, of close Nordic

[1] Cf. Richards, A.: *Hunger and Work in a Savage Tribe*, London, 1932. This book must be considered as the first sociological work in which the importance of the nutritional instincts are recognized.
[2] Keith, A.: *Antiquity of Man*, p. 109.
[3] Ibid., p. 142.
[4] Keith, A.: *New Discoveries*, p. 410.
[5] Keith, A.: *Antiquity of Man*, p. 91.

affinities, and those later and more round-headed Rheinlanders, who are believed to have carried the Beaker-culture overland to England at the beginning of the Bronze Age. Hardly any trace of this round-headedness remains. It is thus reasonable to suppose that the heads of the Beaker-folk were temporarily modified by iodine-deficiency, and that the further change undergone in England allowed a reversion to something of the previous type. The land forming the present Dogger Bank was probably a temporary home of this people ; and one may expect iodine-shortage wherever water has recently been removed—at all events if evaporation has assisted the process.

The theory that bodily characters can be altered by environment in no way invalidates the conception of race as primarily an affair of heredity ; but it does call for a considerable modification of the more common view. We have seen that even the Neanderthal inhabitants of the Danubian region (Krapina) were brachycephalic, and we now find traces of the same character in the Aurignacian of France and Belgium, while it becomes intensified in the Azilian. Ofnet lies at the head of the Danube, and the fact is certainly suggestive when we consider the subsequent invaders who have used that corridor from Asia to the Rhine. It seems quite likely that the Ofnet type of broad-headed inheritance was ultimately derived from much further east—possibly from the western slopes of the Central Asiatic highlands, since this region was presumably subject to great climatic changes at the time when mountain ice-caps were in retreat. We must wait until about 2500 B.C. for the first clearly recorded movement along the Danube ; but by this time it was definitely a movement of round-headed grain-growers, though mixed with long-heads who may be regarded as horsemen from the steppe. Peake and Fleure regard these horsemen as the descendants of the Upper Palæolithic hunters, a point which brings us back to the original and rather unanswerable question how, and by whom, animals were first domesticated.

ENVIRONMENT AND ANIMAL DOMESTICATION

Without attempting to propose an adequate solution of this fundamental puzzle, it may perhaps be useful to outline a theory whereby several basic types of civilized Man may be associated with a like number of domesticated animals. The horse is the animal of the steppe ; though it must remain in doubt whether it was first domesticated by the dolichocephalic peoples of the Caspian region, or by the Mongoloid brachycephals further East, about whom even less is known On a theory of diffusion, the Mongoloid Man at the centre must be given the benefit of the doubt ; and we may reflect that the same iodine-deficiency responsible for the Mongoloid characters in the man might possibly have assisted in making the horse more docile. There seems little doubt that some wild animals are less tameable than others. The Aurochs, the African Elephant, and the Zebra have defied classical or modern attempts to domesticate them. The environments in each case supply very adequate amounts of iodine ; for deficiencies of this element are rare in Africa and are by no means universal in Europe. I suggest, therefore, that mineral-deficiency, and especially iodine-deficiency, may have played a part in encouraging an inhibition of the aggressive instincts in both man and beast, thus assisting the co-operative symbiosis of the two. Indeed, the psychological requirements of the domesticated animal and the civilized man are not altogether dissimilar.

A combination of iodine- and calcium-shortage, such as might have characterized the soils of Central Asia at the time of the Glacial retreat, would be extremely favourable to the domestication of any type of grazing animal. The size, both of the individual and the herd, would almost certainly be reduced, so that speed would be lessened. Also, the small size of the herds would facilitate rounding up ; and I suspect that calcium-shortage could co-operate with iodine-shortage to promote docility. In the case of Jersey cattle, which are adapted to calcium-shortage and iodine-abundance, there is both an extreme sex-dimorphism and a marked difference of character between the sexes. The cows are small and easy to handle ; whereas the bulls are much bigger, and prove most unreliable of temper as compared with other British breeds. I mention the possible influence of calcium-deficiency as an agency having possibly contributed towards animal-domestication, since it could have operated at a time of extreme precipitation. Thus it offers an alternative to the theory that wild animals and Man were both drawn to the same oases, and that domestication became an alternative to death by drought.

This latter theory, however, has also much to commend it. The camel and the humped ox, *Bos indicus*, are both adapted to desert conditions ; and neither possesses any wild relatives. There are, however, two other primary strains of ox that have also probably contributed towards the inheritance of the modern domesticated beast. There is the short-horned inheritance and the hornless strain. The short-horned cattle probably entered Europe from at least two directions, so that their origin is doubtful. I suspect, however, that the purer lines of descent were introduced by Mediterranean peoples of Neolithic culture, who spread across the North of Africa and entered Europe through Spain. Short-horned cattle are found in the West of Africa. The same strain of *Bos brachyceros* or *longifrons* also reached the Western Isles of Scotland, and probably persists in the Kerry and Breton and Channel Island breeds. There has occurred, however, an almost inextricable mixture with the less common short-legged, hornless strain, *Bos aceratos*, found on the Swiss lakes, in the Dutch Terpen, and probably imported into Great Britain from Scandinavia by the Vikings or by earlier Nordics of the Bronze Age culture. In addition, long-horned cattle, which may be related to *Bos indicus*, were later arrivals in Europe. I have elsewhere suggested that this hornless strain may be ultimately connected with the Asiatic brachycephals, and I suspect it of having been domesticated by the inventors of the Azilian culture.[1]

Even the big aurochs, *Bos primigenius*, might possibly have become domesticated ; but, if so, I suspect religious rather than economic motives to have supplied the reason. The wild white cattle of England seem to be the direct descendants of the aurochs, which, nevertheless, were black or red. This white is a dominant Mendelian character, differing therein from the white in other breeds, which is recessive. It might thus have been preserved by the common taboo placed upon the killing of white animals, and would persist as a pure strain after the last coloured individuals were killed off. Such white animals, being sacred, would be specially preserved for sacrificial purposes. White bulls were sacrificed by the Druids, and indeed by most cultures of Keltic origin. The aurochs, and especially its white variant, may thus have come to represent the spirit of the forest, and as such would be reverenced by the agriculturists at its borders. As the forest diminished, it would be perpetuated in its turn as the sacred grove.

MEDITERRANEAN MAN

Here I wish merely to point out the possible parallelism between the brachycephal in association with the hornless cow, on the one hand, and the long-headed Mediterranean type of Man with his small, short-horned, but more normally proportioned, type of animal on the other. *Bos longifrons* resembles a diminutive aurochs, just as the short-statured and long-headed Mediterranean Man is otherwise little different from the larger long-headed Caucasians. It seems probable that a full understanding of the circumstances leading to the evolution of either would explain that of the other also. The short stature of Mediterranean Man seems to be a most definite and prepotent character. It displays itself in the close correlation ($R = 0{\cdot}72$) between small size and the proportion of Italians in the modern American population ; as also in the existence of a centre of short stature in Southern Italy.[2] This strongly suggests a definite racial strain, such as might have been produced by in-breeding and selection within a small area ; of which the primary constituents would presumably have contained some small proportion of Negroid blood.

Egypt might possibly be the cradle of the modern Mediterranean race, since its powers of supporting large populations can only have grown with the size of the Nile, which is relatively recent. North Africa retained the Caspian culture (which is a Southern variant of the Aurignacian) throughout the whole long Upper Palæolithic, while Western Europe went through the successive stages of Solutrean and Magdalenian. It is possible that these last represent Asiatic thrusts, and that the first wave of the Aurignacians represented a less specialized

[1] Marett, J. R. de la H. : *Island Cow*, Jersey, Sept., 1932.
[2] Wissler, C. : *The relation of Nature to Man in Aboriginal America*, New York, 1926, p. 138.

and more dolichocephalic people in whom the genes for brachycephaly were more firmly repressed. The earliest civilized Egyptians, the Badarians, differ in no essential from the predynastic Egyptians, or from the modern inhabitants of the Kharga Oasis.[1] Keith describes them as " a lightly made people of short stature and with small heads." The cranial index of the skulls is 72, the skull vault being low.[2]

According to the theory relating skull-form to physiology that I have put forward, the small size of Mediterranean Man would indicate a race adapted to calcium- or phosphorus-deficiency; while the ill-filled type of low-vaulted skull might indicate an adaptation to an abundance of iodine, whereby tissue hydration and brain expansion might be inhibited. Possibly a diet rich in other salts, such as would be obtained from flood-lands, could help to produce a similar result. This form of body seems thus to represent a small variant of the typical Caucasian. The modern Berber is also of Caucasian type; though the stature is greater, and the skeleton more massive. We may in this connection refer to Hooton's theory that the Guanches of the Canary Islands were belated representatives of the Cromagnon race.[3] I suggest, therefore, that Mediterranean Man is a small and ultra-feminine variant of the main Caucasian stem, and that he owes his secondary somatic adaptation to the growing of grain. This last operation seems more likely to have been invented in Asia than in Europe or Africa, and was probably the result of a reaping-culture which eventually led on the art of sowing and cultivating.

THE POLISHED AXE

By the time that the Neolithic cultures arrived in Europe, they were so fully developed that we have small chance of discovering the origins of any of the components. Pottery, domesticated animals, textiles and corn-growing were all in regular use. There also suddenly appears the polished-stone axe or celt, which rapidly takes on a large number of functions. Now it is remarkable that this polished-stone technique found its way to, or was independently invented in, America where much of the other flint work is of the high quality that we are wont to associate with the pressure-flaking of the Solutrean and pre-dynastic Egyptians. It seems probable, therefore, that the second, if not the original, batch of immigrants arrived in America with the polished celt. Wissler suggests a date of 6000 B.C. for the polished-stone industry.[4] If so, it may well have been developed in Eastern Asia a very long time

[1] Keith, A.: *New Discoveries*; cft. Stoessiger, B. N.: *Biometrika* (1927), XIX, 110; also Hrdlička, A.: Smithsonian Publ. (1912), Vol. 59, No. 1.
[2] Ibid.
[3] Hooton, E. A.: *Harvard African Studies*, Vol. VII, Cambridge, Mass. (1925).
[4] Cf. Wissler, C.: *The American Indian*, 2nd edn., p. 301, New York, 1922.

before its appearance in Europe. America, however, seems never to have had the Tardenoisian Pygmy flints ; and we may reflect that for the cutting of maize, if not of its probable ancestor teosinte, no composite implement would be of much value. Each stalk would, in any case, need to be dealt with singly. If, then, the polished celt has any close connection with agriculture, as seems probable, it would be radically a cultivating rather than a harvesting implement. Indeed, the polish might have been initially obtained by using a stone hoe, and it is not beyond the ingenuity of Man thereupon artificially to copy this polish. This would in any case become a regular feature of old, and therefore lucky, implements to which ideas of fertility and general sacredness would have become attached. If so, Thor's hammer was originally a hoe, and only later became a weapon. Its association with a male deity suggests that, unlike the digging stick, it originated in the hands of men ; and this, in its turn, argues for an exclusively agricultural society, in which neither hunting nor herding could offer the more pleasant alternative.

Even if all this rather wild guessing could be accepted, it does not solve the problem, Who first invented the polished celt ? Once more, however, we are driven to the idea of Central Asia as the point of evolution and subsequent diffusion. For the sake of consistency I would suggest some branch of the Caucasian proto-Nordics as the inventors of the polished celt ; for in the earlier chapters it was assumed on very doubtful evidence that a similar type of man had manufactured and used those other heavy core-implements, the Chellean and Acheulean bouchers. Very similar, though inferior, "picks" appear in the kitchen-middens immediately preceding the period of the polished axe ; and this latter age seems also to mark the turn in the tide of rising brachycephaly which marked the earlier Epipalæolithic.

I submit that this extreme degree of theorizing is not altogether barren. If we are to understand the evolution of Man we must make a thorough study of all aspects of his environment besides familiarizing ourselves with the possible variations of mind and body. So far the cultural remains have been used by anthropologists mainly for purposes of dating, so that an understanding of their functional significance has not been vital. If, however, there is a true and calculable relationship between anatomy and physiology, it will become necessary to work out the full nature of the ecological adjustment at each stage. To do this an exact knowledge of the past climates will be the first requirement ; but, in addition, the improving technical ability of Man must be given due consideration.

THE DIFFUSION OF MIXED FARMING

Modern civilizations seem all to be products of racial mixtures, and, as far back as archæology can guide us, the same cause may be suspected to be at work. For, wherever domesticated animals are found to have been in use side by side with the cultivation of grains, the human population must be suspected of uniting comparatively pure strains of the two sharply differentiated types of humanity. In the next chapter it is suggested that the best kind of Man, the type most easily adjustable to conditions of war or peace, is the product of racial mixture. If this be so, it becomes unsatisfactory to divide the human elements composing civilization into any arbitrary divisions supposed to originate as pastorals and cultivators respectively. At the same time the distinction must be borne in mind, and will serve, like some obsolete boundary, to mark modern deviations from the old cleavage.

There can be no doubt that, when the pastoral enters the plough lands, he comes as a conqueror. The alternative is to stay outside. His best grazing may be slowly encroached upon by the squatters, and he may sometimes, in a half-hearted and shame-faced manner, undertake a little tillage in the more suitable portions of his range. On the whole, however, this peripheral encroachment of one system upon the other will be unimportant. The pastoral races affect civilization either by harrying and constricting its boundaries, or by capturing and invigorating its seat of government. Whenever this latter feat is accomplished, the phalanx of the defending townsmen is led to the assault of the next city-state ; and the wars for empire have begun.

There are good *a priori* grounds for supposing that these cultural clashes would introduce genetical, political and economic changes that are roughly in harmony with each other, and will provide both lords and serfs with an advantage over their own next of kin. For if competition between close relatives is apt to be fiercest, this outdoing of former associates may count for more in the struggle for existence than any rivalry between the more distantly related rulers and ruled.

The new composite civilization places the pastoral as a captain at the head of a loyal and easily disciplined band. He can use his powers of decision to overthrow his less organized and still nomadic relatives. His followers gain in safety whatever they have lost in liberty. In other matters the balance of mutual advantage, if measured in survival-value, goes to the ruled. Assuming the pastoral to have been well adjusted to his earlier environment, there can be but little advantage in exchanging it for the grain-food of civilization. He must retain his strong physique and aggressive character if he is to avoid being deposed. His best chance of so doing will be to maintain strictly pastoral food-habits, and to practise a close endogamy. Harems filled with the daughters of cultivators will not breed him sons like himself, even if they can raise the general standard of physique for the group in general.

Now assuming pastoral domination to imply the modification of specialized grain-growing into mixed agriculture, the opportunity of maintaining an improved physical type will be provided. The strengthened military organization will extend the territorial boundaries so as to include neighbouring grazing lands from which pure pastorals have been driven out. Cultivation will then follow behind the herds, and the manure of the latter will permit a more permanent occupation of the same lands. For without animal manure the cultivator must rapidly exhaust his soil, and is apt to perish by war, famine, and pestilence before securing fresh country to till. Only where floods renewed the soil-salts was he formerly enabled to develop a settled culture. The new composite agriculture can flourish away from the rivers, and so may colonize colder and wetter countries where flood plains remain marshy.

After this composite agriculture is established it could doubtless undergo respecialization. Cold and rain-soaked countries would discourage the growing of grain. In more favoured spots an increasing pressure of population would tend to crowd out the domesticated animals. Nevertheless, this secondary specialization will never assume the extreme form that it took in the days before the ox became yoked to the plough.

CHAPTER XIV

SKY GOD AND EARTH GODDESS

Sex and the Food Instincts: Clothes and Concealment: Cannibalism and Sexual Selection: The Ambivalence of the Food Instincts: The Evolution of Ambivalence: Religion and Environment: Thought and Belief.

IN THIS THIRD AND LAST EXCURSION INTO PSYCHOLOGICAL IMPONDERABLES I shall attempt to bring the important instincts concerning food within the ambit of the theory of sexual selection and the sex-instincts already outlined. In the main, I wish to draw attention to the psychological aspects of those same two types of apparently opposed heredities whose ecological and cultural adjustments, as manifested in plainsman and settled agriculturist, were dealt with in the last chapter. It will be argued that life in arid surroundings, especially when supported by pastoral activities, develops a tall, and often dolichocephalic, type of man, in whom a masculine aggressiveness is well developed and freely exercised. The cultivator, on the other hand, fights only under a real or imagined provocation. He shows less tendency towards self-assertion, and is thus better enabled to co-operate with his fellow-men. The object, then, of this part of the enquiry, is to discover what grounds there may be for putting trust in a racial psychology as the key to a proper understanding of cultural evolution and of our present social adjustments. How far do we act merely in response to the mechanical requirements of the economic situation, and how much is the economic mechanism itself a mere expression and externalization of inborn and deep-seated tendencies of the mind? Are these last the products of analogous situations that affected mind and body alike during the remote past?

As a starting-point, it is worth while to ask whether there is any psychological explanation of the fact that the agriculturist in general both supports and defends himself by collective activity, whereas the pastoral tends both to fight and live as an individualist. Is there any purely technical difficulty great enough to forbid the communal enjoyment of flocks and herds, or to prevent the individual occupation and unaided working of cultivated land? We have only to turn to the modern mixed agriculture to witness both of these theoretical anomalies. In Europe the old common field and communal digging and ploughing has given way before the jealous land-hunger of the modern peasant proprietor. The village no longer works as a unit, and the independent smallholder is held up as an ideal even where he has not already sprung into being. In India, on the other hand, where the village herd occupies the common grazing land, the individual ownership of the beasts does not prevent a communal and equal sharing of such grazing as is available. In both these cases the result is due to cultural, and probably racial, fusion. In the North, however, individualism, as may be expected, shows an increase in cultural dominance. In the South, on the other hand, it tends to give way before collective, if not communal, activities. Even where there is an individual occupation of land, irrigation is often organized and regulated by mutual agreement. If, however, the pastoral enters the corn lands, the canals are at once allowed to silt up.

I propose, however, to defer economic questions, and to point out at once how male and female deities seem roughly to vary in relative importance in accordance not only with the type of employment, but with the type of marriage and sexual selection, prevailing within the group. Agriculturists, especially grain growers, tend to worship a female, often a virgin, deity ; such as the Maize Mother in America, or the Great Mother of the Mediterranean corn lands. Pastorals, on the other hand, are faithful to a male god. So far as it is legitimate to postulate a single train of causality, it can be argued here that the environment influences the body and that the latter reacts upon the mind. Aridity encourages an ontogenetic and phylogenetic increase of masculinity ; which becomes the more marked if a pastoral culture still further improves the mineral and protein balance of the food. This in its turn leads both to a pugnacious temperament and, by promoting fertility, provides a wealth of male rivals, whose sisters, wives and cattle are offered as a prize of victory. Thus strength and fighting efficiency are ideals having survival-value. I have already given my reasons for believing in the great antiquity of a single and Supreme God—a super-male of one's own group, in whose sight all sexual activity is a sin fraught with danger, who more especially punishes incest, and thus commands exogamy by implication.[1] To these common attributes of his exteriorized super-ego the pastoral is wont to add an invincibility in war ; and, since his equal anxiety is water and grass for his beasts, his ideal self becomes also a Sky God.

Let us look now to the case of the cultivator ; imagining an extreme instance, where food of a sort is plentiful, but death appears frequently and mysteriously as a result of mineral-deficiency. Here the battle is not to the strong. It is waged against no living enemy, nor even with a sky which will not rain. Unseen forces strike straight at the mother and child, leaving the man a helpless bystander. Successful motherhood amounts to more than any masculine triumph. In such a situation it is no wonder if men count their descent through their mothers. The female blood-line, or " mogya " as they name it in Ashanti, will be a matter for greater pride than the " ntoro " or masculine strain of

[1] Cf. Freud, S. : *Totem and Taboo*, London, 1919.

father-to-son inheritance.[1] Fertility will depend upon an activity of the sex-linked factors, and these are not conveyed in the male line. Some families of females will be more prolific than others ; so that the idea of an indefinite and ideal fertility will become attributed to a remote Ancestress from whom all may claim ultimate descent.

Only theology will trouble to marry the Great Mother to the All-Father. The latter was first and foremost a monitor and later an all-powerful ideal self. Moreover, supposing a matrilocal and to some extent polyandrous organization, paternity will be a matter of no practical importance. Indeed, under such conditions it might be long before the physiological function of the male aroused sufficient interest to merit the inclusion of such knowledge within the store of tribal wisdom.

SEX AND THE FOOD INSTINCTS

Many students of the life of pastoral peoples have drawn attention to the intensely emotional attitude of the herdsman towards his flock. Often this takes the form of sheer appreciation of numbers, the utility and state of health of the beasts being quite secondary to the joy of possession. We must explain it, I believe, in terms of masculine self-assertion and sex-display. It is an extension of the same sort of instinct and behaviour that leads the strong male to collect a plurality of wives ; and the pastoral, we may reflect, with his patriarchal tradition, glories almost equally in the number of his beasts and in that of his wives, sons, daughters, and grandchildren. He feels a strong rivalry towards his equals, and strives to outdo them, not only in wealth, but in deeds of valour, and in the showing of hospitality. Covetousness with him is a crime, since it implies the acknowledgment that another's possessions and status are greater than one's own. Thus the whole mental attitude is orientated by an instinct for self-assertion and display. Tolerance and kindness are shown to all who slavishly pander to this superiority. In practice, however, such feelings are seldom manifested outside the blood-kin ; and even here they are mainly displayed by the elders towards the young, and then only so long as an iron discipline is maintained. The son stands in awe of his father, and regards his mother as a chattel.

Turning now to the theory that the cultivator tends to be more feminine in body and mind, it remains to enquire how the female instincts towards food and sex-display may be elaborated into a culture-complex. It will be recollected that sex-linked genetic repression was held to inhibit full masculine development ; and thus to leave the female and the less masculine male in a permanently childish state of growth, whereby the domination of some actual or imagined super-male was easily accepted, as well as unconsciously desired. If, then, we transport ourselves back to that hypothetical stage of animal or human society wherein the Œdipus repression is deemed to have been evolved,

[1] Rattray, R. S. : *Ashanti*, Oxford, 1923.

it becomes obvious that the young male must steal and hide his food, or otherwise must eat it during one of the rare moments when all appetites of the dominant male happen to be satiated. Even under these circumstances, to go by Zuckerman's observations, it will be necessary to adopt a supplicatory attitude, wherein all signs of masculine behaviour must be repressed or actually reversed.[1] Feeding will thus be bound up with an ambivalent attitude towards the super-male; and this will become of increasing intensity as size, the demand for food, and the danger of exciting jealousy, increase together. As an example of a " high god " embodying little beyond this narrow concept of a food-rationing father, one is reminded of the storm-riding deity of Terra del Fuego who forbade the slaughter of young ducks ;[2] or of the Andamanese Puluga, who denied the blessings of the monsoon to those who gathered yams out of season.[3]

Of course, there are other and earlier food-instincts of a more pleasurable kind, and with these the idea of the ideal and eternal mother has probably become involved. The suckling is safe while it clings to the maternal body. The element of danger arises only in the event of getting lost. Should this occur, it is vital to distinguish between males and females, since the former are more dangerous ; and, if possible, the young animal must likewise perform the harder task of distinguishing its own mother from the remainder of the adult females. It seems possible that myths and dreams concerning persons of double sex are due to this evolved and infantile anxiety. If so, they too may be bound up with the instincts and behaviour relating to sex and food. If, then, either of these two arguments is valid, it would follow that both in the infantile and in the adolescent stage a strong linkage between the feeding and self-protective instincts will have had survival-value ; so that a connection between the emotions of hunger and fear has probably been forged. Other dangers too, such as the risk of poison, would contribute towards the same effect. The result will be a strong counteracting tendency whereby the sight or thought of food will not always lead to its immediate consumption. Nevertheless, this evolved repression will probably serve to intensify, rather than weaken, the emotional attitude towards food in general. It may further help to regulate its storage, which will be performed in a spirit of fear, and with a view to concealment. There will be none of the pastoral's glory in the unnecessary numbers of his beasts. Corn will be instinctively concealed, and every rational justification for this action will be later explored to the full.

To revert for one moment from psychology to technology, this fear of consuming might be held responsible for the art of sowing and planting. The essential step is to leave a portion unconsumed. A piece of the root is replaced in the hole ; or with grass or grain some is left

[1] Zuckerman, S. : *The Social Life of Monkeys and Apes*, London, 1932.
[2] Darwin, C. : *Descent of Man*, p. 145.
[3] Man, E. H. : Andamanese. J. (R.) A. I. xii, 85.

ungarnered so that the seeds are blown over the remainder of the ground. In these days farmers are taught that no weeds should be allowed on hedges or headlands ; yet the idea dies hard that a " Devil's garden "—a patch left entirely wild—will not somehow or other bring luck. Indeed, if only the best plants were thus set aside, the first stage in the evolution of grain-crops would have come about.

In so far, then, as differences of psychology have contributed to the evolution of the two contrasted types of animal and plant culture, it is interesting to note that these almost polar opposites, male display and feminine inhibition, should have alike prompted the same practical device, namely, the hoarding of reserves in times of plenty, such as can support life in times of want.

CLOTHES AND CONCEALMENT

A psycho-social outcome of this inhibitory attitude may be the tendency towards the concealment of knowledge, as well as of food or other material objects. Starting as a fear-reaction it may be rationalized into a sense of latent power, which can solace an instinct of self-assertion inhibited in childhood. It receives further gratification from the imparting of the secret to novices of a lower social grade. Within the guarded confines of the lodge, the common man casts off his sense of inferiority, and is free to deck himself in magnificent regalia, while safe from the jealous ridicule of the uninitiated.

Clothes, on their part, appeal at once to the instinct for concealment and the instinct for display. Starting with a tendency to hide the genitals, which is rationalized as a fear of black magic, the further elaboration of the garment tends rather to pander to the personal pride ; though its removal would in most cases recall the spirit of shrinking modesty in which it was assumed. Only the warlike and ultra-masculine giants of the Upper Nile scorn the use of clothes. The rest who prefer and can afford to wear them strip off their garments only as a result of a nervous breakdown, when the inhibitory centres cease to work and all unmodified assertion bursts forth. To dance naked before the ark is a sin ; for it is punished by a returning sense of guilt as soon as ever the momentary flame of self-assertion has died down. The suppliant priest goes covered, often in woman's attire ; for even his virgin manhood might provoke the wrath of God. Only the naked pastorals dare shout abuse at the heavens when rain is denied them.

CANNIBALISM AND SEXUAL SELECTION

Another way in which the food instincts may be supposed to have affected culture is in the matter of cannibalism. This is so common a custom of the modern savage, and has so frequently been suspected by the excavators of prehistoric sites, that one cannot fail to bring it home to some members of any of the larger divisions of humanity. As a normal means of obtaining food the practice smacks too much of a mutual exchange of washing. As a method of accelerating evolution and adaptation, however, it could be of use. A race of cannibals might be expected to advance ahead of its rivals if the test was to be fighting efficiency; since only the more successful of the warring individuals and sub-groups that had so strong a reason for destroying life would survive to breed. Later contacts with non-cannibal, and less warlike, neighbours would result in the extinction of the latter.

Now, on the theory of sexual selection already discussed, it was pointed out that large size and strength would be favoured by the Northern and arid habitat; and that adaptation towards a necessary size and full utilization of the abundant lime-salts would be accelerated by a sexual selection for male strength as decided by battle. Such a theory favours the idea that cannibalism would start among the vegetable-feeding inhabitants of an arid habitat. It is consistent with the common view that the special proteins in flesh-food may afford relief from a continuous diet of vegetables. This again suggests that the first Hominidæ may have been cannibals before they acquired the skill to catch game. At the second hypothetical stage, when Neanthropic Man is deemed to have become reduced in size in response to tropical conditions, cannibalism would tend to inhibit any sexual selection for femininity that might otherwise have assisted the required change. Assuming it to have existed beforehand, however, some of the same instincts would be of value in changing the diet from vegetables to meat. Nevertheless, when once game became a regular part of the dietary the original association between the killing and eating of an enemy would tend to break down.

These considerations may possibly explain why cannibalism is more in vogue among the Oceanic than the African negroes. For the latter have more access to game, even when domesticated animals are not available. In Oceania the pig is about the only substitute for human flesh. The theory can also account for why Negroes, on the whole, are probably rather more addicted to anthropophagy than is the case with the two other colour-types. That is to say, it fits in with the previous theory that the Negro evolved as a vegetable-eater of the park-lands. It also agrees with the view that the Negro is basically ultra-feminine, but that natural and sexual selection have decreed a more recent secondary movement towards strength and masculinity.

THE AMBIVALENCE OF THE FOOD INSTINCTS

A point that requires investigation is the relationship of cannibalism to aggression and the blood-lust; for the latter, in various more or less sublimated or ambivalent forms, may be suspected to be the energizing factor behind many forms of ritual and religious sentiment. Indeed we may well enquire whether the aggressive instincts are not more closely associated with the unconscious desire for one particular form of food rather than for another. For both animal experiments and common observation do certainly indicate remarkable powers of capricious choice. These are usually described under the head of *pica*, or depraved appetite. Nevertheless, they are clearly evolved reactions, even if harm may sometimes result. Thus cows on phosphorus-deficient pasture will eat old bones, and may suffer from bacterial infection.[1] Similarly, the coprophagy resorted to by rats starved of vitamin B_2 cannot be wholly beneficial ; but it is better than death. In these last examples the aggressive instincts are also stimulated ; or would it be more correct to say that the friendly feelings are reversed into aggression ? In any case, rats that had been tamed and handled became fierce, suspicious, and liable to bite with no provocation. Human beings suffering from pellagra also became fractious and suspicious.[2] The fact that domesticated animals (pigs) can to a large extent regulate the protein-to-carbohydrate balance of their diet, when offered free choice, say, between maize and fish-meal, has been established and may be legitimately included within this class of phenomena. At the same time it serves to remind us that all animals, including even the much abused Modern Man, have a fairly accurate instinct for the right kind of food ; though admittedly the instincts can be altered by habit, which in its turn is decreed by environment. Probably a good proof of an instinctive bias is when it overrides a social convention. White children in India have been punished for eating lime scraped from the house-wall. Of course geophagy, the eating of lime- and iron-rich clays, is common in many lands. I maintain that the practice is rooted in instinct, and is merely strengthened by social convention.

It seems, then, that there is a more or less complex neurological mechanism that not only assists a choice of the right food, but can reverse or re-direct the food-seeking behaviour whenever the normal food cannot adequately supply some special demand. Such an arrangement is probably of great evolutionary age, involving the interaction of the eyes, nose, and taste-buds on the one hand, and the emotional and motor centres on the other. In the case of Man it seems safe to say that most of those selective processes take place below the level of consciousness. Possibly the "gastronomic Unconscious" has little to say in the choice between beef and mutton ; but it will seldom permit a rigid adherence to any special and narrowly defined diet, especially if the latter has been externally and intellectually imposed, and is not itself dictated by some spontaneously arising prejudice—in other words, another manifestation of unconscious mental processes.

This whole class of instinctive predispositions in regard to food shows some analogy with the ambivalence of those aggressive instincts which have already been discussed. In each case one seems to encounter complete reversals of behaviour. Just as an inhibition of the aggressive instinct would appear to manifest itself in the masochistic

[1] Orr : *Minerals in Pasture*, cf. Theiler.

[2] Findlay, G. M. : *J. Path. Bact.*, Vol. 31, p. 353 (1928).

attitude of the female and adolescent, so too the normal food-instincts may be reversed ; and apparently in this instance as the result of a general or specific deficiency. As an analogous physical parallel I drew attention to the influence of strychnine in changing inhibition into motor activity. Another phenomenon of more evolutionary significance is the influence of adrenalin upon the sympathetic nervous system. Small quantities dilate the capillaries, while large amounts constrict them. If these are indeed fair comparisons, they suggest that chain-reflexes responsible for the reactions to food may likewise be reversed by alterations of the internal environment. Possibly, too, the synapses of the neural arcs in question may be sensitive to a rise and fall in the concentrations of the particular blood-constituents for which they are chiefly responsible. According to this view the rat's normally strong instinct to avoid eating excrement could be put down to an evolved inhibition of an evolved behaviour that had formerly conserved vitamin B in this very way. Similarly, earth-eating or salt-licking would be the reversal of instincts that had likewise once been useful in causing the avoidance of such substances. It is late, at this stage, to enquire anew into the evolutionary history of all ambivalent behaviour ; but it does seem possible that this mechanism whereby complete reversals of feeling and behaviour can alternate may have come into being in relation to the food instincts, and have later required no more than modification and extension in order to become applicable to the aggressive and libidinous impulses. Indeed, supposing the first vertebrates to have been carnivores, aggression and feeding must have associations of great antiquity. In the herbivore these connections must have been broken down ; or else arrangements have been made whereby one set of instincts is able to inhibit the other.

THE EVOLUTION OF AMBIVALENCE

Fisher has pointed out how the preservation and improvement of any hereditary character seem to depend upon its constant utilization.[1] Indeed, when it is removed beyond the focus of natural selection, decay and random modification are apt to set in. Now, if slight modifications in the environment of the nervous system, or of its separate parts, may result in a direct pivoting of behaviour, it becomes clear that natural selection must have been kept in very full and useful employment. Any such violent reaction must be definitely for better or for worse, and will thus be actively encouraged or fiercely suppressed.[2] In the struggle for organ-superiority either alternative is better than the indefinite and fluctuating state which must arise when the failure of an effector is allowed to pass almost unheeded. In the latter case, the structure can only regain employment in the

[1] Fisher, R. A. : *The Genetical Theory of Natural Selection.*

[2] Thus the nervous system has attracted the maximum share of the total incidence of natural selection, and has thereby become more complex than any other system of structures.

event of a return to former conditions. A less passive attitude demands active suppression with a gain in economy; or, alternatively, even greater survival-value may await the discovery of a new use. At the cost, then, of this digression, I suggest that, whereas other bodily mechanisms may display many organs and tendencies that are of no present value, the nervous system on the other hand has tolerated little of such even temporary waste. If an evolved instinct becomes disadvantageous, it can be at once reversed; and if this reversal proves unsuccessful, it can be dropped. To survive, an instinct must be useful both in office and in opposition. Besides, it seems probable that it can be divided and sub-divided, so that some channels retain the primary direction, while others are dammed.[1] The flexibility of the race, or the individual, has become so great that there is no need to retain structures pertaining to non-functional and disintegrating instincts.

The mind works as a whole. Each class of behaviour is more than the mere result of some single evolved instinct. At the most the latter serves merely to ordain a line of advance to which all other sympathizers may rally. Opponents, however, will be no less active, and will hamper the activities of the initial and gathering force. Thus any behaviour will involve a stimulation of all reflex arcs alike. Some, however, will respond positively, and others by inhibition. This inhibition is here regarded as a refusal to convey the impulse, a decision that is consequent on a prior acceptance. The impulse, instead of being transmitted, is rejected like an echo into the conductor whence it came. The greater the capacity and resonance of the inhibitory arcs, the more strength will be added to the initial impulse.

RELIGION AND ENVIRONMENT

The anthropologist's conception of the term religion—at all events as applied to primitive people—is so wide that he is apt to wonder whether any aspect of primitive culture can be altogether excluded from this category. Here, however, I propose merely to touch upon a few apparently hereditary, or else geographically controlled, differences of ritual and belief; my object being to discover causes of a physiological nature such as link differences of ethnic temperament either with differences of heredity, or else with the interactions between that heredity and the environment. The combined influences of the food and sex instincts will require consideration in each case; for as life is at bottom an affair of assimilation and reproduction, the management and mutual adaptation of these functions must continue so long as each remains a necessary confederate of the other. In particular,

[1] *N.B.* Indeed, the evolution of epicritic sensitivity might be explained after some such fashion. Each afferent and efferent branch from the common path could be assumed to differ in its threshold of sensitivity so that every gradation of feeling tone would be due to one of the parallel tracks changing from inhibition to response.

then, I propose to discuss the way in which the mineral-deficiencies characteristic of a hypothetically cold and arid North and a hot and humid South have acted in concert with the type of sexual selection operative in each case.

This, of course, implies gross simplification. There are humid areas in the North, and aridity is now common if not most common in the South. Cultural modification, however, seems in some ways to have restored the trend of remote evolutionary history, at all events if the latter was in truth an alternation between a phase of heat, humidity, and calcium shortage, and another of cold, aridity, and a lack of iodine. When culture has neutralized the influence of soil on nutrition, race reacts to temperature alone. In the Old World the anomalous humid area of cold North-west Europe has been occupied by tall peoples of pastoral culture, who have been thereby enabled to withstand the decalcification of the soils. In the hot, but more arid, regions that lay nearer both to the Equator and to the centre of the continent, the river-valleys became filled with settled agriculturists of smaller stature. The same seems roughly to hold good of America. It is true that the wheat and rice lands of the Old World would be too wet for maize, and vice versa. Nevertheless, the low mineral-content of the Indian-corn is such that it seems legitimate to look for certain similarities in the physiological and psychological foundations when comparing the agricultural civilizations of the two hemispheres; even if we must also remain on guard so as not to overlook differences due to the special American conditions. Indeed, civilization itself may be encouraged by these lime and phosphorus shortages. If so, a greater instability should be expected as a result of its later diffusion towards the North.

Two types of religious phenomena that can be discussed more or less apart from the influences of phylogenetic change through sexual selection, are, firstly, the practice of confession, and, secondly, a whole complex of ritual proceedings based upon mental dissociations, and including the shamanism, the contemplation of the mystic, and lastly, a great part of advanced logical, and specifically theological, thinking. Confession is of interest, since a full understanding of its motives would go far to explain the mechanism of abreaction in psychoanalysis. Moreover, if we turn to ancient Mexico, it is of great interest to note how sexual offences constituted the main class of sins for which custom decreed this form of relief. The practice is found among the Eskimo, and is common throughout North and South America. Among most Mongoloid peoples except the Eskimo, and especially in North America and Siberia, the sweat-house is valued as a physical aid to the process of spiritual purification. An alternative means to the same end is the use of violent emetics. The latter custom appears to have a distribution throughout the tropical regions of the New and Old Worlds; being found, for instance, in the Amazon Basin and the

West Indies,[1] while, again, it occurs among the Kikuyu of East Africa. A third way of quieting the conscience is by bleeding. This practice is found in the bison area. The source of its introduction into European medicine is a subject that would merit investigation. I suspect it of being a characteristic of mineral-rich environments. When diffused, however, into agricultural areas of deficiency it might be expected to become ritualized. In extreme cases the blood of a victim would be substituted for that of the original donor, the latter's emotions swinging round to a lust for slaughter. Indeed, the desire to shed one's own blood may be but a reversal of an instinct to drink the blood of others. This possible ambivalence of the food-instincts has been already discussed.

The other two forms of psycho-physical purification seem equally well designed to correct an electrolyte balance impaired by the extreme nutritional conditions of the habitats in which they are found. They are also after a fashion calculated to suit the racial physiology of the peoples who practise them—at all events if the latter have as close a relationship to their environment as I suspect. Thus the sweat-bath will exercise the poorly developed sebaceous glands of the dry Mongoloid skin; and will also be of value in extracting sodium chloride, which will probably be present to excess in the foods obtained from arid soils. The maize-eaters will have least need of this relief, since grain food probably imposes a tax on all the fixed base. Even here, however, the forcible removal of sodium might possibly encourage a compensatory intake of the rarer and even more necessary calcium. To pass on to the vomiting practised by the tropical agriculturists, this seems explicable as an almost reverse procedure whereby the influence of salt-hunger rather than salt-abundance may be annulled. The acid chlorides in the stomach are removed, while the slender store of sodium used by the pancreas is left untouched. In such cases one suspects a close correlation between acidosis and a conviction of sin. Supposing that all these suggestions were proved up to the hilt, it would not invalidate the idea of sympathetic magic as a most important influence in human culture. It would, however, show that certain forms of symbolism have survival-value in particular situations; and that they become institutionalized on that account. Some associations of ideas, such as that connecting the idea of death with the abandoning or burial of the corpse, will be of value to all branches of humanity, since all are liable to attack by infectious disease. Others, however, will display distributions of a racial and geographical order.

I propose now to turn to the question of mental dissociation, which seems also to be something that can be treated as both an hereditary and environmental character. Although accurate observations of such cases are mostly confined to the literature of pathology, it seems unjust to assume that dissociated individuals have always brought ruin upon themselves and their group. Indeed, the unlettered man,

[1] Wissler, C.: *The American Indian*, pp. 213–214, II, New York, 1922.

often hampered by the limitations of a primitive language, seems bound to resolve his problems with the aid of emotional crises. Doubtless a liability to such nerve-storms must impair the efficiency of the man of action ; but for this reason the group may well afford to maintain at least a single shaman or medicine-man, within whose tortured soul the conflicting perplexities of the people at large may be experienced and, if possible, resolved.

The shaman is universal throughout the New World, and persisted side by side with the more learned and lettered priest in the centres of the indigenous civilization.[1] In the Old World his range extends throughout the Tundra region. Shamanism is therefore almost confined to the Mongoloid race, and is strongest in the cold, arid, and often iodine-deficient barrens. It is thus a feature of the culture developed by the most infantile, and probably latest evolved, of the three main stocks of humanity ; and it flourishes best in the situation where the ontogenetic development of the individual is most liable to arrest. In Siberia a reversal of the sex-instincts is held in great awe, and is itself regarded as a sign of mystical powers.[2] Such a condition might well arise through an overburdening of the heat-promoting powers of the anterior-lobe and the thyroid ; more especially if the activity of the former is reduced by the Mongoloid heredity, and the nutrition of the latter impaired by a shortage of iodine. Both these secretions appear to combine in promoting differentiation and the secretion of sex-hormones by the gonad, in the same way that they again co-operate to promote the basal metabolism. Thus overwork of the one function would leave the other powerless.

Of course the psychological basis of this reverence for the intersex need not bear any very close relation to the physical causes of the condition. I have already put forward one possible reason why an infantile anxiety to distinguish the sex of the adult should possess survival-value ; and, to my mind, it is at least as satisfactory as Roheim's ontogenetic explanation, based on the infant's supposed emotions towards the " primal scene."[3] In any case it is of interest to note that the worship of the intersex may quite possibly have been diffused widely before it died out. Intersexual pigs are now especially bred in the Pacific and used for sacrifice. In Australia the practice of sub-incision appears to have entered from the North. The operation suggests an attempt artificially to deform the male sex-organs to the condition found in the hermaphrodite. The word used is applied also to describe the female genitalia.[4]

There are probably metabolic and neurological differences between the typical dancing and raving shaman and the contemplative, though equally dissociated, itinerant and immobile monks of Tibet and

[1] Wissler, C., loc. cit.
[2] Czaplica, M. A. : *Aboriginal Siberia*, Oxford, 1914, p. 243.
[3] Roheim, G. : *The Riddle of the Sphinx.*
[4] Roth, W. E. : North Queensland Ethnography.

India. Although iodine-deficiency might be the main cause in each case, secondary conditions involving heredity, and both the physical and social environments, could be made responsible for the differences. We have the striking contrasts of behaviour between sufferers from exophthalmic and from simple goitre. The quieter mien of the contemplative orders may be based on an heredity, or food supply, such as can either economize calcium or provide it in additional quantities. When this substitution is unsatisfactory the wandering life opens up every possibility of striking a new balance of diet.

There can be small doubt that the influence of dissociated persons upon human affairs has been enormous. On the whole I am prepared to assign survival-value to the primitive man's willingness to place himself under the orders of the seer, as also to follow his own visionary promptings when these come to him. It is not necessary, though it may be fashionable, to adopt the present psycho-analytic formulæ, and thus interpret nearly all apparitions in terms of the Œdipus complex. It is certainly remarkable that the Mongoloid inhabitants of America, in common with their relatives of the Himalayan region, have developed a strictly personal religion. The American Indian may be said to be largely instrumental in initiating himself. Many, though not all, individuals are enabled after fasting to see their Manitu ; and the recognition of this frequently zoomorphic apparition appears to assist the integration of the adult personality. There is a striking difference between this method and the conventionalized drama that is enacted before his eyes in order to make the young Australian feel that he is a man. The more easily dissociated, and perhaps for that reason suggestible, Amerind requires only the general tradition and his own faith to make him see his future totem for himself.

Moving to a higher stage, we may compare this susceptibility to inward experience with the willingness with which every young Tibetan and Shan assumes the yellow robe and spends his years of adolescence under the tutelage of the monks. The mind proves receptive to suggestion whether obtained from within or from without. The more tractable dispositions of teacher and pupil breed far less of that thinly disguised and mutual aggression which arises when even the rudiments of manners and education are instilled into the youth of the pastoral or other gerontomorphic races. One need not deny the influence of tradition in such cases, but neither must the force of heredity be forgotten. Doubtless the unconsciously sadistic master can engender similar repressed tendencies in his pupil, such as will later be handed on in full force to the third generation. Nevertheless, this or any other cultural phenomenon, will flourish better in one soil than another. It was probably by no accident that age-grades were developed in the secret societies of the Plains Indians, who are the American equivalents of the tall and aggressive pastorals. The same arrangement crops up among the warlike Masai and among the fighting peoples of Oceania.[1] Minds suited to such masculine bodies find difficulty in accepting any equality as between man and man, unless they are drilled to it. The system, while stressing the difficult duty of brotherly love, conveniently restricts the numbers to whom this somewhat artificial attitude need be maintained.

The point, however, on which I wish to lay stress is that dissociation may have survival-value, and is in any case a racial character such as may be intensified by environment. I suspect that its gross physical cause is tissue-hydration due to mineral, and especially iodine, deficiency. A tendency towards the sub-division of the brain through inhibition at various of the more delicately adjusted synapses might be engendered. The result would be a pattern of behaviour of a somewhat childish nature ; for few outward activities would be pursued with full energy. In the growing child and the lactating female electrolytes are withdrawn for purposes of growth, and the aggressiveness of an adult is inhibited for the sake of future survival. So too, then, in the more infantile races of Man, the permanence of this state of the internal environment encourages the continuance of an adolescent and feminine inhibition. Stimuli are duly received, but response is seldom full or adequate. Behaviour resembles play, no course of conduct being pursued to a finish. At the same time this inhibition of active response serves probably to intensify and prolong the internal reverberations through the mind. If no door permits an escape, all doors are likely to be tried in turn. Thus the mind contemplates all possible excursions while at the same time blocking any obvious outlet. Hence the inhibited individual must act tortuously or not at all. As a man of action he will be a failure. For this very reason, however, he will excel as a man of thought. The shaman, then, is a thinker, though a sub-conscious thinker—one, however, whose directions his followers may be wise to follow.

THOUGHT AND BELIEF

The nature of the logical and conscious thinker is more complex. He must be enabled to follow his own mental processes and this requires less in the way of evolved inhibition. Logical thought is, I suggest, a feature of minds governed by a more adult and masculine heredity. Such minds, moreover, will be resident in the less infantile kinds of body. I shall return to this point when mentioning and attempting to explain Kretschmer's association of mental with bodily characters. In the meantime such a theory serves to explain why our own highly logical systems of law seldom agree with the more acceptable revelations arising in the minds of our mystics. The hardness of law is a product of the masculinity that conceived it. The same lowering of the threshold of unconsciousness that allows each step in the reasoning to be recorded and recalled serves also to unblock the channels through

[1] Wissler, C. : *The American Indian*, pp. 382 and 392, II, New York, 1922.

which an aggressive spirit is infused. A regard for truth is an outcome of unleashed aggression. The taboos that comfort and reinforce the inherited repressions of the feminine type of mind are subject to deliberate attack. Daring to think, and to publish abroad the fruits of one's thinking, is gratifying to the autosomal instincts of masculine self-assertion. Belief, to the logical man is no self-imposed restriction whereto he delights to submit. Rather is it a fetter to be filed through or burst. Truth, for him, indeed, consists in no doctrine, but rather in an adventure. Mystics, on the other hand, including those whom Western Europe has elected to revere, tend to be feminine and infantile in their mental type. Thus the freedom of giving and taking, which is a feature of the mother and child relationship, becomes idealized as a pure disinterestedness, and crystallizes into articles of faith. These prove tough fare for the logical minds, if accepted as fundamental truths and then subjected to integration according to other instinctive standards. Such digestive exercise, however, has been to the good. The taboo-principle has been applied to the search for knowledge, and has served to coagulate the latter and preserve it from a too rapid and incomplete disintegrative analysis. Faith has held cynicism in check. Of course it would be a mistake to assume that all mystics are peaceful and all realists aggressive. A mystic born from a fighting race may repress, but will only thereby intensify, his aggressive instincts. To aid him in this inhibition he may seek to bow down before a cruel predestination for whose moral and intellectual inferiority he may nevertheless be forced to stifle his contempt. When this expedient fails, he is liable to impose himself upon his fellows, and lead them in a treasonable revolt or a holy war. All symbols of the alternative tender emotions will provoke wrath. For these are founded on a sex-linked appreciation of the human form, and are energized at the expense of the aggressive instincts which, for the moment, are allowed to seek every means towards their own intensification. Thus the ambivalence of a consciously suppressed love can be used as a rod to castigate either the upper self or super-ego as represented by God ; or to attack the lower half of the personality, the id, for whom the sinner to be reformed stands deputy. The armed man may fear God and honour his King since, by this limited inhibition, he is the better enabled to hate the enemy. Similarly, the social reformer uses a love of his fellow-men to reinforce his inherent pugnacity towards an abstract but overawing political system. Love of the higher thing may help the hate of the lower, and vice versa. In some cases there seems to be no need for an external direction of love before a supreme instinct of aggression can dominate the intellect. Perhaps in these cases it is a diffuse love of self that serves as a sound-box to intensify aggression to a berserk fury. Ajax defies the lightning, since to court death is to cast aside all feelings of tenderness or fear. On a higher intellectual plane a passionate agnosticism offers annihilation of the Self and the Deity in one. The preaching of this creed will in its turn stimulate a destructive criticism of itself. Live thought, unlike passive belief, cannot stand still.

CHAPTER XV

BODY, MIND, AND CIVILIZATION

Race and Type-Psychology : The Strata of Dissociation : The Inheritance of Dissociation : The Ego Trinity : Strong Minds and Weak : Leaders and Led : Mind and Brain : Race and Education : Conclusion.

IT MUST REMAIN AN UNSOLVED BUT NONE THE LESS VASTLY IMPORTANT and intriguing problem of human genetics to discover just how this supposed blend of aggression and dissociate inhibition can sometimes realize itself in the imaginative yet logical thinker. For there can be little doubt that such minds—however they may be produced—have conferred survival-value in no small degree upon whole racial and national groups. Even a few intelligent leaders can sometimes save the multitude from complete disaster. Doubtless there will ever continue the age-long competition between the masculine and the feminine orientations of the germ-plasm ; but their several effects on the bodily characters will become less and less significant with each step of technological and cultural advance. Rather it is their influence upon the mind that will count. Thus we may expect each type to try to frame the economic machine in a manner suitable to its own survival and equally disadvantageous to the other. We must expect rivalry between logical and unfeeling folk on the one hand and insensate emotional masses upon the other. The buffer, however, will be provided by the mixed inheritance of those in whom thought and feeling can combine. Moreover, it is possible that the maintenance of pure-bred stocks may remain a biological necessity if there is to be a continuous supply of fresh and mentally vigorous hybrids.

If we look to the past it would probably be a mistake to suppose that a capacity for logical thought had conferred intra-specific advantage upon the individual genes or combinations of characters concerned. There is every chance, however, that in the future it may of itself so alter the human environment that, like other characters in the past, it may slowly select in favour of its own intensification. In this case a relatively unbridled aggression and a strong bias towards dissociate inhibition have each been specially useful in their respective surroundings ; though, of course, throughout each has had to be restrained by some touch of the other. When fertility is high, male combat serves to reduce numbers, and to maintain a sufficiency of the good-quality food for the physiologically less efficient type of body that must emerge victorious from the fighting.

Where conditions are unfavourable to reproduction, on the other hand, a sex-linked repression of anatomical efficiency is equally of value; and to survive it requires the assistance of its own psychological extension in the form of an inhibitory ambivalence, whereby more of the *élan vital* can be directed towards self-perpetuation in the launching of new lives, while less of it is devoted to the no longer necessary destruction of adult competitors.

Actually there is more than a suspicion that nature has learned somehow to over-allow for these alterations in the quality of the food-supply. The impairment of food-quality seems positively to increase numbers, presumably as a secondary effect following from the modification of the individual. This in its turn may re-introduce the struggle for mere food-quantity, and so, to some extent, may restore the *status quo ante*.

If these two rival types of correlated traits, physiological, anatomical, and psychological, have developed in different classes of habitat, the stability of their combination within the individual will be rare and impermanent. Had it not been for conditions that allowed of a huge expansion of all human groups, leading to repeated racial mixture, the two types might have come to amount to specific differences.

RACE AND TYPE-PSYCHOLOGY

Now it will be noticed that this fundamental, if theoretical, division into two polar opposites of physique and correlated psychology does not fit in with Kretschmer's recognition of two main categories, the "asthenic" and the "pyknic"—the tall romantic Don Quixote, and the short realistic Sancho Panza.[1] The reason, I suggest, is that both may well be hybrids, the products of civilization. We are moving forward from the consideration of ideal prototypes, each specially adapted to an extreme class of environment; and, on reaching civilization, are dealing with a mixture probably not subject to so strict or at least cramping a control on the part of natural selection. As a matter of fact, however, Kretschmer also recognizes two other variants, the "athletic," and the "dysplastic." These may afford nearer parallels, though they may not be identical, with the two constituent extremes of masculine or feminine racial development.

Kretschmer's very nomenclature, indeed, offers the hint of a possible solution. Asthenic means "without strength" or weak, and many tall individuals do look ill-nourished. Nevertheless, the tall heredity should rather be regarded as a product of favourable ecological conditions. For that very reason, however, it will be the one most liable to malnutrition under conditions in which all racial types and mixtures are offered the same class of food, and are bred in much the same surroundings. To some extent, then, one might resolve the difficulty by regarding all asthenics as starved athletics. Similarly, the energetic pyknics could be set down as overfed dysplastics.

[1] Kretschmer, E.: *Körperbau und Charakter*, 1921; also Miller, E.: *Types of Mind and Body*.

In addition to the foregoing somewhat over-simple, and hence probably inadequate, explanation, the same facts might to some extent be met by considering the possibility of racial mixture alone, and discounting the effects of environment. Thus one might adopt the rather dangerous hypothesis that the genes controlling the activity of an endocrine can be frequently inherited apart from those concerned with its reception by the tissues. This possibility was mentioned in an attempt to explain giant and pygmy forms in terms of a racial mixture between two less extreme types.[1] On this theory the athletic and dysplastic types could still be considered representative of the pure parental strains. The former, with an active pituitary, and with tissues adjusted to its hormone concentration, would represent the perfected human animal, the hunter evolved to run down steppe animals. Similarly, the dysplastic would be the ill-formed and less mobile type, adapted to live by gathering in an unfavourable and humid environment.

Next, as regards the asthenic type, this would have to be explained in terms of an "athletic," that is to say, an active, pituitary acting on some genes originally evolved to control the tissues of a dysplastic. The problem, however, is more complicated than when it is attempted to explain a giant or a dwarf. In the asthenic we may have the stature of a giant combined with an inferior girth and thoracic development. The axial growth-gradient is active, while the transverse development is damped down. This might be explicable on the assumption that the pituitary, or one hormone of the anterior-lobe, is specially concerned with growth in height ; which is probably an autosomal character that has been recently accentuated by sexual selection. This might get married to a strong dysplastic inheritance governing the inhibition of thoracic girth, upon which it might have little or no modifying influence. Conversely, the pyknic type could be explained as a northern and mountain form of thoracic development, combined with a repressed and feminine activity of the stature-promoting hormone of the anterior-lobe.

There seem no serious objections to combining these two sets of considerations, the hereditary and the environmental. Assuming the civilized environment to provide a medium balance as between structural and energy-producing nutrients, it would follow that the asthenic with his great height and small thorax must be no less as economical, and probably rather more so, than the fully developed athletic. Thus, under civilized conditions, the numbers of asthenics might increase. Nevertheless, if the development of the individual is variable in response to nutrition, this fact does not wholly invalidate the first theory, namely, that children with a potentially athletic inheritance could develop into asthenics. The same theory had assumed that girth is more subject to environmental inhibition than height. If this were definitely disproved, one might look upon the asthenic as an elongated

[1] See Chapter I. Actually an alternative, and I think more satisfactory, theory will be advanced.

dysplastic, in whom improved conditions had influenced the pituitary, but had failed to affect the thorax ; whereas the pyknic would become a dwarfed athletic.

If these last explanations were to be adopted, the sharp demarcation between the two types would have to be explained, not in terms of a levelling of the primitive extremes of environment, but rather as a result of sharply contrasted social conditions affecting the high and the low in rank. We are tempted to re-examine the assumption that the enlarged civilized population must necessarily involve a lowered incidence of natural selection. Perhaps it has only selected in favour of an increased fecundity, and has thus actively countered the lethal influences of urban existence. The asthenic could, on that view, be the product, rather than the producer, of aristocracy, and his children would develop as full-grown athletics. Similarly, the pyknic could represent the first stage along a downward path leading to a type of dysplastic slum-dweller. The scantiness of our data will account for the plurality of the hypotheses whereby the same few facts might be explained.

The difficulty, which none of the foregoing theories attempts to solve, is to discover why the short fat type should be an energetic practical realist, and the long thin asthenic a romantic when he is not, as he often is, a languid and cynical character. We can use the rather vague but useful word dissociation to explain certain features of both types. The inhibited self-assertion of the asthenic can be interpreted as a general and diffuse dissociation whereby the contemplation of any line of conduct serves only to stir up a host of countervailing considerations. The pyknic, on the other hand, who is here assumed to embody Jung's extravert type of mind, thinks rapidly and concisely.[1] The conscious mind seems to be more shallow, so that one suspects more activity in the depths of an unconsciousness wherein the passions fight out their battles unobserved. Here the power of dissociation seems concentrated at a stratum, or level, which becomes the sharply defined threshold of consciousness. Above, and possibly also below this plane, thoughts tend to coalesce rather than to inhibit each other. One idea recalls another at once, though often with the flimsiest of logical pretexts. Similarly, behaviour is rapid and calculable. The extravert is content to do the obvious. He feels no hankering after subtlety for its own sake.

A useful way of distinguishing between the extravert and introvert is to say that the first adapts himself to his environment, whereas the latter, being less plastic, seeks to adapt his environment to himself. It has been further suggested that the conscious extravert is an unconscious introvert, and vice versa.[2] Now there can be little doubt that of our two theoretical types, the masculine and the feminine, it is the male who is least adaptable, and who tends to alter his environment to suit

[1] Jung, C. G. : *Psychological Types*, 1923.
[2] Jung, C. G., loc. cit.

himself—usually by killing his rival. The female, on the other hand, submits to social as well as to other environmental pressures. Combining these views we arrive at the conclusion that the introvert is consciously male and sub-consciously female ; while the extravert is less consciously aggressive, but with more unbridled passion below the level of consciousness. This would further fit in with what, I think, is a just observation, namely, that women are in general more " practical," that is to say, more extraverted, than men.

THE STRATA OF DISSOCIATION

All this suggests that, when we ascribe its evolutionary significance to a particular type of psychology, the unconscious rather than the conscious elements may have hitherto deserved more credit for promoting survival. The conscious manifestations are often mere mirror-images, the inverted counterparts of the forces responsible for their being. One is reminded of the ease whereby nerve impulses may be inhibited and instincts ambivalently reversed. Can it be that the threshold of unconsciousness virtually coincides with an evolved correspondence in the conditions needed to inhibit one set of instincts and throw another into gear ? Rivers implies this when he points out that forgetting is essential to a tadpole if the neural activity responsible for swimming is to be kept distinct from the new behaviour of the legs.[1] The adult state, entailing a higher ratio of solids to water, has come to inhibit the whole of the aquatic behaviour, so as to allow the terrestrial reflexes free rein. In such cases it must have been the synchronization of the change in all opposing types of behaviour that was vital to success. Perhaps in Man similar common thresholds of ambivalence have continued to have survival-value, and have been used for a variety of purposes during the long history of the species. For instance, to repress all adult behaviour until childhood is over is better than to embark upon impulsive and unpremeditated adventures for which the remainder of the mind and body is unprepared. It is far better to build up a repressed, and therefore strong and coherent, adult behaviour, such as can finally burst forth in full spate, and soon remove all trace of the dykes behind which it was dammed.

To continue along this line of thought, one might expect the active behaviour of the infant to be forgotten when the first main advance in mental growth occurred. What would then manifest itself in action would be the mass of previously repressed or reflected tendencies—all that the child had hitherto been unable or unwilling to do. These might appear in consciousness as memories even if they had never before influenced behaviour, and it is a nice point whether, in such a raw state, they can rank as memories at all. They would tend later to be interpreted in terms of recent rather than of remote sensations, and will then take their place among the springs of action. It may be that their very repression is responsible for part of the activity they can

[1] Rivers, W. H. : *Instinct and the Unconscious*, Cambridge, 1920, p. 68.

generate at a higher level. The practice of psycho-analysis reveals how a forgotten memory ceases to motivate the behaviour, when once its emotional tone is clothed in a mantle of real, or perhaps imagined, sensual experiences.

It does not seem improbable that there may be many strata of dissociation. Every specific change has entailed violent changes of behaviour. Moreover, as suggested in chapter VI, it seems probable that these changes have been sudden, and have involved an immediate inhibition of independent and aggressive activity ; though this has afterwards slowly reasserted itself under the stimulus of male sexual selection. Man has, at the least, changed from a ground-dweller to a tree-dweller, and returned to earth again. Now the change from pre-natal to separate existence fits in between two major expansions in the index of cephalization, and is followed by a third increase ; which last, as I previously suggested, might mark the dawn of humanity as such.[1] It is not impossible, therefore, that the psychologists may find three thresholds of unconsciousness corresponding to these three crises of ontogenetic development. Indeed, it might almost be said that Freud has already pointed out two of them. For, first of all, he interposes his so-called narcissistic stage of emotional development between the unorganized libido of the child and the adult's heterosexual behaviour ; and, later, he has similarly divided the mind into three persons, each of them unconscious of the rest.[2] Likewise it might be claimed that the first and pre-natal brain-expansion served to cut off the voluntary from the involuntary behaviour.

Each of these breaks in the continuity of consciousness may divide compartments which are mirror images of their neighbours ; and if so, the directions, if not the details, of the infantile and adult states, as also the first and last developing persons of the Ego Trinity, who will be mentioned later, ought to correspond with each other and show a direct reversal to that found in the narcissistic adolescent. This seems to be true in fact. The full adult directs his activities outward ; whereas the adolescent's main conscious interest is in himself. In the infant the main interests are also directed externally, even the organs of the body being treated as interests in themselves. One can see survival-value in this. Such a method is useful in making a first acquaintance with a complex system of effectors, and with an external world of animate and inanimate objects.

In regard to the next narcissistic phase, it has already been argued that a repression of anything beyond a feminine sex-attitude has been dangerous as liable to provoke attacks ; and it is the border-line between this and the final stage that seems of most importance in discussing the influence of heredity upon the psychology of the man in the masculine and feminine races. In regard to the woman, it does not

[1] Cf. Chapter VI, diagram p. 128.

[2] Freud, S. : "Zur Einführung des Narzissmus," *Jahrbuch für Psychoanalytische*, 1914, VI, p. 1. Freud, S. : *Das Ich und das Es*, 1923.

seem impossible that an extreme degree of racial sex-linked repression might inhibit a full development of even the second self-loving class of emotional behaviour. In such cases some adjustment, perhaps through translocation, might correct such a state of affairs. Indeed, it might well correct itself by inhibiting any further instinct towards a sexual selection for feminine characters.

THE INHERITANCE OF DISSOCIATION

I have strayed some distance from the original point, namely, the discussion of the causes leading to the asthenic introvert and the pyknic extravert. The conception of a stratification in the levels of ambivalent dissociation offers, however, some hope of providing a partial solution. We required a theory to explain why dissociation was diffuse in the long thin type, and less frequent, but concentrated and final, in the pyknic. This might be explained in terms of racial mixture, were it assumed that some hereditary blends would result in a correspondence between the strata inherited from each parent, while in others the two heredities would act apart. In the one case, that of the short build of Man, the mind would have but three stories, each of the two floors being of double thickness and soundproof. The other would have five stages, each division being more permeable to the gossip circulating in the flats above and below.

It seems probable that the asthenic introvert is the rarer type, and one hardly the result of any direct process of natural selection. Possibly, therefore, there is some strong normal tendency for the homologous genes and chromosomes of the two parents to become fused, and then to act as one ; though in some mixed heredities this fusion of influences fails to occur. This is suggested by Painter's recent discovery of "somatic synapsis" in the giant chromosomes of the salivary glands in Drosophila.[1] Fusion is not always perfect along the whole length, and it is conceivable that it might be further inhibited in the case of a sub-specific cross. Mules, we may reflect, are subject to chromosome aberrations. It would be of first-rate interest to know whether somatic synapsis occurs in the case of Goldschmidt's *Lymantria* intersexes. I suspect that it does not. It is but a long shot, but I submit that gross differences of psychology may be found reflected in the arrangement of the body's chromosomes. Perhaps a genius is a somatic polyploid ! To follow out this theory, it must be noted that the sudden enlargements of the brain were on other grounds believed to have been associated with, and indeed caused by, three corresponding arrests of bodily development ; while these in their turn had caused organ-inferiorities requiring compensations in the form of altered behaviour. One would expect, therefore, that a racial mixture, or other cause, such as resulted in a failure fully to synchronize the processes responsible for laying down their respective strata of dissociation, would also prevent the primary evolved requirement, namely, the inhibition of the body's

[1] Painter, T. S. : *J. Hered.*, Vol. XXV, No. 12 (1934), p. 467.

growth in size. We must expect the tall thin type to be subject to twice as many partial arrests of development. None, however, will be so final as in the pure-bred type. The hybrid's development will be delayed, but it will be less rapidly arrested. Of course this theory,

Influence of Growth-arrests on Formation of Dissociation Strata.

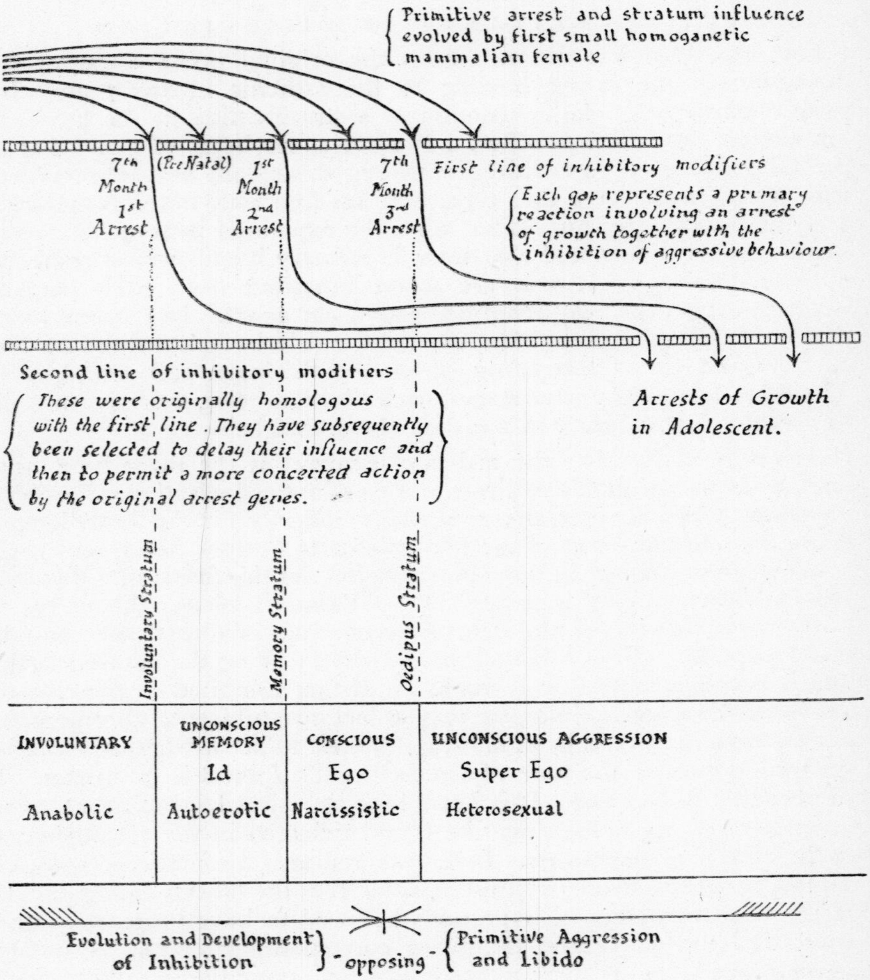

too, takes an all-too-easy road through what is quite uncharted country. The increments of growth in the child's brain and the arrests of growth in the adult body need not have any close genetical connection or linkage. If, however, the former are in truth the traces of past specific change, the notion is not altogether fantastic. I have attempted to outline these ideas in the above diagram.

There is little doubt that physiological states ungoverned by heredity can also affect the mind. Tuberculosis has often been associated with mental brilliancy ; and H. G. Wells has recently drawn attention to the clarity of thought that followed upon a severe hæmorrhage.[1] We know that the brain expands in response to a lowering of the electrolyte concentration of the blood, and that the lower and more primitive portions react most strongly.[2] We may recollect that the specific changes to mammal, anthropoid, and Man have been attributed to epochs of severe mineral-deficiency, in the last of which iodine-shortage is held to have caused the most serious deprivation. If, then, the strata of dissociation were evolved at those times, it should follow that the activity of the unit-characters responsible will still retain a certain sensitivity, and will react most actively when they meet with the same type of environment as that wherein they were initially selected.

All this suggests that a moderate degree of mineral-deficiency may be a useful factor in encouraging cerebral development in general, together with a mild dose of diffuse dissociation as a necessary ingredient. The tall asthenic may be expected to demand more mineral than his digestion will be able to supply, whereas the hereditarily swollen brain tissues of the pyknic—the " rond digestif " of Brown Séquard—will be more fully nourished, at all events so as to satisfy their diminished demands. Perhaps on this account the cells will be less liable to accumulate pathological quantities of water, and so to separate the ions involved in the happenings at the synapses. Illness, which is so often associated with mineral-deficiency, may result in complete splitting of the mind when the asthenic breaks down. The pyknic alternates between maniac activity and complete inhibited depression. Both cases seem explicable in terms of a thickening of the insulating strata. The maniac depressive is cut off from all contact with his unconscious wherein the uncertain attitudes of youth lie hid. He enjoys an over-full liberty of action, until suddenly the barrier breaks down, and the repressed doubts and fears burst forth to swamp his mind. In the disintegrated and schizoid asthenic no such complete blockage occurs, and no spectacular explosions will follow. At every stage, however, there is difficulty in converting feeling into thought, or thought into action, until finally each is left marooned either to exist in isolation or to die through lack of stimulus.[3]

[1] Wells, H. G. : *Autobiography*.

[2] Haldi, Rauth, Larkin, and Wright (1927) : *Amer. Jl. Physiol.*, 80, 631–638.

[3] It is later suggested that epileptic seizures may result from a similar thickening and subsequent bursting of a lower, or " involuntary," stratum. Similarly, it would fit the theory were one to attribute hysterical symptoms, involving loss of voluntary control, to failures affecting the so-called memory stratum dividing the ego from the id. The maniac depressive symptoms are thus believed to follow from maladjustments of the last-formed or " Œdipus " stratum.

THE EGO TRINITY

It may prove little more than a superstitious juggling with a magic number, but it does seem worth while to try to associate the three hypothetical strata of dissociation with Freud's three active anthropomorphic persons of the mental trinity, the moral " super-ego," the conscious " ego," and the unconscious " id," ; as well as also with his three stages of emotional development, the " auto-erotic," the " narcissistic," and the adult " object love."[1] One could assume each to be an ambivalently reversed reflection of the next ; so that the super-ego and the id might stand furthest apart but parallel, whereas the intervening conscious ego would face its opposites upon each side. Such an arrangement tends to identify the ego with the narcissistic phase of emotional development. This suggests that consciousness is essentially self-consciousness, and as such is energized by self-love.

On this hypothesis the super-ego becomes an exciting charge inducing an opposite potential upon the inner or ego side of the insulation ; so that hate becomes love, and vice versa. Only if the dissociation stratum is weak will conduction replace induction. In such a case, which, it is suggested, may be exemplified in the adult male in whom the top, or " Œdipus," stratum is weakened, the emotions of the super-ego would slowly leak in to swamp the ego ; changing the general charge from love to aggression, or vice versa, but thereby inducing contrary charges in the super-ego itself. Part of this concept has already been used in the case of the maniac depressive. In the schizoid, in whom each of the double strata will be weak, the pulsations will be regular and gradual ; whereas in the better insulated type the dissociation will break down in a flash. Inhibition, like excitation, results in fatigue.[2]

In regard to the id, the true unconscious must now be situated below the bottom and earlier formed barrier separating the auto-erotic from the narcissistic compartments. Here memories can be stored as feelings relating to the separate parts of the body. The fact that they may undergo inversion during each process of banishment and recall seems of importance only in regard to the possibility of impaired dissociation, such as is deemed to occur in the schizoid. The cyclothyme pyknic, with his good memory, can accurately dissociate his bodily activity from his conscious thought, so that it records itself by contraries at the lower level. The less accurate memory of the schizoid could then be explained in terms of the same mechanism already used to account for his fluctuating emotional states. The bad insulation allows past and present to become confused. Strong emotions break through directly to the unconscious, and will later be reflected back as unrecognizable inversions of themselves. Moreover, supposing two imperfect strata of dissociation to stand deputy for the single efficient

[1] The first formed stratum is assumed to isolate the involuntary.

[2] Bayliss, p. 422.

echo-board of the practical man, it will follow that part of every conscious thought must undergo a double reversal before it finds bottom in the memory ; though an unreversed fraction will continue unchanged. This double forking of stored feeling will not assist clarity

Ontogenetic Development of Psychological Types.

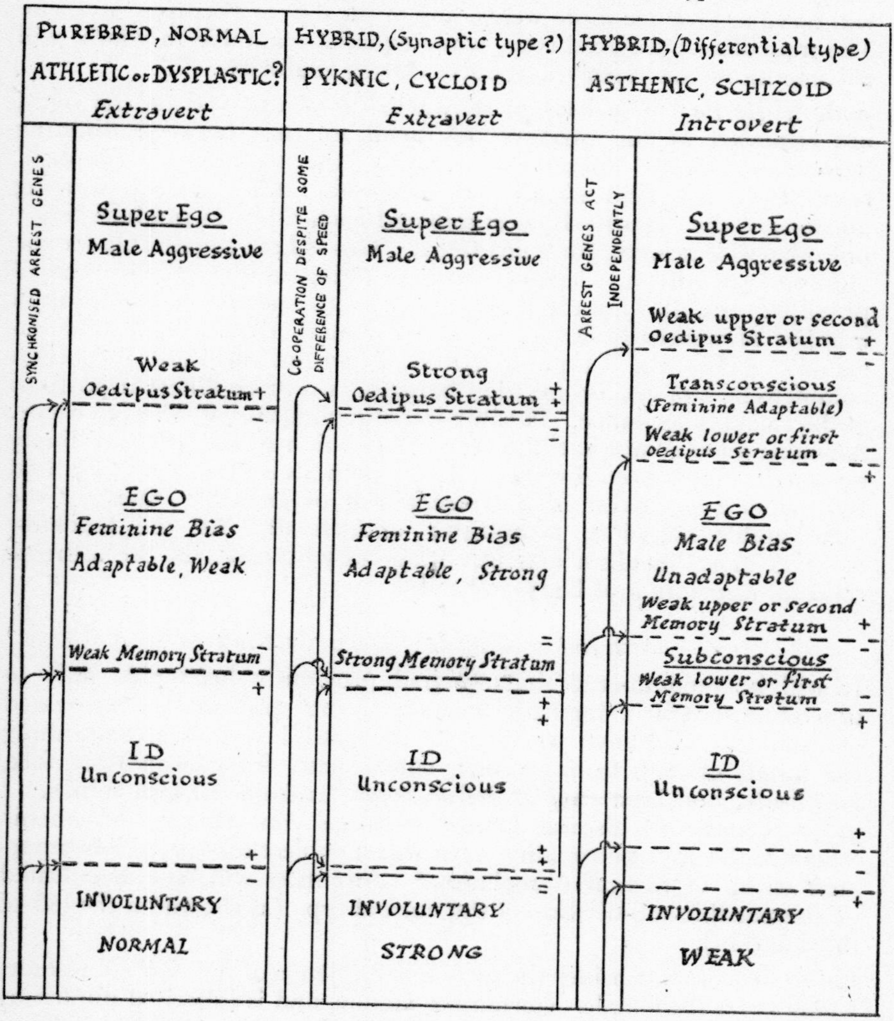

of recollection ; even if it may add to the complexity of association, when each fragment seeks to return along some new and tortuous path.

I have tried to represent these ideas in a diagram. On the left is outlined the supposed order of physical happenings governing the mental development in either of the two pure-bred types—the masculine athletic and feminine dysplastic. In both these cases the two parts of the heredity are considered to work at the same speed, and thus to co-operate in the laying down of single dissociation strata. The minor psychological differences will appear after puberty. In the athletic, the great strength of the masculine portions of the autosomal heredity will serve to produce more weakening of the top, or Œedipus, stratum. The masculine pure-bred type, while equally adaptable in youth, will become more consciously aggressive during maturity.

Both of the two hybrid types, shown in the centre and on the right, are regarded as the products of racial mixture between differing hereditary strains. The first, however, the so-called "synaptic" type, shows a hybrid vigour due to the fact that the two warring portions of the heredity have stimulated each other to produce large, but otherwise normal, somatic effects. This is held responsible for the vigorous growth and definite arrest resulting in the pyknic type of physique, and also for the laying down of the normal and minimum number of unusually strong strata of mental dissociation. The so-called "differential" type of hybrid, shown on the right, displays a complete lack of synchronization between two more different portions of the racial inheritance. Possibly somatic synapsis has failed to occur. A double set of somewhat imperfect dissociation-strata are accordingly assumed to have been formed. This hypothesis is able to account first for the delayed arrest in the mechanism of growth; then for the unadaptable conscious mentality; and, finally, for the tendency towards moral idealism and loss of memory observed in the asthenic schizoid association of body and mind.

STRONG MINDS AND WEAK

It will be remembered that we had previously been able only to suggest reasons for a single division of types into split and well integrated personalities, and have said little of the possible causes distinguishing the minds of men from women, contrarients from suggestible folk, and lastly, and least easy to define, vigorous from sluggish minds. I propose, then, to dismiss further questions concerning the asthenic schizoid, the split personality regarded as subject to four widely separated strata of mental dissociation.[1] Attention will be concentrated on the possible sub-division of the normal type (as shown on the left of the diagram).

Let us first of all consider the probable influence of the X chromosome, which bears the female-determining factors, and is inherited duplex by the woman. It was held to be an accelerator of ontogenetic differentiation, and for that reason, paradoxically, to be also responsible for accelerating the arrests of development; as indeed also for intensifying

[1] Besides the two or four "mental" strata there may be lower, or earlier developing, strata such as that isolating the voluntary from the involuntary behaviour.

the evolved tendency to stop growing. The hereditary strains marked as masculine and feminine were held to differ in the degree in which this acceleration affected both sexes ; for even the male is influenced by one X chromosome, and there is always the possibility of X-borne genes becoming detached and translocated to the autosomes, which are inherited equally by each sex.[1]

Dealing first, then, with the ontogenetic development of the female, we may suspect that the two upper composite strata of dissociation will tend to be laid down earlier than in the case of a male. If so, we may consider that the unconscious id will be more rapidly isolated from the influence of the unmodified aggressive tendencies, inhibited in the infant ego, and not yet isolated by the upper, and last to be developed, level of super-ego ambivalence. Quantitatively, therefore, the id of the female will contain fewer of the aggressive impressions, and may possibly be built up by a relatively longer continued process of feminine reversal during the time between the establishment of the last and that of previous stages of isolation.

Let us now, however, consider the laying down of the Œdipus or last stratum. This will also take place faster than in the case of the male, so that the free bombardment of the super-ego upon the insulation of the id will likewise be curtailed. The id will thus contain less of either raw emotion, and one must hesitate before assuming the balance to be preponderantly more female than male, or vice versa.

If, however, ontogeny is a logarithmic extension of a similar phylogenetic compression, one might almost expect the time-lags due to the differences of masculine and feminine heredity to increase with the development of the individual. If so, the time-differences at the second stage will be greater than at the first ; so that the balance of raw to reversed aggression in the female id will be increased, despite the absolute reduction of both classes of emotional content.

Almost the opposite would appear to hold good of the super-ego. It also would be cut off earlier, and, as suggested already, the insulation would probably be more complete. Thus there would be every chance of accumulating a large store of repressed aggression ; which, in the female and in the less masculine men, would seldom gain free discharge without undergoing an ambivalent conversion to love. Thus one may conclude that the aggressive and male form of body contains actually a less aggressive but more freely discharging super-ego, and that this shortage is compensated in a larger and more femininely orientated id. In the feminine races the id is starved and less-feminine, while the super-ego is strong and well nigh permanently isolated. It is these feminine racial types that, in the next chapter, are accused of the folly of modern war.

[1] *N.B.* I have neglected the possibility of Y-borne genes affecting racial evolution. Their influence would not be very different from that of autosomal characters.

LEADERS AND LED

We are still short of an important key to the garden of sociological understanding. It may be sufficient to write down the masses as a dysplastic, ultra-feminine horde with a starved and aggressively orientated Unconscious, leading to an alternation between listless suggestibility and irrational blood lust. We have still to take into consideration the two types of leader. One the asthenic, schizoid Savonarola has been mentioned. A word must now be said of the other, the sympathetic, yet heroically aggressive, Lloyd George, of the typical pyknic build of body. It was suggested that both the pyknic and the asthenic might be hybrid types ; so it remains to imagine a mechanism whereby this curious blend of feminine sympathy and aggressive driving power could have been combined.

Now if the unconscious id of the common man is assumed to bear a masculine bias, due to the early intervention of the second stratum of dissociation, the same mechanism might be assumed as a means of explaining the suggestible, and presumably femininely orientated, ego of the pyknic leader—the demagogue, as his enemies must call him. On the other side of the conscious field, however, it would be then necessary to assume a large degree of continuous conduction, whereby the raw aggression of the super-ego could gradually and progressively seep in, to fluctuate and finally to revolutionize the conscious mind.

This process of strong but impermanent stratum-formation can be explained in terms of the same hypothetical genetical mechanism as that used to explain the four strata of the schizoid.[1] It is only necessary to imagine the same influences working with a more curtailed range of action. The fast and slow types of Southern and Northern—ultra-feminine and masculine—heredity tend to conflict with each other, though they never finally quite agree to a divorce. At every stage of development the differences become more acute ; so that, by the time puberty is reached, the inevitable and evolved weakening of the top stratum in the man is carried out to a somewhat extreme degree. Probably the decline in the insulation of the super-ego goes on until middle life. Such characters can begin as socialists and end as dictators. They are never quite deserted by the sympathetic capacity of their suggestible youth ; but the power and experience of age is accompanied by a hardening and simplification in the conscious outlook.

A difficulty must be admitted in explaining the great difference between the pyknic and asthenic physiques, assuming the former to be genetically a less extreme example of the latter. We are again baffled by our great ignorance of the causes of hybrid vigour. Assuming, however, a fight between the two halves of the inheritance, it is not impossible that, before partial separation took place, the homologous portions would each strive to master and outdo the other. If so, the

[1] See centre section of last diagram.

first effects would be exaggerated, while the subsequent ones would fall below average results. It is possible, therefore, that the arrest of growth in the pyknic, together with the initial insulation of the ego, might be abnormally complete and final ; so that growth would be actively arrested, and the conscious and unconscious departments of the mind given every chance of full and clear development. Only in the later stages of adult life would the contesting genes begin to tire and their influences to abate.

MIND AND BRAIN

Now reference was made to the revolutions between maniac enthusiasm and depressed inhibition that are liable to overtake the pyknic cyclothyme, the man of action. It was suggested that these arose through a breakdown in the insulation between the conscious and the unconscious, so that the aggressiveness inhibited in youth is able to flood in and alter the emotional charge of consciousness. We are reminded by this of the " short circuit " theory of epilepsy, in which the whole upper, and on the whole inhibitory, part of the brain is held to fail, thus allowing the lower and more primitive portions to exert themselves in uncontrolled " all or none " reactions. Although the matter is abstruse and highly technical, it all has an important bearing upon the questions at issue. We have a connection with the general mineral-hypothesis in the fact that deprivation of mineral, and the dilution of the blood through the inhibition of diuresis, have been shown to predispose towards the spontaneous outbreak of attacks.[1] Moreover, the brain of the epileptic is often found to contain pathological amounts of accumulated fluid ; which reminds us of its swelling under experimental conditions, when the blood is similarly diluted and its electrolyte concentrations reduced.[2]

All this suggests that there may be even more primitive and earlier developing strata of inhibition, as well as the two that divide the conscious mind from the super-ego and the id. It may be the penning up and bursting out of neural activity of the lower and more primitive reflex arcs that is responsible for the epileptic attacks. We may return to the suggestion of Dr. Rivers that the change from water to land life must have demanded a most complete change of habit. If so, it seems conceivable that this old stratum has still been conserved intact, and is now of use in separating the voluntary from the involuntary behaviour. It does not, however, seem easy to associate the earliest stage of cranial expansion with this first stratum. Actually, I have had to adopt a rather more complex hypothesis, parts of which are outlined in the diagram in chapter VI.[3] If the first cranial expansion marks the dawn of mammalian evolution, it has served to inhibit the independent, and perhaps aggressive, behaviour of the primitive land-mammal. The change from water to land life was

[1] McQuarrie, I., and Peeler, D. P. : *J. Clin. Invest.*, 10, 915 (1931).
[2] Lennox, W. G., and Cobb, S. : *Epilepsy*, London, 1928.
[3] See p. 139.

earlier. Moreover, I suspect it to have involved a change from less to more masculinity ; whereas the change from proto-mammal to true mammal is supposed to have introduced a phylogenetic shift towards femininity. As a further complication, it must be remembered that a sex-reversal was deemed to have occurred between the times of vertebrate emergence on to the land and the much later evolution of the small homogametic mammalian female. Thus both the emergent amphibian and the newly-evolved mammal must alike have been subject to a selection for ultra-sexuality, despite the fact that in one case this implied more masculinity, while in the other femininity was increased. We must suppose this old sex-reversal to be recapitulated in the individual development. Thus some of the earlier-acting sex-linked genes of the mammal may still encourage the old amphibian and proto-mammalian inhibition of feminine anabolism. If so, it is not impossible that the genes responsible for the three cranial expansions might produce an inhibition of feminine reactions below a certain level of the nervous system, while they encouraged it in the centres above. I suggest, therefore, that each brain-expansion is due to a temporarily increased interaction of the sex-inheritance, and of the genes derived from it, with the other autosomes ; and that this process will encourage an inhibition of masculine and aggressive behaviour, some of which will tend to record itself at permanent, or semi-permanent, strata of dissociation.

The foregoing question would be of importance if any attempt were to be made to relate differences in the working of the conscious behaviour to measurements of involuntary movements of any sort. It might furnish part of the explanation why the pyknic type, although shorter, is both more muscular and more voracious than any other type. If his arrest of growth is due to the hybrid vigour of two initially-feminine parts of the inheritance, one would have expected less muscular development and tonus, and a more inhibited and feminine attitude towards food. The foregoing theory explains this in terms of a heightened masculinity at the lower level, coupled with more femininity above it. It saddles us, however, with the difficulty of explaining the differences between women and men. Perhaps the reduced muscularity and tonus, and the probably less active gastric nerves characteristic of the latter, are the result of a subsequent selection for femininity, occurring after the previously discussed sex-characters had become autosomal.

Turning now to the inevitable philosophical difficulty that must arise whenever we attempt to relate the mental to the material, I must confess to thinking in terms of a strict psycho-physical parallelism. The dominant activity of certain parts of the brain as manifested at certain times has been held responsible for Freud's three separate stages of emotional development, as well as for his three aspects or components of the self. It seems improbable that any one of these distinctions could be said to exist without the others to serve as a foil. Indeed, each may be considered as a product of its difference to its neighbours. If one admits a serial development of emotional phases, it seems necessary to imagine each stage as implying its own capacity for individual memory, even if the symbols or patterns used may vary somewhat in kind, and may be energized by differing degrees of conative stimulation. I conceive of the id as consisting mainly of inhibited manipulative behaviour appropriate to a small social tree-dweller. Similarly, the less complex but more forceful nature of the super-ego might be equated with the unrestrained ferocity of an adult giant-anthropoid. This too, however, has come to be inhibited by the last-evolving, or so-called Œdipus, stratum, though previously we may assume that such behaviour would have acted by releasing activities appropriate to the id as well.

I have tried to represent some of these concepts in the form of diagrams, but it must be clearly understood that the latter are intended as no more than mechanical analogies such as may possibly be of assistance to some minds in order to grasp the ideas it is wished to convey. A stratum of dissociation is a psychological rather than a physiological concept. That is to say, the relationship between the parts of the brain that are thereby dissociated does not seem necessarily to imply a close anatomical nexus ; though I do suspect it of implying a correspondence in respect to evolutionary and developmental age. If Professor Dubois is right in his suggestion that the evolution of the brain proceeds by a bi-partition of cells, it seems possible to think of the human brain as possessing all fundamental portions in quadruplicate.[1] If so, the warring sections of the human mind might be considered each to actuate, and be actuated by, its own appropriate neural mechanism. Moreover, the first evolved task of each successive portion would appear to be that of inhibiting the instinctive behaviour of its predecessor. If so, consciousness might be the product of these conflicts.

My object in drawing attention to these difficulties is to explain, and in some sense excuse, the plan here adopted of displaying the parts of the mind as though the latter were actually contained within the walls of compartments, and isolated from each other by strata. To these strata I have, alternatively, attributed the properties of an electrical insulator, or dielectric, whereby a positive charge upon one side induces a negative potential upon the other. At the same time I have assumed it as possible that this insulation might break down. This would follow either from the great strength of an externally applied impulse, or from the internal induction of too strong a charge.

This diagrammatic treatment seems to necessitate the placing of the conscious ego in a position at which it is in communication with the two other parts of the mind, the super-ego and the id. For this reason I have shown it at the centre. The super-ego, which is believed to be formed last, is accordingly placed above ; so that the id, which is held to consist mainly of inhibited bodily activity, must be relegated to the

[1] Cf. Chapter VI.

lower position, and is thus set immediately above the involuntary stratum.

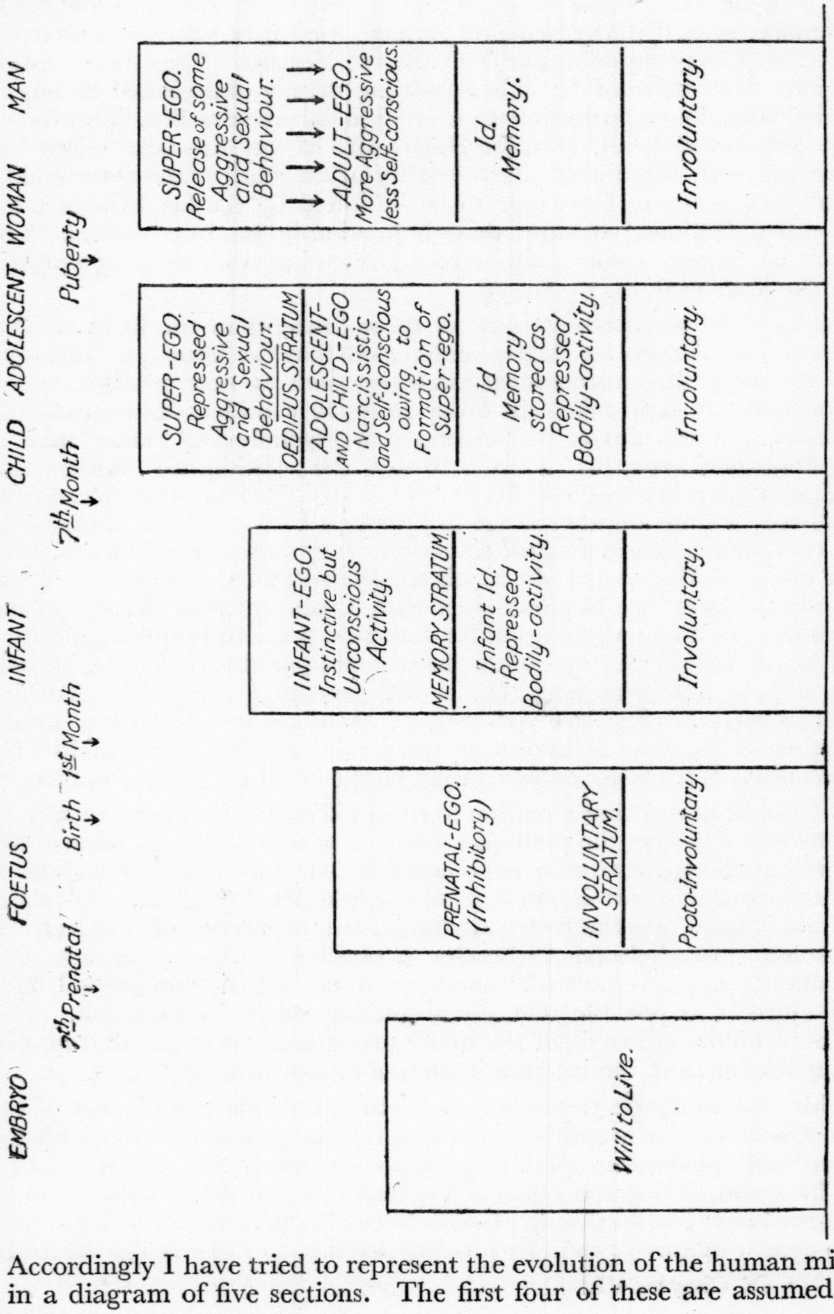

Development of three strata of Dissociation.

Accordingly I have tried to represent the evolution of the human mind in a diagram of five sections. The first four of these are assumed to represent important stages of ontogeny and phylogeny. The last represents the development of the adult from the child. Much the same scheme—though developed in another manner—was outlined in chapter VI. Starting from a relatively undifferentiated stage corresponding to an aquatic form of life, it is there suggested that a first stratum is formed when the relatively automatic behaviour of the fish is removed to the purely involuntary department on the occasion of the change to terrestrial existence. The nature of the possibly complex association between this lowest stratum and the first cranial expansion has already been discussed.

Let us then imagine the needs of a previously aquatic creature following on the change to terrestrial existence. Food must be marked down and attacked and not merely sucked in during the process of swimming; while, again, a mate of the opposite sex must be recognized. It is no longer enough to discharge gametes into the sea. Thus at this stratum of dissociation aggression is divided from the involuntary, and on the whole more anabolic and so feminine, behaviour of the aquatic creature. Sex evolves in the first instance as an increase of catabolic masculinity.

This evolution of aggression and male sexuality needs, of course, to be inhibited in the unborn child. This inhibition, then, is attributed to the first stratum. It is represented by the rebound of the aggressive tendencies from the upper, and essentially inhibitory, portions of the brain. The latter accept and amplify, but they must discharge back in the same general direction as that from which they were originally stimulated. In the fœtus they find no outlet. In the infant, however, after the development of what must now be called the second stratum, these inhibitory processes are converted into love of the mother, which is essentially a feminine attitude and one useful in obtaining nourishment. They here become elaborated into the whole complex of bodily activity that is learned at this time, and retains the tone imparted to it by the reversed aggression, or love. Such love is later conveyed to the id proper, and may be allowed to flood upwards so as to reinforce the self-loving content of the next stratum, namely, the isolated narcissistic conscious ego of the child and adolescent. For it has been necessary to postulate the formation, and subsequent weakening, of the stratum in question in order to allow for the greater aggression of the adult male. If this occurs in the one case, it seems more probable than not that the other strata will likewise have a period of maximum efficiency, after which greater conduction will be permitted.

Lastly, then, after the development of the infantile memory, constructed from inhibited bodily movement below the level of the probably more conscious child-ego (which is more aggressive in its food quest and bodily activity), we postulate the development of the last stratum. This cuts off the upper aggressive portion of the mind, and thus creates a new intermediate compartment in which all conscious activity is supposed henceforth to reign. During the whole long course of youth and adolescence this super-ego, a magazine of aggression, will tend to be charged by all affections felt and ambivalently reversed in the consciousness ; as also by any strong aggressive feelings that may force a direct entry during the period before or after insulation is complete. Mild degrees of hate experienced at this period will correspondingly reduce the emotional charge ; and will be the cause of a reduced aggressiveness in the later life of the man, after this last stratum has weakened, and the final period of super-ego discharge has set in.

RACE AND EDUCATION

It merits careful consideration how far the same type of educational treatment will produce like results when applied to children of the masculine and feminine races respectively, as well as to the boys and girls of each. Restricting ourselves to purely tentative and unverified hypothesis, we might assume that in boys, and in all older children of the more masculine races, the insulation of the super-ego will be weaker. That is to say, direct hate induced in the ego will tend to be merely " suppressed," and thus stored in an unconverted rather than in an ambivalently reversed or " repressed " form. In girls, on the other hand, and in younger boys of the more feminine races, cruel treatment would induce love as a repression in the super-ego whose charge would thus tend to be weakened, so that its subsequent influence on adult behaviour might at most alter it somewhat in the direction of sadism. The opposite holds good of kind treatment. This will invigorate the super-ego of ultra-feminine youth of either sex, and will normally be reflected back in the same form in which it was applied. Only when the barrier breaks down in individual or mass neurosis will it flood back as raw aggression.

Now boys of the ultra-male races would appear to receive less benefit from kindness. It may strain the insulation of the super-ego, perhaps never so strong, by inducing an over-charge of aggression, that may then tend to find a premature escape in sadism. Alternatively, or in addition, love could leak in to swamp the same stored and isolated aggression ; so that, in either case, a lower potential would be available when the final barrier is lifted to energize the adult-masculine behaviour. At all events, if a fighting man is required, the existence of some mechanism such as is here suggested can be postulated in connection with the well-recognized if now unfashionable theory (if not matter of observed fact) that some youths are the better for a stern and even cruel upbringing. In such cases, to withhold the rod would appear only to spoil the super-ego of part of its possible content ; though to apply it is to run the risk of a discharge into individualistic activity of an antisocial kind. The remedy is to devise socially beneficial outlets for this aggressive initiative. If this proves impossible, there would seem to be no future for the masculine form of inheritance, and that though, on the whole, it seems the best champion of free will.

Freud's theories can thus be interpreted in more than one way. To treat the masculine heredity as if it were feminine, or vice versa, may be as great a mistake as to treat the healthy as though they were sick. In either case we may be robbing Peter to pay Paul.

As a practical suggestion it may be mentioned that the "paliers," or arrests of bodily growth during the life of the infant, prove easily measurable, and may be correlated with the laying down of the strata of dissociation. If these were recorded they might serve as a guide to the educational treatment in later life.

As a very general statement it seems fairly true to say that the pastoral is cruel to his growing sons, though he cherishes the mother and the infant. The agriculturist, like the hunter and gatherer, on the other hand, is most indulgent towards his growing children ; though he may be more addicted to infanticide, at any rate before the first *rite de passage*, when the new arrival is admitted to full membership of the group. All this can be interpreted in terms of a cultural intensification of pre-existing hereditary tendencies, which as such assists adaptation to the environment. The pastoral does everything to stimulate his own natural and inherited aggression in his son. The more feminine peoples similarly adopt means to encourage group-affection and restraint, the potentialities for which are in any case firmly established in their inheritance. In so far as the treatment of the infant can have any influence upon the emotional tone of the id, the same parallelism holds good. The affection of the pastoral could reinforce the aggression in the infant id ; which in its turn could later react by intensifying the charges of love and hate in the newly-formed ego and super-ego of the child and adolescent. The possibly less affectionate attitude of the other type of mother would tend permanently to impoverish the emotional content of the whole mind, and this also may have temporary survival-value in a collectivist and static society.

This cruelty in the upbringing should not be confused with the temporary infliction of pain, possibly conjoined with ridicule, at the time of the puberty ceremonies. This seems best explained as an attempt not to build up the super-ego, but to liberate it and promote its discharge. If only hate or aggression can be suppressed, without undergoing ambivalent repression into love, part of the same breach may remain open for its return. The fact that this so-called cruelty is carried out impersonally and with the full approval of the group, and in the group-interest, is of importance. It is the law of the tribe that inflicts the pain, and it is upon the law itself, not upon its obedient, and often masked, servants, that the aggressive super-ego of the initiate will focus itself. When his turn comes, he will carry out the same rites in the same impersonal spirit ; and on the fringe of the immediate focus of ideas connected with his initiation he will likewise adopt an essentially aggressive, if somewhat unsympathetic, attitude in all matters concerning tribal lore and custom. In theory, the need for a painful and terrifying initiation would seem to increase with every advance of racial femininity, assuming, that is, a thicker and more persistent wall of inhibition in such cases. If the facts do not fit this hypothesis, it might be argued alternatively, that originally, and so perhaps now, the male races had most need of an adolescent inhibition, since this was evolved to protect them from the wrath of the adult male. At this early stage the first blood shed in battle may have served to liberate the adult aggression.

CONCLUSION

Civilization is held to have produced so great an intermixture of racial types that it becomes wellnigh impossible to distinguish the separate component elements when considering the physical form and its relation to the behaviour of civilized individuals and groups. Although this racial classification breaks down, the organic differences, in the light of which we have hitherto sought to understand its evolution, appear to hold good and to have been retained. Strong is still distinguishable from weak, tall from short, ultra-masculine from ultra-feminine, and the aggressive unadaptable folk from the subservient suggestible individuals, classes, and even nations. In addition, however, to this sharp division between the more and less manly types, two other common and less easily defined classes of individuals have arisen. These are the asthenic introverts and the pyknic extraverts, the schizoids and cyclothymes that emerge from the type psychology of Kretschmer and Jung. I have tried to account for both in terms of a racial mixture between a fast- and a slow-maturing type of heredity. In the case of the tall asthenic the evolved arrests of stature-development are held to have failed through lack of synchronization ; whereas in the short fat pyknic I believe the same result to have been narrowly averted. In this case the tension between the opposite types of heredity may have accentuated the influence of each ; the tendency to act together being just strong enough to prevent an independent behaviour such as was postulated in the first case.

The psychological differences of the two types seem amenable to explanation by the same mechanism. It has been argued that arrests of growth were evolved as a result of in-breeding at the times when one species gave rise to another. At these times behaviour must also have altered, so that an inhibition of much previously evolved behaviour—and especially of aggressive individualistic action—became imperative. These arrests of bodily development are accordingly identified with certain presumed strata of dissociation within the mind : regions at which nerve-impulses are inhibited and induce reversed influences, or emotions of an opposite kind, operating beyond the stratum in question. The three main increments in the index of cephalization—already referred to—are equated with the laying down of three corresponding strata. The lowest and first of these (which is dealt with last) is held to mark the change from aquatic to land life, and to provide at present the break between voluntary and involuntary behaviour. The serial development of the upper two is held normally to divide the brain into three compartments, mental manifestations of which are the same as those recognized by Freud as the id, the ego, and the super-ego ; their formation being attributed in the same order to his three stages of emotional development—the auto-erotic of the child, the narcissistic self-love of the adolescent, and the hetero-sexual object-love of the adult.

In the pyknic these two upper strata are believed to have been well-established ; that is to say, they will ambivalently reverse a large majority, if not all, of the impulses impinging upon them. In later life, however, the upper, or Œdipus stratum, is assumed to break down, allowing the outflow of stored aggression to energize the adult behaviour, and so exhaust the moral super-ego.

In the asthenic, the failure to integrate the two halves of the inheritance produces four upper strata instead of two. In addition to the three divisions of the normal mind there is a " transconscious " between the super-ego and the ego, and a " subconscious " between the ego and the id.[1] Since the sex-bias of each compartment induces an opposite in its neighbour, this results in the conscious mind of the asthenic schizoid being masculine and therefore unadaptable ; whereas that of the pyknic extravert and other normal individuals is more feminine and thus more adaptable. The same theory is made to account for the oscillation and dullness of feeling, as well as for the inferior memory, and greater subtlety, that mark the schizoid type of mind.

The super-ego is the repository of male aggression. This evolves out of a formerly less active form of feeding at the embryonic and aquatic level ; this passive assimilation being segregated by the first stratum where it continues to energize the involuntary behaviour. The aggression then activates the less diffuse consciousness of the fœtus, until it is further divided into the inhibited bodily activity of the infant id and the remainder consisting of the more conscious and more aggressive ego and super-ego in combination. When these separate at about the seventh month from birth, after the last expansion of the brain, the super-ego tends to store all conscious love in the form of hate, and vice versa. Since, however, it is probable that the quality of the dissociation strata is dependent upon heredity (and physical environment), it follows that the same educational methods may not have the same results when applied to different types. In the more masculine of these the conduction of the upper stratum is believed to increase at the expense of its power of ambivalent reversal. Thus in such types, as represented by the pastoral races, cruelty will drive through to the super-ego and will be held as

[1] Probably most of the same facts could be accommodated to a theory involving the doubling of a single threshold of unconsciousness.

suppressed but not as repressed emotion. It will thus help to build up the super-ego. In the more feminine races, however, the same cruel treatment would serve to induce love in the super-ego and would thus reduce its emotional content. A similar argument was applied to the case of the id.

of the heredity itself being modified by environment.[1] Even if the genes remain potentially unchanged, their interaction and influence upon the organism may be slowly alterable in the direction that proved generally useful during previous similar episodes in the past. The full influence of a given environmental change may need three or more generations to reveal itself.

THE SOCIAL LADDER

Having arrived at this rather damping conclusion concerning our vast ignorance both of the causes and effects of changed ecological conditions, it is nevertheless necessary to try and foresee some of the more probable influences of urbanization upon society as a whole and upon the individuals whom it brings into interaction. Conditions are at the moment so unstable that it seems probable that some partial and temporary periods of improved equilibrium may lie ahead. We have the not quite irrelevant object-lesson of the many gradations of primitive and barbaric society, which through lack of a recorded past seem static, yet bear the scars of cultural contacts or internal revolutions suggesting epochs of most violent social change. It seems possible that organic and cultural evolution may voyage in company under stress of gales relieved by calm intervals, rather than by holding any straight and separate courses, or proceeding at some steady or gradually accelerating speed. We may assume, in short, that the moments of cultural evolution will correspond, and will not alternate, with the epochs of bodily change. If so, each should be considered as complementary elements in a greater whole ; and, despite the cultural cushioning of Modern Man, it does not seem impossible that the psycho-physical, and especially the emotional, changes may still dominate the partnership. I doubt whether there is, or ever has been, a constant or calculable human nature.

The immediate problem is to enquire into the history of the rural recruits who have flooded the ancient and modern cities, so as to see how they begin and in what ways they most often end. For the ancient world, and I think in the case of the modern city too, there is sound reason to suppose that the newcomers would tend to be drawn from the weaker, more feminine, more suggestible, and more adaptable, parts of the rural population.[2] In so far as this still retained any of its old stratification into pastorals and grain-growers, it would be the latter, the relatively servile element, who would first forsake the land. There can be little doubt that town life has an emotional as well as an economical appeal ; and one would expect this gregarious instinct to be strongest in the hereditary types whose aggressive instincts were most completely repressed. Moreover, it would be these same smaller physical specimens who would stand the best chance of survival in

[1] Boas, F. : *Changes in the Bodily Form of Descendants of Immigrants.*

[2] *N.B.* This would not hold good of emigrants unless organized for the profit of others.

the city. Their lower calcium-requirement would give them an initial advantage, such as would then favour further specialization along the same line. If, as I suspect, the latter type of phylogenetic change is one that increases fecundity, we have before us the mechanism responsible for producing the urban proletariat. Of course, the change of environment will reduce the birth-rate ; but, if a prolonged residence in cities can to some extent mitigate this effect, it seems to follow that poverty will come to possess survival-value. This, of course, fits in with the observation that the poor are, in fact, the more prolific. The point is of further interest since it fails to reveal any clear means whereby the established town-heredity can have been selected in favour of a greater aggression, such as is almost certainly needed in the pursuit of modern trade, or in the undertaking of anything beyond some rigidly conventionalized form of economic activity. If the psychological and bodily characters are to remain linked, the wage-slave appears to have more chance of survival than his master. So far, however, we have detected no method whereby the officers can be promoted from the ranks, unless, to some extent, these social-climbers may be regarded as urban misfits who rise to the top as scum during the brewing and maturing of this standardized but somewhat insipid beverage.

Now the vigour of Western civilization must be admitted, however much we deplore its other faults. The formula that has been outlined might possibly fit the caste-system in the cities of the ancient world ; though even in that case the additional, if periodic, invasion of the pastoral must be discounted. In a veiled form, however, the same old influence may well be at work, even if it has given up its former militancy and adopted methods of peaceful penetration. We must remember that besides the aristocrat and the serf there is a middle class in rural society. The fallen nobility and prosperous peasant combine to form a small central body that is accustomed to employ and handle labour. Moreover, we may reflect that there are great differences between countries. In some the family holding, without hired help, is well-nigh universal. In others farms run to all sizes, and social importance depends upon wealth and acreage. In the small holding the labourer is rare. Landowners seem unwilling or unable to take command ; but are content to do their own work, their reward being often a hoard hidden beneath all the signs of poverty. In the large holding, the big farmer seldom works with his own hands. Of course there are complex reasons for all this ; but the main one, I contend, is that the corn-lands have evolved their own type of man, who is not good at organizing others. So, too, I would argue that the grazing land has attracted the less industrious and more domineering personality, who thrives as an organizer, and has often made money from both large scale and subsidiary cultivation carried out under his guidance. The large, self-assertive man makes the best master, since his domination is instinctive though controlled by conscious thought. On the whole, he is reasonable even in his most aggressive moods, and can be friendly and jocular when these become ambivalently reversed. The true peasant, on the other hand, being naturally less assertive, has all the time a greater unconscious hate and fear of his employee. The effort of maintaining an unnatural mastery will strain his reduced powers of rational behaviour ; so that the least mutiny of the hind will be followed by a passionate outburst ending in a dissolution of the contract. There will be none of the mutual relief and stability achieved through the artistic blasphemy of the master and the philosophical grumbling of the man.

It is the contingent of potential officers that would appear to run the greatest risk of extinction under urban conditions, and it seems legitimate to regard them as the chief participants in the economic struggle for social pre-eminence. Unless they can undergo a rapid somatic transformation, and thus assume the drab uniform of the dysplastic proletariat, they will rarely survive even a temporary fall in the social scale. Both their bodies and their minds will turn against them. They will be less able to live on poor food in the crowded and sunless quarters of a city ; and they will feel a deeper resentment against what will be felt as an intolerable, and vindictively applied, force of economic pressure. They will similarly be unable to appreciate the possible pleasures of their lot. Crowding will be felt as an irritation, rather than as a stimulus to direct and diffuse activity of an erotic, if femininely orientated, description. They will not know how to enjoy the circus, since they will be unable to suppress their jealousy of the performers. They will prefer to remain dissatisfied. If the social ladder offers no hand-hold at its bottom rung, they will lead an onslaught against the foundations of the whole edifice. As leaders of the suggestible proletariat they may succeed in pulling down their cousins at the top ; while the latter, with no less intuitive accuracy, will pick out the ringleaders for persecution, or promote them back into the ruling caste. All this is a condensation of history ancient and modern, and is not gratuitous prophecy. We have arrived at a time when the aggression of these leaders has brought power in plenty within the grasp of themselves and the masses whom they command. Unless phosphorus-deficiency and over-population again insist on a return to bread-eating and a low standard of living, there is no reason to expect an improved ratio of animal-food and dairy-products to reduce further the fertility of the aggressive " pituitary " types. Meanwhile, we may hope to have come near to an arrest of that differential birth-rate whereby the dysplastic masses survive at the expense of their betters. This must ever remain a menace ; but it has been temporarily staved off and awaits permanent or long-continued suspension at the hands of the growing, or less rapidly diminished, numbers of the stronger and more expensive hereditary strains. Even if the numbers of the latter are still on a comparative decline there can be little doubt that their power over the remainder has, for the moment, masked the effect. Only in the ancient East is there a voiced wish to return to the simple life.. The peoples of the West have no real fear of the machine, since is offers them the sole chance to live on the fat of the land.

It must remain a matter of extreme doubt how far racial development is influenced by these changes of external conditions. If this influence is as large as I suspect it to be, there seems only a remote danger of any immediate swamping of active individuality in favour of the illogical suggestibility and dangerously repressed aggression of the mass.

WAR AND THE MAN

Future generations will owe a deep debt of gratitude to Freud for his inspired, if somewhat ruthless, leadership in the cause of self-knowledge. Of his followers none will be considered to have better digested and applied his lessons than those who are now seeking to understand, and therefore control, the psychological causes of war. Part of this activity of theirs might well be directed towards an enquiry into the organic and hereditary basis of the different forms of warlike behaviour ; and it is to illustrate this possibility that I have rather deliberately excluded much reference to the influence of various suggestions and ethical ideals and have drawn attention to the probable differences between the receptive capacities of one sort of mind and other.

On the whole physical anthropology would appear to have taken its heredity for granted, and to have contemptuously turned its blind eye towards such few and indistinct signals of environmental change as have hitherto come within its notice. Similarly, the social sciences have proceeded from the opposite hypothesis, and have scarcely reached that pitch of maturity when castle building is suspended and the fundamental postulates themselves call for repair. As Hogben has recently pointed out, there is good practical reason to assume an alterable environmental control rather than to fall back on a pessimistic determinism ; in which mood all ills of the flesh are put down to heredity, and their mastery is postponed as something still outside the field of practical politics.[1] This also has been the wise policy of the physician. Thus it is no wonder if psycho-analysis tends to remain weakly attached to the genetical and physiological sciences.

What, then, can we conjecture about the causes of war, if we assume hereditary, racial, and national differences to exist according to the degree in which the primitive aggressive instincts are restrained by the influence of subsequent gene mutations ? Following in the footsteps of Freud and such followers of his as Money Kyrle[2] and Glover,[3] we look at once to the forces of repression as most probably to blame for the strength and periodicity of the outbursts. If, then, differences of

[1] Hogben, L. : " Heredity and Human Affairs," essay in *Science To-day*, London, 1934.

[2] Money Kyrle, R. : *Aspasia.*

[3] Glover, E. : *War, Sadism and Pacifism.*

heredity affect the degree of repression, it should be the smaller and more sex-inhibited types who may be expected to fight least often, but with the greatest ferocity. The larger gerontomorphic people, for all their permanent and sustained aggressiveness, might be expected to exhibit fewer and less startling paroxysms of *mania sanguinis*. They may be guilty of some degree of thoughtless bullying, and it is possible, though by no means certain, that this may be responsible for retaliatory outbursts on the part of the peoples so suppressed. The most dangerous kind of interference would be one that affected the emotional and religious life. If this, through any cause, became upset, the repressed libido might well find a scapegoat in a conqueror whose economic and military domination had hitherto passed almost unnoticed.

We may reflect that wars occur with a great mixture of overt motive. Nevertheless, dismissing for a moment the psychological complication of religious struggles, it seems fair to include honour and security as two tattered standards that each side thinks to capture by the defeat of the other. From this it is but a step to the next thesis, namely that a masculine race will fight for honour, but that a feminine people may be doubly dangerous in the cause of security. Of course motives will differ in the diverse social strata. The officer class will feel little of the fear that fills the hearts of the ranks they command. Born to plenty, they will know nothing of the repressed anxiety of the poor home. Nevertheless, it may be the very listlessness whereby the poor hereditary types repress their unconscious fear of starvation that is from time to time transformed into patriotic zeal. This so-called fear, held responsible for the normal listlessness, might equally well be explained positively as a manifestation of repressed aggression. It is the common mental orientation of the social animal. Mutual co-operation rouses a need for an outlet in a common cause. There is a vast difference between the adventurer and the man who defends his hearth and home. The former fights for excitement, loot, and renown ; each oarsman hopes one day to command the ship. There was much the same spirit of adventure abroad in the days when the Spaniards broke up the agricultural empires of America ; and it is worth noting that, in the course of subduing certain independent communities of Peru, the invaders met with the most heroic resistance, some communities perishing to the last man.[1] Communal life may sap the springs of individual initiative ; but it does not, as we well know, induce an inability to face death. Neither the conscientious objector nor the shameless profiteer need be cowards, even if they refuse to be patriotic at the dictation of the crowd. Conscious aggression could in fact offer a certain guarantee of world peace. The evolution of war, from the light-hearted raiding of wifeless youths to its present mass-influence over both sexes of whole populations, is the result of a phylogenetic shift towards racial femininity. In place of the sparring of the stags we

[1] Wissler, C. : *The American Indian*, p. 156 ; cft. Joyce, T. A. : *South American Archæology*, New York, 1912.

have reached the cold and desperate fury of the female fighting in defence of her young.

If these conclusions are upheld, it would follow that some large part of the inhibited aggression both preached and honoured in modern society is an effect, rather than a primary cause. If so, the remedy must lie in a control of the organic inheritance, or in the reaction of the phenotype as influenced by ecological conditions. This brings us to a consideration of two most interesting and almost diametrically opposed theses: Money Kyrle's idea that wars are mainly the product of inhibited libido;[1] and Unwin's claim that civilization itself depends upon this very control.[2] The former regards the pressure as already risen far beyond the margin of safety; while the latter hopes to stem the tide by screwing down the safety-valve. The practicability of either of these recommendations depends on how far this pressure of inhibition is and has been within rational control. Culture may be but a coach-dog running ahead in the direction that it is in any case destined to travel. Of the two suggested methods I prefer the difficulties of the psycho-analytic approach, even if it endangers the unity of the mind, to the plain man's artless method of whole-hearted ethical repression. The machine that has been stripped for inspection can usually be re-assembled; whereas it is cowardly and dangerous to be content to remain its ignorant slave. False confidence will end in over-driving and hence in irreparable disaster.

Some faint light may possibly be shed upon the unconscious ends of civilized striving if we consider the evolution of the instincts of sexual selection and assume differences to exist between the masculine and feminine racial types. The feminine races were characterized as the products of a sexual selection energized by an appreciation of the female and adolescent body. Such people will live and die for love. There will be a passionate self-identification with the mother, the mate, and the family group; and, by a further extension of the same instinct, the nation, the homeland, and the linguistic group will fall within the scope of the same set of ideas.[3] Such peoples will only attack in the interests of defence; but such paranoiac patriotism may prove a fatal incentive if fear arises between one such group and another.

To turn now to a consideration of the other hypothetical example, it seems possible that we have so far been guilty of a certain lack of subtlety in attributing raw aggression to the masculine type, and disregarding the possible complexities of conversion necessary before it can find outlet in any approved activity. We do not know how many phylogenetic changes may have gone to produce the present strains that are less feminine in their physical and psychological

[1] Money Kyrle, R.: *Aspasia, or the Future of Amorality*, London, 1932.

[2] Unwin, J. D.: *Sexual Regulation and Human Behaviour*, London, 1933; *Sex and Culture*, Oxford, 1934.

[3] The degree of this substitutional extension will depend upon the social inhibition of the primary instinctive outlet.

heredity. It may be worth while, therefore, to consider the possibility that some sorts of masculinity may be a product of inhibited femininity rather than part of the raw material out of which the latter was first formed. This might hold good of the schizoid.

Now if femininity leads to an appreciation of the human body alike in all its forms and in their direct representations, it might follow that these instincts of feminine sexual selection could have been secondarily repressed in certain of the more highly evolved male types. In such an event one would expect to encounter a sublimation of this physical love along channels that lay, as far as possible, in the same line as the old unsubstituted primitive aggression. The first result of this would be an instinctive revolt against bodily contacts. The same super-ego that had originally dictated the inhibition of the masculine outlet of libido would now extend his beat so as to guard the feminine outlet also.

If this interpretation is correct, a mere lowering of the defences erected upon the ancient incest-barrier will be insufficient to enervate the aggression of the masculine attack, though it might possibly relieve the tension within the ranks of the feminine defenders. It could, however, serve to nullify the dangerous, if otherwise desirable, anxiety and love for the security of the homeland and nation. For if physical love were to find a fuller outlet within the immediate circle of acquaintanceship, there would be less of the pent-up and explosive libido, liable to erupt in its most primitive form on any flimsy excuse, such as will always be provided by the necessary complexities of the substituted interests. I argue, therefore, with Money Kyrle that inhibited sex is one of the main causes of modern war ; but I suggest that it is the inhibition, not of a simple masculine aggression, but of a feminine type of love, that is mostly to blame.

If this diagnosis is at all near the mark, the cure will be difficult ; for it is the more feminine people who are most completely under the sway of the sexual taboo, even if schizoid masculine preachers have been in no small part responsible for their condition. The latter, by impressing their own dislike of bodily contacts upon a medium that was all too ready for the unreasoning acceptance of prohibitions of all kinds, have thus built up a wall that they must now demolish. For it is the restraints imposed by this very love and mutual forbearance that consciously irk the aggressive character. If love is to exist at the borders of the logical and purposive mind, the central part must be free to indulge in variety and adventure. To satisfy this essential craving, in a taboo-ridden society, is hard ; though in circles where no taboos existed it might prove harder still. From that war at least—the conflict between the impulsive and the repressive forces of human nature—there is no release.

GLOSSARY

ACHEULEAN. A palæolithic culture phase of Europe between the Chellean and Mousterian.

ACHONDROPLASIA. A pathological condition named from the failure of normal, cartilage development.

ACID, BASE, ALKALI, SALT. A molecule of water, consists of two atoms of oxygen and one of hydrogen. A minute proportion of water is normally dissociated (ionized) into one hydrogen atom carrying a positive charge (hydrogen ion) and a group of one hydrogen and one oxygen atom carrying an equal negative charge (hydroxyl ion).

An ACID is a substance containing hydrogen, which, when dissolved in water, increases the number of hydrogen ions present. Such solutions have a sour taste, turn litmus red, set free carbon dioxide from washing soda. Part or all of the hydrogen in the acid may be replaced by a metal, forming a salt.

BASES are substances which contain hydroxyl groups and which when dissolved in water increases the number of hydroxyl ions present. They turn litmus blue, and combine with acids to form a salt and water, e.g., caustic soda, ammonia, etc.

An ALKALI is a readily soluble base ; an alkaline solution is one containing an excess of hydroxyl ions over hydrogen ions.

A SALT is formed together with water when an acid combines with a base.

ACIDOSIS. An acid condition of the animal and human body.

ACROMEGALY. A pathological condition involving an over-growth of the hands, feet, face, and jaw, due to an over-activity of the anterior-lobe of the pituitary-gland. If the hypersecretion of the anterior-lobe occurs before the final ossification of the limb-bones the condition is known as gigantism owing to the great increase of stature.

ADRENAL-CORTEX. The covering of the adrenal-gland which secretes a hormone known to affect the kidney's power of retaining, or re-absorbing, sodium ; and also to favour the production of secondary masculine sex-characters.

ADRENALINE. A substance secreted as a hormone by the medulla, or interior, of the adrenal-glands. It maintains smooth muscle in a state of excitability and thus co-operates with the sympathetic nerve-endings to produce capillary constriction and a rise of blood-pressure. Small amounts have an opposite effect.

ÆTIOLOGY (or Etiology). The study of causes.

ALKALINE. (See ACID, BASE, ALKALI, SALT.)

ALLELOMORPH. The partner of a GENE, situated in an opposite and corresponding chromosome.

AMBIVALENCE. The theory of emotional pivoting, e.g., love becoming hate.

ANABOLIC (Process). Physiological processes whereby energy is stored. (See METABOLISM.)

ANÆMIA. Deficiency in numbers or quality of the red blood-corpuscles.

ANION. (See ION.)

ANTERIOR-LOBE. Here used to indicate the anterior, or front, part of the PITUITARY GLAND.

ARCHEAN. First period of Palæozoic Era.

ASTHENIC. Literally means "without strength." Used in medicine to indicate the results of wasting diseases. Here used after Kretschmer to indicate a special physical type described by him.

ATAVISM. Used here for theory that remote ancestral characteristics may return. Such have been termed atavistic.

ATROPHY. A waste of the tissues of a part or of the entire body; opposite to hypertrophy.

AURIGNACIAN. The earliest of the Upper Palæolithic culture phases of Europe; between the earlier Mousterian and the Solutréan and Magdalenian, which both succeed it.

AUTO-EROTIC. First supposed phase of emotional development in the child. (Freud.)

AUTOXIDATION. A coupled reaction involving the production of a higher and lower oxide in fixed proportion; the energy released in the latter process is used in the former.

AXILLARY. Concerning the arm-pit.

AZOTOBACTER. A soil-organism responsible for the fixation of organic nitrogen.

BASAL-METABOLISM. The heat produced by the body at rest.

BASE. (See ACID, BASE, ALKALI, SALT.)

BLOOD-GROUP. It is found that transfusion of blood is only safe when the donor and receiver possess certain special chemical similarities. All individuals can be placed in one of four blood-groups (I, II, III, IV), and any individual of one group can receive or give blood to any other individual in the same group. Certain cross-transfusions are possible. The inheritance of these characteristics is typically Mendelian; three genes exist, and form a triple allelomorph. (Beilstein's theory.)

BOUCHER. CHELLEAN and ACHEULEAN core-implements named after their discoverer Boucher de Perthes; also known by the question-begging name of hand-axe.

BRACHIATION. Climbing by an almost exclusive use of the arms, used by anthropoid apes.

BRACHYCEPHALIC. Broad-headed.

BROW-RIDGE (or Supraciliary Ridge). Excrescences of bone above the orbits of the eye. In the large anthropoids and palæanthropic fossils these fuse with the glabella to form what is known as a FRONTAL TORUS.

CACHEXIA. A wasting away of the body in the course of a chronic disease. Used here for the dry, dead condition of the skin following failure of the thyroid or anterior lobe, or from excess of fluorine in the diet.

CAPILLARY. The smallest class of blood-vessels, which together contain a greater volume of blood than any other part of the circulatory system.

CARBONIFEROUS. The geological period whose deposits occur above the DEVONIAN and below the PERMIAN.

CARTILAGE. Gristle. A tough and dense tissue both flexible and elastic ; it does not contain blood-vessels. Hyaline cartilage constitutes the precurser of the bony skeleton ; but bone may also be formed by the ossification of membrane before the latter has reached a cartilaginous stage of development.

CATABOLIC. Physiological process in which energy is released. (See METABOLISM.)

CATALYST. A substance capable of hastening a chemical reaction and of being recovered at the end of it.

CATION. (See IONS.)

CAUCASIAN. A useful term used to describe the different physical types of humanity met with in Europe and the Near East. Includes Nordic, Proto-Nordic, Alpine, East Baltic, and Mediterranean ; and excludes Mongoloid and Negroid races. (Blumenbach.)

CEREBRO-SPINAL FLUID. Liquid that bathes the brain and spinal cord.

CHELLEAN. An early palæolithic culture-phase preceeding the ACHEULEAN and characterized, like the latter, by large flint implements chipped from a whole " core."

CHROMATOPHORE. Skin cell of fish and amphibia containing a yellow, red, and black pigment which can expand to cover the nucleus or contract to a point. By this means the colour of the skin can be changed.

CHROMOSOME. Small bodies in the cell nucleus which stain with basic dyes, and can be seen forming from fine threads preparatory to the time when cell-division will take place. They contain the genes responsible for the organic inheritance. All the cells in a human being contain forty-eight chromosomes with the exception of sperms and ova, in which the number is halved. All except two are arranged in pairs of corresponding size. These are known as autosomes. An odd pair, one larger than the other, are known as the Y and X, or male and female, sex-chromosomes. The cells of a man contain a Y and an X, while a woman inherits XX. For this reason the woman is said to be of the HOMOGAMETIC sex while the man is HETEROGAMETIC.

CRETACEOUS. The last of the secondary or Mesozoic periods. The age of chalk between the JURASSIC and EOCENE.

CRETINISM. An arrest of bodily and mental development due to a failure of the thyroid secretion ; this in its turn, may be due to hereditary or *environmental* causes. Cretinism differs clinically from Mongolian idiocy since in the latter cases there is no thickening of the subcutaneous tissues and much greater alertness of mind ; from

ACHONDROPLASIA, where there is often no mental impairment; and from infantilism—a term used to cover a group of symptoms where the primary and secondary sexual-characters fail to appear at the proper time. Cretinism is cured by thyroid feeding.

CROMAGNON. A supposed race of Upper Palæolithic culture, taking its name from a cave in the South of France where skeletons were found. Here the term has been used somewhat loosely to designate all human remains found in association with the hunting cultures of Upper Palæolithic.

CYCLOTHYME (Cycloid). A person subject to regularly recurring periods of mental derangement; often maniac activity followed by extreme depression. On KRETSCHMER's hypothesis some physical types (the PYKNIC) are considered most liable to develop this form of disorder; they are called cycloid.

DENTITION. The arrangement and form of the teeth.

DEVONIAN. Primary geological period between SILURIAN and CARBONIFEROUS.

DIPLOID. The fertilized ovum and the remainder of the body cells growing from it are diploid since they carry the full number (forty-eight) of chromosomes. Sperms and unfertilized ova are said to be haploid.

DISJUNCTION. The longitudinal splitting of CHROMOSOMES during the division of cells.

DISSOCIATION. The mental phenomenon whereby one set of thoughts or behaviour can work independently of another.

DOLICHOCEPHALIC. Long-headed; opposite to BRACHYCEPHALIC.

DOMINANCE. A gene is said to be completely dominant to its recessive ALLELOMORPH, or partner, if, when inherited together, the latter can produce no observable influence upon the development of the individual. Dominance is usually, if not always, relative. Original, or "wild type," genes are usually dominant to their newly arising mutant allelomorphs. See EPISTATIC and PREDOMINANCE.

DRYOPITHECUS. An extinct order of anthropoid apes known only by fragments representative of different species. Dryopithecus is considered to have been closely related to the ancestors of the living large anthropoids.

DUPLEX. A gene is said to be inherited DUPLEX when it occurs double, thereby occupying both the corresponding LOCI of a pair of CHROMOSOMES.

DYSPLASTIC. Form due to abnormal and often incomplete development.

DYSTROPHY. Growth that has taken an abnormal course.

ECOLOGY (also spelt Œcology.) The study of the dependence of organisms upon each other, and of their relations to the inorganic aspects of their ENVIRONMENTS.

ECTODERM. The outer parts of an animal which develop from an early differentiating class of embryonic cell. The ectoderm is thus distinguished from the mesoderm and endoderm.

ECTODYNAMORPHIC (Soils) owe their salient features to external conditions, notably to climate. They are thus distinguished from ENDODYNAMORPHIC soils whose main characters are due to their parent material. As a rule the soils of coastal regions are considered to be endodynamorphic, whereas the continental extremes of climate create ectodynamorphic phenomena.

ELECTROLYTE. (See ION.)

EMBLEM. Here used to indicate the external display of a feature, the admiration of which will lead to a process of sexual-selection leading to a more extreme development of itself, and also of other, possibly more useful, characters associated with it.

ENDOCRINES. Also called ductless glands and organs of internal secretion ; elaborate and discharge into the blood or other internal circulating fluids substances known as hormones or autacoids which are chemical messengers. These in some way control the behaviour of other structures. A theory of their evolution and action has been outlined.

ENDODYNAMORPHIC. (See ECTODYNAMORPHIC.)

ENVIRONMENT (Surroundings). Distinguishable into physical, organic, and social aspects according as the features in question are the result of dead matter, or living organisms, or organisms of the same inter-breeding group as the one whose environment is under consideration. The state of the internal body-fluids which are external to the cells is known as the internal environment ; and I have referred to conditions inside the cell and its nucleus, but outside the genes, as the INTRA-NUCLEAR environment.

EOCENE. First period of Tertiary or Cænozoic Era.

EOLITH. Supposed stone-implements from Pliocene and other early horizons, concerning which there has been much discord in archæological circles.

EPILEPSY. A pathological condition involving the recurrence of fits.

EPIPALÆOLITHIC (or Mesolithic). Culture phases later than Upper Palæolithic and before Neolithic and Early-Bronze Ages.

EPISTATIC (genes). Favour the outward, or PHENOTYPIC, expression of others in the same chromosome.

ETIOLOGY. (See ÆTIOLOGY.)

EXOPHTHALMIC GOITRE. A disorder characterized by prominence of the eyeballs, tremor, rapid heart action, high metabolic rate ; due to excess of its hormone by the thyroid gland. (See GOITRE.)

EXOGAMY. Marrying on and of the kin or natal association ; opposite to endogamy. Incest is the violation of the exogamic rule.

EXTRAVERT. One whose main conscious interest is in his surroundings ; the opposite to INTROVERT. (Jung.)

FIXED BASE. Non-volatile bases. (See ACID, BASE, etc.). Here used of the non-volatile, metallic component of salts ; mainly sodium potassium, calcium, and magnesium, retained in the blood and in the tissue cells, where it is used for the purpose of buffering acidity.

FŒTALIZATION. Supposed process whereby the development of the organism, is, at some points, arrested at a fœtal stage.

FŒTUS (fœtal). Unborn child during later stages of pregnancy.

FRUCTIVORE. Eater of fruit.

FRONTAL TORUS. (See BROW-RIDGE.)

GAMETE. HAPLOID marrying cells ; sperms and ova.

GENE. The material body embedded in a chromosome held responsible for the particulate transference of a unit hereditary character both from parent to offspring and from the fertilized ovum to all cells of the adult body.

GENETICS. The study of inheritance.

GERM-PLASM. Tissue from which gametes are produced.

GERONTOMORPHIC. Formed like an aged individual ; opposite to PÆDOMORPHIC.

GLACIATION. The formation of ice either on mountains or in sheets stretching across continents.

GLOMERULI. Parts of the kidney responsible for the extraction of waste products from the blood.

GOITRE. Enlargement of the thyroid gland ; may be simple (Derbyshire neck) when it is associated with hyposecretion of the thyroid hormone, or connected with exophthalmos. (See EXOPHTHALMIC GOITRE.)

GONAD. Organs containing the germ plasm in either sex, and in the mammal differentiating into testicles or ovaries, which act on the rest of the body by means of sex-hormones.

GRAVES' DISEASE. Same as EXOPHTHALMIC GOITRE.

GROWTH GRADIENT. Increment in the speed of growth according to the position of the tissue in relation to some fixed point.

GÜNZ. The earliest Alpine glaciation of late Pliocene or early Pleistocene date.

HERMAPHRODITE. Organism of double, and often alternating sexuality.

HETEROGAMETIC. (See CHROMOSOME.)

HETERO-SEXUAL. Attraction between males and females ; opposite to homo-sexual.

HETEROZYGOUS. Cross-bred, opposite to HOMOZYGOUS or pure-bred in regard to a particular gene or group of characters whose alternative allelomorphs are absent.

HOMINID (Hominidæ). Term used to embrace all the living and extinct races of Man.

HOMOGAMETIC. (See CHROMOSOME.)

HOMOZYGOUS. (See HETEROZYGOUS.)

HUMUS. The black organic portion of the soil.

HYDRAMNIOS. Excess of water in fœtal membrane.

HYDROCEPHALUS. Water on the brain. Excess of cerebro-spinal fluid due to HYPERSECRETION or blocking of outlets.

HYPERSECRETION. Over-production of its secretion by any gland.

HYPOSECRETION. Under-production of its secretion by any gland.

ID. Term used by Freud to indicate the amoral portions of the unconscious mind responsible for memory.

IN-BREEDING. The mating of close relatives.

INFRA-MASCULINE. Here used to indicate males of ULTRA-FEMININE races in whom the PREDOMINANCE of the female-determining genes of the X chromosome is deemed to have overthrown much of the influence of the autosomes and Y chromosome.

INFANTILIZATION. Arrest of racial development at an infantile stage. (See FŒTALIZATION.)

INTERSEXUALITY. An incomplete differentiation of primary- and secondary-sexual characters leading to a blending of masculinity and femininity.

INTER-SPECIFIC (rivalry) or (variation). That between two or more species each viewed as a whole. Opposite to INTRA-SPECIFIC.

INTRA-NUCLEAR. (See ENVIRONMENT.)

INTRA-SPECIFIC (rivalry) or (variation). That between individuals of the same species.

INTROVERT. One whose main conscious interest is in himself; the opposite to EXTRAVERT. (Jung.)

ION. Atom or group of atoms carrying a negative charge; they are present in all solutions that conduct electricity (classed together as ELECTROLYTES), that is, in solutions of acids, bases, and salts. ANIONS carry a negative charge, and include the hydroxyl ion (see ACIDS). CATIONS carry a positive charge and include the hydrogen and all metallic ions.

The charge on an ion, expressed in terms of that of the electron as unit, is termed the VALENCY of the ion.

ISOTONIC. Two solutions are said to be isotonic if, when separated by an animal membrane, no liquid passes from one side to another.

JURASSIC. Middle period of SECONDARY OF MESOZOIC. After TRIASSIC and before CRETACEOUS.

KAMASIAN. A pluvial period of the Early Pleistocene in Kenya.

KETOSIS. A condition in which acetone and acetoacetic acid are found in the blood.

LABIA MINORA. Part of the female genetalia.

LAMARCK (theory of). Suggestion that acquired characters are inherited; a view which, though popular, is mostly rejected by modern biology.

LATERITE. A class of tropical soil.

LEGUMINOSÆ. Plants such as clover, peas, and lupins which fix atmospheric nitrogen on account of nodule bacteria living in symbiosis with them.

LINKAGE. Genes frequently inherited together are said to be linked. This is due to their close association on the same chromosome and to the absence of genes favouring breakage and "crossing-over."

LOCUS. The position in a chromosome occupiable by a gene or its allelomorphs.

LYMANTRIA. Gypsy moth. Used by Goldschmidt in his experiments on intersexuality.

MANDIBLE. Jaw-bone.

MARGO VERTEBRALIS (of scapula). Inner edge of shoulder-blade.

MARSUPIAL. Pouched mammals like kangaroos.

MELANESIAN. Negroid inhabitants of Pacific Islands between New Guinea and Fiji.

MELANOPHORE. Skin-cell containing diffusable black pigment. (See CHROMATOPHORE.)

MENDELIAN. Inheritance in which the particulate transmission can be demonstrated.

MESOCEPHALIC. Medium size of head.

MESOLITHIC. (See EPIPALÆOLITHIC.)

METABOLISM. The physiological term for all processes where substances change their form. If they become more complicated, and thereby store energy, such metabolic processes are termed ANABOLIC. The reverse, where energy is released as heat or work, is termed CATABOLIC.

MICROPHTHALMIA. The state of having small eyes.

MINDEL. The second Alpine glaciation. Between Günz and Riss.

MIOCENE. The third division of the Tertiary Era. After the Oligocene and before the Pliocene.

MODIFIER. A gene which assists the dominance of another (Fisher). See EPISTATIC.

MONGOL. A DOLICHOCEPHALIC Mongoloid horse-culture folk of Central Asia.

MONGOLISM. A pathological condition in which some features of the racially Mongoloid peoples is reproduced.

MONGOLOID. Term used to embrace the whole of the straight-haired third of humanity all of whom have a pigmented skin usually of yellow colour.

MONOTREME. The most primitive of the three grades of mammals, still represented by the Platypus and Echidna.

MUTATION. Here only used to indicate a gene-mutation, also called a mutant. The external effect, and presumably the internal structure, of a gene can be changed by short-wave radiation. This also occurs naturally.

MYXŒDEMA. Symptoms following from thyroid-deficiency in the adult ; include loss of hair, tissue hydration and mental dullness.

NARCISSISTIC. Second supposed phase of emotional development in the child and adolescent. (Freud.)

NEANDERTHAL. An extinct race of coarse-boned Hominidæ.

NEANTHROPIC (or Modern, Man). Here extended to embrace earlier hypothetical fine-boned races.

NILOTE. Very tall "stove-black" and mainly Hamitic-speaking inhabitants of the Sudan and Abyssinia.

NITRIFICATION. The conversion of ammonia or nitrogen to nitrous and nitric acids ; effected in the soil by bacteria.

NORDIC. Fair haired, tall, dolichocephalic and moderately coarse-boned inhabitants of Western Europe usually speaking a Teutonic form of the Aryan languages. Differ from the Proto-Nordics (e.g., Ainu) and other Caucasians in the matter of hair- and eye-colour.

ŒDIPUS-COMPLEX. System of ideas resulting from a hereditary or environmentally imposed fear of the adult by the child. (Freud.)

OLIGOCENE. The second period of the Tertiary Era. Between the Eocene and the Miocene.

ONTOGENY. The development of the individual as contrasted with phylogeny, the development of the race.

ORGAN-INFERIORITY. An organic handicap leading to a compensatory specialization in other directions.

OSSIFICATION. The formation of bone from membrane or cartilage.

OSTEOMALACIA. Adult rickets.

PÆDOMORPHIC. Formed like a child. (See GERONTOMORPHIC.)

PALÆANTHROPIC. Here used to embrace all the coarse-boned and extinct Hominidæ, together with their presumed ancestors.

PALÆOLITHIC. Early culture phases characterized by use of chipped stone implements ; no ground implements or Pygmy flints.

PARATHORMONE. Active substance isolated from the parathyroid glands, having the property of causing calcium to be released from the bones into the blood.

PARATHYROID. ENDOCRINE tissue situated near the thyroid. (See above.)

PARIETAL. Bones rising from the temporal and sphenoid to the vault of the skull ; joining each other at the sagittal suture and also with the frontal and occipital bones.

PERMIAN. The last part of the PRIMARY ERA.

PEROXIDASES. Enzymes that activate hydrogen peroxide, enabling it to oxidise substances not otherwise attacked by it.

PHENOTYPE. The external aspect of an organism, as contrasted with its genotype or inherited potentialities.

PIGMENTATION. Colouring of the skin and other cells.

PITUITARY GLAND (or Hypophysics cerebri). The most complicated and important endocrine attached to the bottom of the brain.

PLASMA. The non-cellular parts of the blood.

PLEISTOCENE. Together with the Holocene, or crescent epoch, constitutes the earlier part of the Quaternary Period ; follows after the Pliocene.

PLIOCENE. The last part of the Tertiary Period.

PODZOL. Acid soil produced by heavy rainfall and lack of surface evaporation.

POLYANDRY. (See POLYGAMY.)

POLYGAMY. Includes POLYGYNY, where a husband has two or more wives ; as well as POLYANDRY where a wife has two or more husbands.

POLYGYNY. (See POLYGAMY.)

POLYPLOID. Having additional sets of chromosones.

PREDOMINANCE. Here given a special meaning similar to that of genetic DOMINANCE, but embracing a whole chromosome, linkage-group, or set of chromosomes. When considered in their relation to others.

PRESSOR. Causing a rise of blood pressure.

PROLIFERATION. Growth by the splitting of cells.

PROTOPLASM. The structureless contents of cells.

PYGMY. Dwarf races of the tropical rain-belt.

PYGMY FLINTS. Small implements found in Tardenoisian (Epipalæolithic) strata ; probably used for composite tools.

PYKNIC. Used by Kretschmer as opposite to ASTHENIC. Short, thick-set, but fine-boned.

QUATERNARY. The fourth geological era, including the Pleistocene and Holocene (Recent).

RATIONALIZE. To find intellectual justification for an instinctive act or emotion.

RECAPITULATION. Theory that the main events in the history of the race (phylogeny), are re-enacted in the growth of the individual (ontogeny).

RENDZINA. Soils of limestone origin common in Italy.

RICKETS. Failure of ossification and consequent distortion of the skeleton usually due to calcium or vitamin D deficiency or (rarely) to loss of calcium through the kidney. Known in German as " The English disease."

RISS. The third Apline glaciation. Between Mindel and Würm.

RITE DE PASSAGE. Religious ceremony marking and emphasizing the individual's change from one social status to another. (Van Genep.)

SAKAI. A Pygmy race of Malaya.

SCHIZOPHRENE (schizoid). Split personality to a degree considered pathological. On Kretschmer's hypothesis the ASTHENIC physical types are considered most liable to these forms of mental derangement. This tendency, when not pathological, is termed SCHIZOID.

SEX-BIAS. Supposed degree to which the masculine or feminine potentialities of a race or individual are developed at a given moment.

SEX-CHROMOSOMES. (See CHROMOSOME.)

SEX-DIMORPHISM. The degree to which males and females of the same race differ in form.

SEX-LINKAGE. The association of genes in the sex-(X) chromosomes.

SEXUAL-SELECTION. Intraspecific and sex-limited competition, here considered to be of interspecific advantage.

SINANTHROPUS. Pekin Man of Lower Palæolithic age.

SOLUTRÉAN. A horse-hunting hunting phase of Upper Palæolithic Europe characterized by pressure-flaked core implements and interposed between the Aurignacian and Magdalenian flake-industries.

SOMATIC. Concerning the body as contrasted with the germ-plasm.

SOMATIC MUTATION. Gene-mutation in a soma-cell, which therefore cannot be inherited.

SOMATIC REVOLUTION. A supposed happening whereby a disturbance of the INTRA-NUCLEAR ENVIRONMENT might alter the relative PREDOMINANCE of linkage groups.

SOMATIC SYNAPSIS. The observed fusion of chromosome pairs in body-cells. The hypothesis is advanced that points where this fails to occur correspond to conflicts between dissimilar genes.

STEATOPYGIA (steatopygous). Projection and abnormal development of the buttocks.

STEPPE. Country whose climate and soil has favoured a growth of grass.

STRATUM (Geological) level, or layer, corresponding to a given period of time. (Psychological) I have used the terms stratum and strata of dissociation in a way that extends the concept of a threshold or surface dividing the conscious from the unconscious mind.

SUBCONSCIOUS. Here applied to the threshold of memory and contrasted with the TRANSCONSCIOUS considered as the threshold of moral ideas.

SUPER-EGO. An anthropomorphic concept embodying the aggressive and hetero-sexual components of the mind considered as the unconscious source of moral behaviour. (Freud.)

SYNAPTIC MEMBRANE. The supposed boundary between one nerve fibre and another, across which the transference of impulse takes place.

TARSIOIDS. A once numerous genus now represented by *T. spectrum*, and probably standing close to the human line of descent.

TCHERNOZEM (also spelt CHERNOZEM). " Black earth " soils.

TERTIARY. Third geological era comprising Eocene, Oligocene, Miocene, and Pliocene.

THYROID. Endocrine gland situated in front of and on either side of the larynx. (See GOITRE.)

TRANSCONSCIOUS. (See SUBCONSCIOUS.)

TRANSLOCATION. The occasional transference of a gene or linkage-group from one chromosome to another not homologous and paired with it.

TRIASSIC. The first part of the Mesozoic Era ; after the Permian and before the Jurassic.

ULTRA-FEMININITY. Excessive development of secondary female characters in the race or individual.

ULTRA-VIOLET (radiation). Shorter than visible violet and longer than that of X-rays and radium-γ rays. Necessary for synthesis and auto-synthesis of vitamin D.

VITAMINS. Accessory food factors without which growth and life cease. Vitamin A is anti-infective ; B (the B complex), anti-neuritic ; C, anti-scorbutic ; D anti-rachitic ; E counteracts sterility. A, D, and E are fat soluble ; the remainder are water-soluble.

WÜRM. Last Alpine Glaciation, after Riss.

INDEX

D

E

R

S

INDEX OF AUTHORS

Figures in italics refer to pages on which the author's name occurs in the text but not at the foot of the page.

NOTE. Abbreviations used in references are those standardised in the Oxford World List of Scientific Periodicals.—*Oxford, 1934.*

J

K

L

M

N

O

P

HUTCHINSON'S
SCIENTIFIC & TECHNICAL
PUBLICATIONS

CONTENTS

RACE, SEX & ENVIRONMENT

A Study of Mineral Deficiency in Human Evolution

J. R. de la H. Marett

"In the pioneer work before us Mr. Marett sets forth a theory of the essential causal action of the environment on the individual and so on the social and political group. His inquiry is 'an attempt to associate the discordant categories of the organic and the inorganic by as close a nexus as the existing evidence allows.' The bridge across the gap is built on the fact that man eats to live."

Times Literary Supplement

342 pages, large demy 8vo, illustrated, 21/-

HEAD, HEART & HANDS

in Human Evolution

R. R. Marett,

F.B.A., M.A., D.Sc. Oxon; Ll.D. St. And.

"The man who is to understand the beliefs and practices of nature's peoples must have a peculiarly flexible and sensitive form of sympathy. He must be able to view things as Alice did in Wonderland. The Rector of Exeter College has this gift. . . . It is just because of his alert mind and quickened sympathy that Dr. Marett is so excellent a guide to the mind of the savage."

Sir Arthur Keith in The British Medical Journal

302 pages, demy 8vo, 10/6

CUSTOM IS KING

Essays Presented to R. R. Marett

Edited by L. H. DUDLEY BUXTON

Contributors

C. G. Seligman	H. J. Rose
L. H. Dudley Buxton	R. S. Rattray
Earnest A. Hooton	Henry Balfour
O. G. S. Crawford	Raymond Firth
T. K. Penniman	A. M. Hocart
Konrad Theodor Preuss	D. Westerman
Diamond Jenness	R. M. Dawkins
Beatrice Blackwood	Marius Barbeau
E. E. Evans-Pritchard	Leonhard Adam
C. von Fürer-Haimendorf	M. Fortes

Edited by L. H. Dudley Buxton

"This volume of essays presented to Dr. Marett, the distinguished and popular Rector of Exeter and Reader in Social Anthropology in Oxford, to commemorate his seventieth birthday, and adorned with portraits of him in prose and paint, gives interesting insight into the latest developments of anthropology and the allied disciplines. A bird's-eye view is obtained of the various fields now being tilled, crops watered and buildings erected in the vast and still unchartered fields of anthropology."

The Spectator

"Anthropological studies in Oxford owe much to Dr. Marett. Not only did he take a prominent part in the movement to institute a diploma, which gave Anthropology an assured place in the University's curriculum, but also by his enthusiasm and his broad philosophic outlook he won an ever-increasing following for studies which admittedly by their very title were human but which only grudgingly, as it were, came to be recognised as 'humanistic'."

Manchester Guardian

256 pages, demy 8vo, illustrated 12/6

Essentials of Modern MEDICAL TREATMENT

Vincent Norman,
M.D., M.R.C.P. Lond.; F.R.C.S. Edin.; D.P.H. Lond.

With a foreword by S. WATSON SMITH

A work of ready reference both for the man in active general practice and for the senior student requiring rapid revision for his final examination. It will also be valuable to those working for the higher examinations in medicine. A valuable feature of this book is its conciseness. The author has, as far as possible, kept strictly to the essentials of treatment, avoiding unnecessary descriptions and details, for which the busy practitioner, for whom the book is primarily intended, has no time.

256 pages, demy 8vo, 10/6

Foundations of SHORT WAVE THERAPY

Dr. Ing. Holzer and
Dr. Med. Weissenberg

Translated by JUSTINA WILSON and CHARLES DOWSE

" Here is to be found the best presentation of the technical aspects of ultra-short waves available in book form. Every practical worker in short-wave therapy should possess a copy of this book."

The Lancet

230 pages, medium demy 8vo, illustrated 12/6

Theory & Practice of
ANÆSTHESIA

M. D. Nosworthy,

M.A., M.D., B.Ch. Cantab. ; Anæsthetist to Westminster Hospital, and Grosvenor Hospital for Women; late Senior Resident Anæsthetist St. Thomas's Hospital

With a foreword by I. W. MAGILL

" This is a first-rate book for any man to study when he is beginning to give anæsthetics. That is not to say that it contains no substance for the experienced anæsthetist ; indeed it is so well conceived and clearly written that the expert may gain much from its perusal. Dr. Nosworthy's attitude towards his subject is throughout scientific and up to date, but he is fully alive to the value of the older methods.

The book contains no superfluous words. The print is of a capital size and clearness and the illustrations plentiful."

The Lancet

" It can be said that the book will be of such satisfaction to experts that their work in teaching will be made much easier and many of their ideas will be reflected independently in the book."

Jnl. American Medical Assoc.

223 pages, cr. 8vo, illustrated 10/6

INSULIN : its Production, Purification and Physiological Action

D. W. Hill, B.Sc. ; Ph.D. and

F. O. Howitt, M.Sc. ; F.I.C. ; Ph.D.

With a preface by Professor E. C. DODDS

" Anyone who has attempted to keep abreast of this subject will be grateful to the authors for the most exhaustive presentation of the work done on its chemistry and preparation that has yet appeared."

The Lancet

" The book attains a highly valuable object in that it is provocative of further research.
The book is attractively presented, and the subject matter most clearly arranged. Above all, the bibliographies at the end of every chapter will be of inestimable value."

Nature

240 pages, demy 8vo, illustrated 12/6

PRACTICAL ZOOLOGY

H. R. Hewer,

A.R.C.S. ; D.I.C. ; M.Sc. Lond.

" Those who are about to teach elementary zoology in universities or schools will do well to refresh their memories by a study of these pages. To students working on their own this book should prove extremely useful."

The Lancet

120 pages, cr. 8vo, illustrated 5/-

EVOLUTION OUT OF DOORS

A study of Sex Difference & Animal Coloration

Major H. J. Molony
late of Indian Police

Edited by J. R. de la H. MARETT

In the study of life, no less than in other intellectual pursuits, it is a rare thing to find a live interest in theory wedded to a masterly command of fact. Moreover, in the recent history of biology, the lure of the microscope has served to intensify this inevitable division between the outdoor man of action and the indoor man of thought.

By presenting Major Molony's life's work to the educated reader the publishers believe that they can thus help to break down this barrier that has stood in the path of science. Yet, it is not only to the scientific public that this book will appeal. Both the junior subaltern fingering his virgin rifle and the seasoned sportsman with a mind well stocked with memories of his own adventures will equally well enjoy this well-marshalled synthesis of observations and experiences obtained among the game animals of India. Similarly, lovers of the English countryside are offered the chance to see it afresh through the eyes of one for whom nature is no faded fresco adorning the walls of an urban existence, but amounts rather to a vital drama portraying scenes of intense parental solicitude, alternating with battle, murder and sudden death.

256 pages, demy 8vo, illustrated 15/-

The Making and Moulding of PLASTICS

L. M. T. Bell,

A.U.C.N.; Lecturer in Plastics Borough Polytechnic

This book is based on the author's unusually wide experience of the practice of this rapidly growing branch of technology and provides an easy means for all those engaged in the industry and for students to study the materials with which they work. It is simply written and discusses the history, the present-day essentials and the probable future developments of plastic moulding. In order to extend the field, the author has also included some discussion of processes of resinification and provided information that will be of interest to those with considerable experience of the trade. This book should lead to a better appreciation of the products and to a wider investigation of the study of plastic mouldings, to the benefit of the industry.

256 pages, medium 8vo, illustrated 12/6

ELECTRIC ARC WELDING Pocket Book

Karl Meller

The authoritative information given in this book will prove invaluable to all design offices, repair works and shipyards. It contains a large amount of information in a condensed and interesting form, and also includes references to the very latest work in arc-welding practice.

200 pages, cr. 8vo, illustrated 8/6